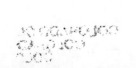

CURRENT TOPICS IN

DEVELOPMENTAL BIOLOGY

VOLUME 22

THE MOLECULAR AND DEVELOPMENTAL BIOLOGY OF KERATINS

WITHDRAWN

CURRENT TOPICS IN

DEVELOPMENTAL BIOLOGY

EDITED BY

A. A. MOSCONA

CUMMINGS LIFE SCIENCE CENTER
THE UNIVERSITY OF CHICAGO
CHICAGO, ILLINOIS

ALBERTO MONROY

VOLUME 22

THE MOLECULAR AND DEVELOPMENTAL BIOLOGY OF KERATINS

VOLUME EDITOR

ROGER H. SAWYER

DEPARTMENT OF BIOLOGY
UNIVERSITY OF SOUTH CAROLINA
COLUMBIA, SOUTH CAROLINA

1987

ACADEMIC PRESS, INC.

Harcourt Brace Jovanovich, Publishers

Orlando   San Diego   New York   Austin
Boston   London   Sydney   Tokyo   Toronto

ACADEMIC PRESS, INC.
Orlando, Florida 32887

United Kingdom Edition published by
ACADEMIC PRESS INC. (LONDON) LTD.
24–28 Oval Road, London NW1 7DX

LIBRARY OF CONGRESS CATALOG CARD NUMBER: 66-28604

ISBN 0–12–153122–8 (alk. paper)

PRINTED IN THE UNITED STATES OF AMERICA

87 88 89 90   9 8 7 6 5 4 3 2 1

CONTENTS

CHAPTER 4. The Experimental Manipulation of Keratin Expression
and Organization in Epithelial Cells
and Somatic Cell Hybrids
LOREN W. KNAPP AND CLIVE L. BUNN

CHAPTER 5. Patterns of Keratin Expression Define Distinct
Pathways of Epithelial Development and
Differentiation
W. MICHAEL O'GUIN, SHARON GALVIN,
ALEXANDER SCHERMER, AND TUNG-TIEN SUN

CHAPTER 6. Developmental Expression of Human Epidermal
Keratins and Filaggrin
BEVERLY A. DALE AND KAREN A. HOLBROOK

PREFACE

Keratins make up the intermediate filaments found in almost all epithelia from fish to mammals and are the products of multigene families. The great diversity in the form and function of epithelia and the tissue-specific expression of the keratins with their "pairing rules" makes the study of epithelial differentiation an excellent paradigm for studying the developmental regulation of gene expression. The availability of specific immunological and molecular probes for the individual keratins is rapidly advancing our understanding of the molecular and developmental events involved in the coordinated expression of the keratin genes in numerous epithelia.

The objective of Volume 22 of *Current Topics in Developmental Biology* is to provide a broad picture of the research being conducted on the molecular and developmental biology of keratins. It would be impossible to provide contributions from all the laboratories actively engaged in studies relative to the research areas discussed in this volume; therefore, representative areas were selected to present the general concepts and the methods in use.

In the introduction to the volume, Howard Green sets the stage by first examining the reasons for the resurgence of interest in the keratins and then posing some significant questions that will undoubtedly receive considerable attention in the years to come. Chapter 2, by Elaine Fuchs and her collaborators, provides the reader with a detailed discussion of the human keratin genes, while the following, by Paul Bowden and his associates, presents information on the modifications of keratins, such as phosphorylation, during terminal differentiation. In Chapter 4, methods for experimentally manipulating the organization of keratin filaments in cultured human cells and examining their organization in somatic cell hybrids are presented by Loren Knapp and Clive Bunn.

Monoclonal antibodies against human keratins have been extremely useful in further defining the "pairing rules" for keratins.

Using these monoclonal antibodies, Tung-Tien (Henry) Sun and his collaborators have shown that keratin expression in human as well as other mammalian epithelia defines distinct pathways of epithelial differentiation. In Chapter 5, Mike O'Guin and his colleagues now provide us with the information that the expression of avian α-keratins also defines distinct pathways of epithelial development and differentiation, similar to those seen for mammals. Again using the monoclonal antibodies to human keratins as well as an antibody against the keratin-associated protein, filaggrin, Beverly Dale and Karen Holbrook present in Chapter 6 the patterns of expression and localization of these proteins during human fetal skin development.

The picture for keratin expression in germ cells and very early embryos is provided by Eero Lehtonen in Chapter 7. His studies employ the laboratory mouse as well as teratocarcinoma stem cells. That many factors are involved in the regulation of keratin gene expression is exemplified by a discussion of the role of epidermal growth factor in development of the mouse palate by Robert Pratt in Chapter 8. Then in Chapter 9, Dennis Roop describes keratin gene expression during differentiation of the epidermal and vaginal epithelia of the mouse.

It is well established that epithelial–mesenchymal tissue interactions play a major role in the cell proliferation, morphogenesis, histogenesis, and terminal differentiation of epithelia. The mechanisms by which these interactions occur remain unknown, yet mutant genes affecting epithelial differentiation are proving very useful in defining when and where critical events of development are occurring. In Chapter 10, Chris Fisher describes his studies with the pupoid (*pf*/*pf*) mutation of the mouse. And finally, Chapter 11, by Rose Shames and Roger Sawyer, provides the current picture of the expression of the avian β-keratin genes during development of normal scale-forming epidermis and the epidermis of the scaleless (*sc*/*sc*) mutant chicken.

Because of his many contributions to our understanding of the keratinization process and his distinguished career in the field of skin biology, Gedeon Matoltsy was asked to present some concluding remarks on the epithelium that protects us all, the epidermis of the skin and its numerous and varied appendages.

Roger H. Sawyer

CHAPTER 1

INTRODUCTION

Howard Green

DEPARTMENT OF PHYSIOLOGY AND BIOPHYSICS
HARVARD MEDICAL SCHOOL
BOSTON, MASSACHUSETTS 02115

Epithelial cell types are ingenious and versatile. They can spe-
cialize in absorption, secretion, or ionic regulation. They can line internal surfaces or cover and protect external ones. The integument can
differentiate further to produce the elaborately structured and fos-
silized cellular appendages known as hair, feathers, nails, and, for ag-
gressive purposes, horns and claws.

The most abundant material of the epidermis and its appendages
has long been known to consist of keratin. The writing of this volume
reflects the fact that research on keratins has undergone a resurgence
during the past few years. The reasons may be easily traced:

1. The use of keratin antisera, including monoclonal antibodies,
demonstrated that the intermediate filaments of nearly all epithelial
cell types consist largely or entirely of keratins.

2. Electrophoretic analysis revealed the diversity of keratin polypeptides. The number of keratins so far identified exceeds 20 and it is
likely that a few more remain to be discovered. This diversity is much
greater than that known for any other intermediate filament protein.

3. Keratins have been classified according to their isoelectric point
as acidic (type I) or basic (type II). The keratins of one type are more
closely related to each other than to keratins of the other type. Filaments are constituted as heteropolymers of members of the two types.
There exist "pairing rules" relating the relative molecular sizes of the
two members of a pair. The overall combining ratio of type I and type
II polypeptides is presumably unity, but there is latitude in the selection of members of each type (keratin polypeptides are not strictly
monogamous). The unit formed by keratins in solution is the tetramer,
composed of two antiparallel double-stranded coiled coils, one containing two polypeptides of type I and the other containing two polypeptides of type II.

1

4. Since each keratin (with rare exception) is translated from its own mRNA, it has been possible to derive the amino acid sequences of keratins from their corresponding cDNAs. This has clarified the coiled coil structure and the relation between the keratins of the two types. All keratin molecules, like vimentin, contain central α-helical segments of about 310 amino acid residues. The differences in size between the larger and smaller keratins are due to variable N- and C-terminal extensions. In type II keratins but not in type I, these extensions contain H-1 subdomains of 30–35 residues and H-2 subdomains of 56 residues. The larger keratins of both type I and type II possess larger V subdomains in their N and C extensions than the smaller keratins. These extensions are likely to determine certain properties of the filaments; for example, the larger polypeptide subunits produce filaments that are more resistant to chemical denaturation.

5. The nucleotide sequence of the genes for keratin and other intermediate filament proteins has disclosed that they share extensive homology not only in their coding regions but also in their intron/exon boundaries. Clearly, intermediate filament genes have common evolutionary origins.

All of these subjects are treated in the chapters that follow. Turning now to the cells in which keratins are synthesized, we need to ask why keratins exist at all, and why there are so many different keratins. Part of the answer must lie in the particular properties of filaments assembled from different pairs of keratin molecules; the requirements of mesothelial cells or renal tubular cells are not likely to be the same as those of the epidermal cell. Epithelia can be classified according to a hierarchy in the size of keratin polypeptides they use, simple epithelia using the smallest and the epidermis using the largest. Each cell of a stratified epithelium synthesizes different keratins as it moves, in the course of its lifetime, from the basal to the outer surface of the epithelium. This is an example of a property of keratins that distinguishes them from other intermediate filament proteins: their synthesis is highly regulated.

Elucidation of the means by which this regulation takes place in different epithelial cell types and the purposes it serves is certain to be an important area of keratin research for years to come. Some idea of the dimensions of the problem may be given by the following examples.

1. The nature of the keratins synthesized by a cell is affected by its growth rate. For example, (human) keratins 6 and 16 are made by

epidermal cells only under conditions of marked proliferation. Depending on the state of the mesothelial cell (resting or growing, stationary or moving, in contact or not with other mesothelial cells) the intermediate filaments will be largely made of keratins or of vimentin.

2. The basal cell of the epidermis makes its intermediate filaments largely out of 58- and 50-kDa keratins. Once departed from this layer, the cells no longer synthesize those keratins but instead make mainly the keratins of 65 and 56.5 kDa that constitute the bulk of the corneocyte. Other terminally differentiating squamous epithelial cell types make slightly different type II keratins. The fate of the 50- and 58-kDa keratins made in the basal layer is not clear: they may be simply diluted as filament subunits by the newly made larger keratins. Such a dilution would most likely occur within each filament, thus modifying the properties of the filament progressively. Intrafilamental dilution might also explain the masking of previously synthesized subunits that sometimes makes them immunologically undetectable.

Why do the keratinocytes of the basal layer not already possess the keratins that will be necessary in the corneocyte? The most obvious explanation is that the proliferating cells of the basal layer might be adversely affected by filaments containing large keratins. Cells of the spinous layer, even if they contain the large keratins, may undergo mitosis; but these are transit amplifying cells with limited growth potential, and their progeny will soon undergo terminal differentiation and programmed cell death. The basal layer contains the stem cells whose progeny must proliferate over a long term. The presence of too rigid a filament system in such cells could produce errors in chromosome segregation, resulting in aneuploidy. Accordingly, the synthesis of the most resistant keratin filaments may need to be delayed until they no longer pose a risk to the stem cell population.

3. The concentration of vitamin A controls the differentiation of numerous epithelia. A deficiency of the vitamin converts respiratory and urinary epithelia to squamous epithelia and unkeratinized squamous epithelia to keratinized. This amounts to a change in cell type, and entails modification of the cellular program of differentiation affecting many proteins, including the spectrum of keratins synthesized.

Studies of cultured keratinocytes have shown that the addition of vitamin A suppresses the synthesis of some keratins and promotes the synthesis of others. These effects could result rather directly from the interaction of a vitamin-bearing receptor protein with the keratin genes. For example, it has been suggested that retinol or retinoic acid binding proteins enter the nucleus and exert effects on transcription. The proteins would have to act as repressors at some keratin genes, and as positive effectors at others. In order for such a control system to work, there might be a specific nucleotide sequence activating transcription in response to the vitamin A binding protein, and another sequence inactivating transcription in response to the same protein. Keratin genes responsive to vitamin A would be linked to one or the other of these controlling sequences and keratin genes lacking both sequences would be unresponsive to vitamin A.

Such a scheme ignores the fact that epithelial differentiation is the execution of a highly integrated program. For example, in terminal differentiation of keratinocytes, there are numerous proteins beside the keratins whose syntheses are activated. These include involucrin, transglutaminase, filaggrin, and cell surface proteins. In metaplasia induced by excess or deficiency of vitamin A, the number of differentiated proteins affected is probably still larger. The vitamin seems able to intervene at a control point for entire sets of differentiated proteins, of which the keratins are only a part. It is likely that the keratin genes respond not directly to the vitamin, but to a regulatory system which chooses the entire set of differentiated proteins. The regulatory system would also have to account for the existence of what might be called exclusionary or at least reciprocal relations in keratin synthesis: a single cell synthesizes at any time only a small number of the possible keratin molecules, sometimes only two, usually not more than four.

Some of the following chapters deal with the very interesting morphogenetic interactions that lead to the formation of epithelia. Mutations that produce errors in epithelial morphogenesis such as pupoid, rhino, and scaleless will be very useful in studying the control of differentiation. It will be important to determine whether these mutations affect regulatory molecules or structural proteins functioning as terminal products. Mutations in keratins and other structural proteins, while not elucidating morphogenesis, would be important for identifying the properties of such molecules. Many such mutations may be neutral, as polymorphism of keratins has already been found in humans.

CHAPTER 2

THE HUMAN KERATIN GENES AND THEIR DIFFERENTIAL EXPRESSION

Elaine Fuchs, Angela L. Tyner, George J. Giudice,
Douglas Marchuk,* Amlan RayChaudhury,
and Marjorie Rosenberg

DEPARTMENT OF MOLECULAR GENETICS AND CELL BIOLOGY
THE UNIVERSITY OF CHICAGO
CHICAGO, ILLINOIS 60637

I. Introduction

As surface and lining tissues, human epithelial cells play a common protective role in the body. This role is manifested by the construction of an extensive cytoskeletal architecture inside each cell. The epithelial cytoskeleton is composed of three distinct components: the 6-nm actin microfilaments and the 23-nm microtubules, both of which are ubiquitous throughout the eukaryotic kingdom, and the 8-nm keratin filaments, which are unique to epithelial cells (Rudall, 1968; Mercer and Matoltsy, 1969). Whereas the actin microfilaments and the microtubules do not seem to show much variation in different epithelia, the keratin filament network seems to be specifically tailored to suit the particular structural needs of each epithelial cell.

The surface of the skin has perhaps the greatest need for a protective cytoskeleton. Figure 1 shows a scanning electron micrograph of two terminally differentiated epithelial cell types: the hair shaft and the outer stratum corneum layer of the epidermis. The design of the cytoskeletons of these cells must be tough and highly structured, but since both cell types have lost all their metabolic functions, the cytoskeletons do not need to be compatible with cell division (for review, see Frazer *et al.*, 1972). Indeed, these cellular skeletons are densely filled with large bundles of keratin filaments. While the filaments in the cortex cells of the hair are arranged in an orderly and rigid fashion, the bundles of filaments in the squames of the epidermis appear to be more loosely packed. The different organization of

---

* Present address: Department of Biology, Hope College, Holland, Michigan 49423.

CURRENT TOPICS IN
DEVELOPMENTAL BIOLOGY, VOL. 22

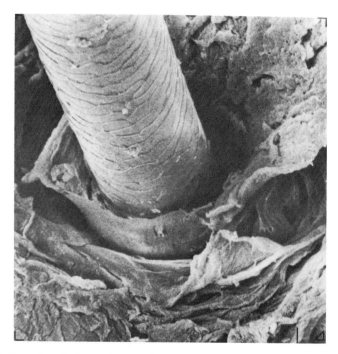

Fig. 1. Scanning electron micrograph of a hair shaft emerging from human scalp. Both the stratum corneum layers of the epidermis and the cuticle layers of the hair are composed of terminally differentiated cells. No metabolic processes or cell division take place in any of these cells, but their architecture and organization in the tissue are clearly different. (Micrograph kindly donated by Tsuneo Fujita, Niigata University School of Medicine, Asahi-Machi, Niigata, 951 Japan.)

cytoskeletal elements within the two types of cells may contribute to the markedly distinct packing of cells within the two tissues.

In contrast to the terminally differentiated epithelial cells on the body surface, the cells of the basal layer of the epidermis as well as cells of internal epithelia must maintain their ability to divide and to undergo normal metabolic processes and cell movement. This may explain why their cytoskeletons are less densely packed with keratin filaments: whereas 85% of the total protein in terminally differentiated epidermal cells is in the form of these filaments, the keratins comprise only 1–30% of the total protein in dividing epithelial cells (Moll et al., 1982; Tseng et al., 1982; Wu et al., 1982).

In addition to the variation in the abundance of keratin filaments, the proteins which make up these filaments are also different for different epithelia. For the human alone, there are at least 20 related keratins with widely varying molecular masses (40–70 kDa) and iso-electric points (pH 4.5–7.5) (for review, see Moll *et al.*, 1982). This family can be further subdivided into two distinct groups of equal size on the basis of their amino acid sequences: the small (40–56.5 kDa) and relatively acidic keratins form the type I class and the larger (53–67 kDa) and more basic keratins form the type II class (Fuchs *et al.*, 1981). From this repertoire, one to three pairs of type I and type II keratin polypeptides are selected by each epithelial cell for expression (Eichner *et al.*, 1984). Different pairs of keratins seem to be expressed in different epithelial cells at different stages of development and differentiation.

Despite the diversity in keratins, the 8-nm filaments of different epithelia cannot be readily distinguished under the electron micro-scope. In each case, a relatively uniform 8-nm structure is revealed, and lengths of up to 40 μm can be attained both *in vitro* and *in vivo* (Steinert *et al.*, 1976; Lee and Baden, 1976; Milstone, 1981). From *in vitro* assembly studies, a type I and a type II keratin appear to be essential for formation of the 8-nm structure (Franke *et al.*, 1983). However, any type I keratin, when combined with any type II keratin, can assemble into 8-nm filaments *in vitro* (Hatzfeld and Franke, 1985). Whether keratins can sort out *in vivo* into filaments containing differ-ent pairs of keratins is likely to be dependent upon their relative affinities for their "true" partners (Eichner *et al.*, 1986).

Some of the major mysteries of this field have been (1) to determine how the differential expression of different pairs of keratins might relate to cytoskeletal design, and (2) to elucidate the molecular mecha-nisms underlying this process. Recent sequence analyses of the ker-atins and the genes which encode these proteins have begun to reveal the answers to these questions.

II. The Keratin Filament: Classification, Structure, and Subunit Composition

A. THE KERATIN FILAMENT IS A MEMBER OF THE INTERMEDIATE FILAMENT FAMILY

The keratin filament is one of a class of intermediate filaments, which have a diameter of 8–10 nm, intermediate between that of the 6-nm actin microfilaments and the 23-nm microtubules. The family of intermediate filaments (IF) was initially subdivided according to the tissue(s) in which the different IF subunits were first discovered: neu-rofilament protein (neural cells), glial filament protein (astrocytes), vimentin (cells of mesenchymal origin), desmin (muscle cells), and keratins (epithelial cells) (for review, see Lazarides, 1980; Fuchs and Hanukoglu, 1983; Steinert *et al.*, 1985). The ultrastructural similarities of the assembled filaments gave the first indication that the subunits of different intermediate filaments might be related. The isolation of a monoclonal antibody that cross-reacts with all classes of intermediate filaments further supported this notion (Pruss *et al.*, 1981), and amino acid sequence data established a substantial relation among the five classes of IF subunits.

Recently, the sequences of nuclear lamins A and C have revealed a striking resemblance to the intermediate filament proteins (McKeon *et al.*, 1986; Fisher *et al.*, 1986). In addition, the lamins assemble into structures that share many of the characteristics of the intermediate filaments. Thus, even though the lamin filaments form a network beneath the nuclear envelope rather than being cytoskeletal in their location, they have been included as a part of the family of intermediate filament proteins.

Of all the intermediate filament classes, the keratins are by far the most complex and diverse group. Both types of keratins share only 25–30% homology with the other IF classes, and the two types themselves are only about 25–30% homologous with each other (Crewther *et al.*, 1980, 1984; Sparrow and Inglis, 1980; Hanukoglu and Fuchs, 1982, 1983; Steinert *et al.*, 1983; Jorcano *et al.*, 1984a,b; Glass *et al.*, 1985; Knapp *et al.*, 1986a,b; Bader *et al.*, 1986; Dowling *et al.*, 1986; Singer *et al.*, 1986). In contrast, desmin, vimentin, and glial filament protein are highly related to one another, sharing 60–90% homology (Geisler and Weber, 1981, 1982; Hong and Davison, 1981; Geisler *et al.*, 1982; Lewis *et al.*, 1984; Balcarek and Cowan, 1985). The three neurofilament proteins also share substantial sequence homology with this group, but they differ in having unusually long carboxy terminal ends that are rich in glutamic acid and lysine (Geisler *et al.*, 1983; Lewis and Cowan, 1986).

If the IF subunits are classified according to sequence homology rather than along histological lines, there are five multigene families of IF subunits: type I and type II keratins, which together form the intermediate filaments of epithelia; type III IF proteins, which include glial filament protein, desmin, and vimentin; type IV, which includes the neurofilament proteins; and type V, consisting of the nuclear lamins. A number of IF sequences are shown in Fig. 2 with their alignment to yield maximum homology with each other. Note that the lamins differ from other IF proteins in that the second helical domain contains 42 additional amino acid residues. The presence of this inserted sequence generates slight differences between the overall structure of the lamin filaments and that of the other IF filaments. Thus, although the filament structure of the lamins is similar to other IFs, the discussions which follow are limited to the cytoplasmic IFs.

B. The Structure of the Keratin Filament

Regardless of subunit composition, the cytoplasmic intermediate filaments have a diameter of 8–10 nm and an axial periodicity of 21 nm (Milam and Erickson, 1982; Henderson et al., 1982). Early X-ray diffraction studies on wool keratin microfibrils indicated that this structure contains an undetermined number of closely packed protofilaments composed of several largely α-helical polypeptide strands intertwined in a coiled coil configuration. A common X-ray pattern has been shown for all intermediate filaments, indicating that the details of their structure are likely to be highly similar even though the sequences of their subunits seem to be quite different (Crick, 1953; Pauling and Corey, 1953; Steinert et al., 1978; Geisler et al., 1982).

Amino acid sequence analyses have led to important refinements of our knowledge about the general structural features of the intermediate filament. Computer-assisted analyses of these sequences have revealed that despite the heterogeneity among IF subunit sequences, the predicted secondary structure of the polypeptides is remarkably similar. For all cytoplasmic IF proteins, a central region of approximately 300 amino acid residues consists of four richly α-helical domains demarcated from one another by three regions in which β-turns (helix disruptions) are predicted with high probability (for review, see Fuchs and Hanukoglu, 1983). The helical domains, which are marked by bars in Fig. 2, seem to be nearly constant in size for all cytoplasmic IF subunits. These domains contain the most highly conserved sequences of the proteins (see Table I). Even so, many amino acid substitutions,

---

Fig. 2. Amino acid sequence alignments of several intermediate filament proteins. Amino acid sequences are from the following sources: HK14 (a human type I keratin), Marchuk et al. (1984); MK10 (a mouse type I keratin), Steinert et al. (1983); WT-I (a wool type I keratin), Dowling et al. (1986); HK6b (a human type II keratin), Tyner et al. (1985); HK1 (a human type II keratin), Johnson et al. (1985); WT-II (a wool type II keratin), Sparrow and Inglis (1980); hamster vimentin (hVIM), Quax et al. (1983); mouse glial fibrillary acidic protein (MGFA), Balcarek and Cowan (1985); mouse 68-kDa neurofilament protein (MNF), Lewis and Cowan (1986); chicken desmin (CDES), Geisler and Weber (1982); human lamin C (HLAM-C), Fisher et al. (1986). Sequences were aligned for optimal homology. Helical domains were determined by computer analyses using the programs of Chou and Fasman (1978, 1979a,b) and Garnier et al. (1978) (Hanukoglu and Fuchs, 1983). The heptad repeats of hydrophobic residues located in the helical domains are shown by dots. Note that the repeat falls out of alignment at two positions corresponding to residues 300 and 368 of the HK14.

Amino-terminus

```
HK14 KER:   1  TTCSRQFTSSSSMKGSCGIGGGIAGSSRISSVLAGGSCRAPNTYGGCLSVSSRFSSG-GAYGLGGYGG-FSSSSSSFGSG-FGGGYCGGLGAGLGGFGGGFAGGDGSSV-GSEK-
MK10 KER:   1  SSTRGSLGGGLSSGGFSGGSFSRGSSGGGCFGSSGGYGGFGGGGSFGGGYGGSSFGGGYGSSFGGGS                    SVLVCSSSKQFSSSRSGGGGGGSVRV

WT-I KER:   1                                                                   SFNFCLPNLSFRSSCSSRPCVPSSCCGTTLPGACNIPANVGSCNWFCEGSFDGNEKE
HK6b KER:   1                                                                           ASTSTTIRSHSSSRRGFSASSARLPGVSRSGFSSISVSRSRG

HK1 KER:    1  SGGLGGACGGAGFGSRSLYGLGGSKRLSIGGGSCAISGGYGSRAGAGYGFGGAGSGFGGGAGICFGLGGPALLCFGGPGFPVCPPGGIQEVTVNQSLLITPLNLQIDPAIQRIGAEER
                                                                             SRQFSSSGYRSGGGFSFGFAGIINYQRRTISSTRRSGGGGRFSSSGGGGSFGAGGGF

WT-II KER:  1  GSRSLAGSGGSIASISGARGGGGSGFGGGYGGGGFGGGGFGGGFGGGIGGGGFGCGFSSGGGGFGGGGGFGGGGYGGYGPVCSPGGIQEVTINQSLLQPLNVEIDPEIQKVKSRER
               (R2,C2,T1,S2,P1,G4,A2,V1,I1,L1,Y1,F1)........                       .RSFCYRSGGVSGPSPCSITTVSVNESLLTPLNLEIDPNDCVKQEE-
STRSVSSSSYRRMFGPGTSNRQSSNRSYVTTSRTYSLGSLRPSTSRSLYSSP---GGAYVT------RSSAVR----LRSSMPGVRLLQDSVDFSLADAINTEFKNTRTNEK-
               ............                                          .MPPRRWSGASGPSRQLGTMPRFSLSRMTPPLPARVDFSLAGALNAGFKETRASER-
               ............                        .QSYSSSQRVSSYRRTFGGTSPVFPRASFSRGSGSSVTSRVYQVSRTSAVPILSTFRTTRVTPLRTYSAYQGAGELLDFSLADAMNQEFLQTRTNEK-
               ............                                       SSFASDPIFSTSYKRRYVETPRVHISSVRSGYSTARSAYSSYSAPVSSSLSVRRSYSSSSGLKPSLENLDVSQVAAISNDLKSIRIQEK-
               ............                                             ....ETPSQRRATRSGAQASSTPLSPTRITTRLQEK-
```

Helical domain I

```
HK14 KER: 116  VTMQNLNDRLASYLDKVRALEEANADLEVKIRDWYQRQR---PAEIKDYSPYFK
MK10 KER: 144  VTMKNLNDRLASYMDKVRALEESNYELEGKIKEVVREARQLKPREPRDYSKYYK
WT-I KER:  57  ETMQFLNDRLASYLEKVRQLERENAELESRILERSQQQE---PLVCPNYQSYFR
HK6b KER: 163  EQIKTLNNKFASFIDKVRFLEQQNKVLDTKWTLLQEQGKTKVRQNLEPLFEQYI
HT1 KER:  181  EQIQSLNNQFASFIDKVRFLEQQNQVLQTKWELLQQVDTSTRTHNLEPYFESFI
WT-II KER: 67  ......RFAAFIDKVR.......RQ-CCES-NLEPL.-YFK   (K5,R2,,C3,B4,T1,Z9,P1,G3,A4,I2,L8,Y2,F3)
MGFA    : 103  VELQELNDRFANYIDKVRFLEQQNKILLA---ELEQLKG---QGKSRLGDLYEE
CDES    :  56  AEMMELNDRFASYIEKVRFLEQQNKALAA---ELNQLRA---KEPTKLADVYQA
68kDaMNF:  91  VELQELNDRFANYIEKVRFLEQQNALMVA---EVNRLRG---KQPTRVAEMYEE
HLAM-C  :  32  AQLQDLNDRFASFIERVHELEQQNKVLEA---GLLVLRQ-KHSGPSRFRALYEQ
               EDLQELNDRLAVYIDRVRSLETENAGLRL---RITESEEVVSREVSGIKAAYEA
```

● ● ● ● ● ●

Helical domain II

```
HK14 KER: 167  TIEDLRNKILTATVDNANVLLQIDNARLAADDFRTKYETELNLRMSVEADINGLRRVLDELTLARADLEMQIESLKEELAYLKKNHEEEMNAL
MK10 KER: 198  TIEDLKGQILTLTTDNANVLLQIDNARLAADDFRLKYENELTLRNSYEADINGLRRVLDELTLSQSVLELQIESLNEELAYLKKNLEEEMRDL
WT-I KER:  108 TIEELQQKILCAKSENARLVVQIDNAKLAADDFRTKYETELGLRQLVESDIDGLRRILDELTLCKSDLEAQVESLKEELICLKSNHEEEVNTL
HK6b KER:  217 --NNLRRQLDSIVGERGRLDSELRGMQDLVEDDFKNKYEDEINKRTAAENEFVTLKKDVDAAYMNKVELQAKADTLTDEINFLRALYDAELSQM
HK1 KER:   235 --NNLRRGVDQLKSDQSRLDSELKNMQDMVEDYRNKYEDEINKRTNAENEFVTIKKDVDGAYMTKVDLQAKLDNLQQEIDFLTALYQAELSQM
WT-II KER: 138 YIETLRREAECVEADSGRLSSELNHVQEVLEGYKKKYEEEVALRATAENEFVALKKDVDCAYVRKSDLEANVEALIQEIDFLRRLTEEIRVL
hVIM    :  151 EMRELRRQVDQLTNDKARVEVERDNLAEDIMRLREKLQEEMLQREEAESTLQSFRQDVDNASLARLDLERKVESLQEIAFLKKLHDEEIQEL
MGFA    :  104 ELRELRLRLDQLTANSARLEVERDNFAQDLGTLRQKLQDETNLRLEAENNLAAYRQEADEATLARVDLERKVESLEEEIQFLRKIYEEEVRDL
CDES    :  149 ELRELRRQVDALTQQRARVEVERDNLLDNLQKLKQEIQLKQEAENNLAAFRADVDAATLARIDLERRIESLQEEIAFLKKVHEEEIREL
68kDaMNF:  141 EIRDLRLAAEDATNEKQALQEEREGLEETLRNLQARVEEEVLSREDAEGRLMEARKGADEAALARAELEKRIDSLMDEIAFLKKVHEEEIAEL
HLAM-C  :   83 ELGDARKTLDSVAKERARLQELSKVREEFKELKA LHDLRGQVAKLEAALGEAKKQLQDEMLRRVDAENRLQTMKEELDFQKNIYSEELRET
```

● ● ● ● ● ● ● ● ● ● ● ● ● ● ● ● ●

RNTKKEGDLIAAQARLKDLEALLNSKFAALSTALSEKRTLEGE

Helical domain III

```
HK14 KER: 260 RQQVGGD-VNVEMDAAPGVDLSRILNEM--RDQYEKMAEKNRKDAEEWFFTKTEELNREVATNSELVQSGKS
MK10 KER: 291 QNVSTGD-VNVEMNAAPGVDLTQLLNNM--RNQYEQLAEKNRKDAEEWFNQKSKELTTEIDSNIAQMSSHKS
WT-I KER: 201 RSQLGDR-LNVEDAAPTVDLNRVLNET--RAQYEALVETNRRDVEEWYIRQTEELNKQVVSSSEELQSCQT
HK6b KER: 308 QTHISDTSVVLSMDNNRNLDLDSIIAEV--KAQYEEIAQRSRAEAESWYQTKYEELQVTAGRHGDSVRNSKI
HK1 KER: 326 QTQISETNVILLSMDNRQFDLDSIIAEV--KAQNEDIAQKSKAEAESLYQSKYEELQITAGRHGDSVRNSKI
WT-II KER: 231 QANISDTSVIVSKMDNSRDLNMCCIVAEEIRAQYDDIASRSRAEAESWYRSKCEEIKATVIRHGETLRRTKE
hVIM    : 244 QAQIQEQHVQLDVDV-SKPDLTAALRDV--RQQYESVAAKNIQEAEEWYKSKFADLSEAANRNNDALRQAKQ
MGFA    : 234 REQLAQQQVHVEMDV-AKPDLTAALREI--RTQYEAVATSNMQETEEWYRSKFADLTDAASRNAELLRQAKH
CDES    : 243 QAQLQEQHIQVEMDI-SKPDLTAALRDI--RAQYESIAAKNIAEAEEWYKSKVSDLTQAANKNNDALRQAKQ
68kDaMNF: 234 QAQIQIAQISVEMDVSKPDLSAALKDI--RAQYEKLAAKMQNAEEWFKSRFTVLTESAAKNTDAVRAAKD
HLAM-C  : 217 KRRHETRLVEIDNGKQREFESRSADALQELRAQHEDQVEQYKKELEKTYSAKLDNARQSAERNSNLVGAAHE
```

Helical domain IV

```
HK14 KER: 329 EISELRRTMQNLEIELQSQLSMKASLENSLEDTKGRYCMQLAQIQEMIGSVEEQLAQLRCEMEQQNQEYKILLDVKTRLEQEIATYRRLLEGEDAHL
MK10 KER: 360 EITELRRTVQGLEIELQSQLALKQSLEASLAETVESLLRQLSQIQSQISALEEQLQQIRAETECONAEYQQLLDIKTKLENEIQTYRSLLEGESSS
WT-I KER: 270 EIIELRRTVNALQVELQAQHNLRDSLENTLTETEARYSCQLNQVQSLLSNVESQLAEIRGDLERQNQEYQVLLDVRAARLECEINTYRGLLDSEDCKL
HK6b KER: 378 EIAEINRMIQRLRSEIDHVKKQCANLQAAIADEQRGEMALQKAKQRGEMALDKAKNKLEGLEDALQKAKQDLARLLKEYQELMNVKLALDVEIATYRKLLEGEECRL
HK1 KER: 396 EISELNRVIQRLRSEIDNVKKQISNLQQSISDAEQRGENALKDAKNKLNDLEDALQQAKEDLTRLLRDYQELMNTKLALDEIATYRTLLEGESRM
WT-II KER: 303 EINELNRVIQRRTA(K6,R2,B9,T4,S9,Z17,P3,G11,A11,V10,L12,Y1)RAKQNMACLLKEYQEVMNSKLGLDIEIATYRRLLEGEEQRL
hVIM    : 313 ESNEYRRQVQSLTCEVDALKGTNESLERQMREEMEENFALEAANYQDTIGRLQDEIQNMKEEAARHLREYQDLLNVKMALDIEIATYRKLLEGESRI
MGFA    : 303 EANDYRRQLQALTCDLESLRGTNESLERQMREQEERHARESASYQEALARLEEEQSLKEEMARHLQEYQDLLNVKLALDIEIATYRKLLEGENRI
CDES    : 312 EMLEYRHQLQSYTCEIDALKGTNDSLMRQMREMERFAGEAGGYQDTIARLEEEIRHLKEMARHLREYQDLLNVKMALDVEIATYRKLLEGENRI
68kDaMNF: 304 EVSESRRLLKAKTLEIEACRGMNEALEKQLQELEDKQNADISAMQDTINKLENELRSTKSEMARYLKEYQDLLNVKMALDIEIAAYRKLLEGETRL
HLAM-C  : 290 ELQQSRIRIDSLSAQLSQLQKQLAAKEAKLRDLEDSLARERDTSRRLLAEKEREMAEMRARMQQLDEYQELLDIKLALDMEIHAYRKLLEGEERL
```

Carboxy-terminus

```
HK14 KER: 426 SSSQFSSGSQSSRDVTSSSRQIRTKVMDVHDGKVVSTHEQVLRTKN . 471
MK10 KER: 457 GGGGRRGGSGGGSYGGSSGGGGSYGGSSGGGGSYGGSSGCGGRGGG . 513
WT-I KER: 367 PCNPCATTNACGKTITPCISSPCAPAAPCTPCVPRSRCGPCNSYVR . 412
HK6b KER: 475 NGEGVGQVNISVVQSTVSSCYGGASGVGSGLGLGGGSYSYGSGLGVGGGFSSSSGRATGGGLSSVGGGS-STIKYTTTSSSRKSYKH . nd
HK1 KER: 493 SGECAPNVSVTVSTSHTS1SGGGSRGGGGGYGGSGSYSGGGGSYGSGGGGGRGSYGSGGGGSYGGGSSYGSGGGGGHGSYGSGSSSGYRG
HK1 KER: 589 GSGGGGGGSSGGRGSGGGGSSGGGSGCGRGSSSGGVKSSGGSSVKFVSTTYSGVTR . 643
WT-II KER: 453 CQ-CVGAVNVSVV-S.......(R2,C9,B3,T4,S8,Z1,P3,G13,A3,V7,L5)....RC . 525
hVIM    : 410 SLPLPNFSSLNLRETNLESLPLVDTHSKRTLLIKTVETRDGQVINETSQIHHDDLE . 465
MGFA    : 401 TIPVQTFSNLQIRETSLDTKSVSEGHLKRNIVVKTVIKDSKQEHKDVVM . 449
CDES    : 409 SIPMHQTFASALNFRETSPDQRGSEVHTKKTVMIKIIETRDGEVVSEATQQQHEVL . 464
68kDaMNF: 401 SFTSVGSIITSGYSGLSQUGFGRSAYSGLQSSYLMSARSFPAYYTSHVQEEQTEVETIEATKAEEAKDEPPSEGEAEEEKEKEEGEEEGAEEEEAAKDES
HLAM-C  : 387 RLSPSPTSQRSRGARSHSSTSQTQGGGSVHKRKLESTESRSSFSQHARTSGRVAEEVDEEGKFVRLRNKSNEDQSMGNWQIKRQNGDDPLLTYRFPPKFTL
                    KAQQVVTIWAAGAGATHSPPTDLVWKAQNTWGCCNSLRTALINSTGEEVAMRKLVRSVTVEVDEDEDGDDLLHHHHVSGSRR . 572
```

11

Fig. 2. See legend on p. 9.

TABLE I

SEQUENCE HOMOLOGIES WITHIN THE HELICAL AND SPACER DOMAINS OF DIFFERENT IF SUBUNITS[a]

		Structural domain						
		Helix I	Spacer I	Helix II	Spacer II	Helix III	Spacer III	Helix IV
I : I	HK14 : MK10	76	43	81	67	64	33	60
	HK14 : WT-I	67	33	63	61	59	17	56
	MK10 : WT-1	64	14	55	39	46	17	52
II : II	HK1 : WT-II	80 (i)	36 (i)	47	44	46	41	65 (i)
	HK1 : HK6b	88	50	73	72	82	58	76
III : III	MGFA : CDES	73	44	62	50	67	50	66
	hVIM : MGFA	77	33	59	39	72	58	71
	hVIM : CDES	83	33	67	67	79	92	78
I : II	HK14 : HK1	42	12	22	17	36	17	33
	WT-I : HK6b	33	5	24	12	36	8	32

I : III	HK14 : hVIM	48	11	35	11	41	17	35
	HK14 : CDES	45	6	38	21	41	17	34
	HK14 : MGF	45	17	37	37	38	33	38
II : III	HK6b : hVIM	60	0	26	22	40	42	40
	HK6b : CDES	42	5	31	18	46	25	43
	HK6b : MGF	60	0	30	6	38	25	41
I : IV	HK14 : MNF	43	5	32	28	46	33	35
II : IV	HK6b : MNF	60	5	25	23	32	17	39
III : IV	hVIM : MNF	57	40	46	44	64	50	56
I : V	HK14 : HLAM	53	5	20	6	19	25	32
II : V	HK6b : HLAM	40	10	22	11	27	8	33
III : V	hVIM : HLAM	57	18	23	17	22	25	35
IV : V	MNF : HLAM	43	16	26	0	22	33	35

[a] Abbreviations of IF subunits are according to the legend in Fig. 2. Comparisons are given in percentage identical residues. (i) indicates that one of the two sequences is incomplete. The comparisons are grouped according to IF subunit type as indicated at the left.

all of which are compatible with an α-helical structure, appear to have been tolerated. An exception is the sequence E-I-A-T-Y-R-K-L-L-E-G-E at the end of the fourth helical domain (see Fig. 2). This sequence is the most highly conserved sequence among the IF proteins.

The α-helical domains of the IF subunits are involved in the formation of the coiled coil. Throughout the helical portions of all IF proteins are sequences characteristic of a periodic interchain interaction, i.e., a heptad repeat of **a** b c **d** e f g, where **a** and **d** are hydrophobic residues (McLachlan and Stewart, 1975; McLachlan, 1978). These heptad repeats are marked by dots in Fig. 2. In addition, an interesting periodicity in positively and negatively charged residues has been observed for different IF subunits, indicating that electrostatic interactions may also play an important role in stabilizing the coiled coil structure (Parry *et al.*, 1977; McLachlan and Stewart, 1982).

Although physicochemical studies initially led to the suggestion that three polypeptide strands come together to form the coiled coil (Skerrow *et al.*, 1973; Steinert, 1978), recent nearest neighbor cross-linking studies indicate that there are only two polypeptide chains involved in the conformation (Ahmadi and Speakman, 1978; Woods and Gruen, 1981; Geisler and Weber, 1982). Model building using keratin sequences supports the two-stranded model (McLachlan, 1978). For the keratins, it seems most likely that a type I and a type II keratin subunit form the coiled coil (Fuchs and Marchuk, 1983; Fuchs and Hanukoglu, 1983; Steinert *et al.*, 1985). Biochemical analyses by Quinlan *et al.* (1984) and Parry *et al.* (1977, 1985) are in agreement with this hypothesis, and further suggest that the polypeptide chains in each heterodimer are parallel and in exact axial register. For other filaments, a single IF subunit is capable of forming this structure (Geisler *et al.*, 1985).

For all IFs, tetramers containing two coiled coil dimers seem to be especially stable, and they can form readily from a mixture of keratins in a solution dialyzed from 8 M to 4 M urea (Quinlan *et al.*, 1984). The dimers comprising the tetramers appear to be antiparallel, but whether they are in register or staggered has not yet been answered unequivocally (Parry *et al.*, 1985; Geisler *et al.*, 1985). This tetrameric structure may serve as the building block for IF filament assembly. Auxiliary proteins do not seem to be necessary for the assembly process, and hence the interactions between the subunit chains must themselves be sufficient to direct filament formation.

The smallest IF subunit known is the 40-kDa keratin (K19), while the largest is the 200-kDa neurofilament protein. Although the large NFP subunit has yet to be fully sequenced, it is clear that the central

300 amino acid residues of these proteins are compatible with the helical structure characteristic of the IF coiled coil (Weber *et al.*, 1983; Bader *et al.*, 1986). In the case of each of the neurofilament proteins, it is the nonhelical carboxy terminus that contains the "excess" molecular weight. In the case of the keratins, variation in this region also accounts for much of the wide diversity in size (40–70 kDa). For example, the smallest keratin K19 has only 13 amino acid residues following the conserved IF sequence at the end of the fourth helical domain (Bader *et al.*, 1986). In contrast, the largest keratin, K1 (67 kDa), has 154 residues after the conserved IF sequence (Johnson *et al.*, 1985). For the keratins, variation in the amino terminal segment also contributes to molecular weight differences. These differences are particularly large when keratins of different types are compared.

Not only is there a pronounced difference in the lengths of the nonhelical terminal segments of different IF subunits, but there is also tremendous divergence in these end sequences. Even when the terminal sequences of two IF proteins of the same type are compared, no distinct homology can be found without introduction of numerous gaps and insertions. Thus, the major differences in IF subunits reside in their termini rather than in their central helical domain.

The role of the end sequences in filament assembly is perhaps best assessed from studies where these sequences have been removed. When intermediate filaments are subjected to limited proteolysis, the nonhelical termini of the subunits are selectively digested, and the filament is partially disassembled. Short cylindrical rods of 2- to 4-nm diameter form that resemble the tetrameric structures described above (Skerrow *et al.*, 1973; Geisler *et al.*, 1982; Steinert, 1978; Steinert *et al.*, 1983; Sauk *et al.*, 1984). Since these rods cannot assemble into IFs, it seems that at least a part of the nonhelical terminal segments must be necessary for the complex interactions required to form the 8- to 10-nm filament.

Electron microscopy has greatly increased our understanding of the higher order structure of the intermediate filament (Aebi *et al.*, 1983; Steven *et al.*, 1982, 1983; Ip *et al.*, 1985; Eichner *et al.*, 1986). Each intermediate filament seems to be made up of four smaller filaments (4.5 nm), called protofibrils. The protofibrils themselves appear to arise from even smaller filaments (2–3 nm), although the precise number of protofilaments in each protofibril has not yet been determined. At least a part of the nonhelical ends of the coiled coils may contribute to the end-to-end and lateral interaction necessary to pack the coiled coils into protofilaments and protofibrils. Collectively, data from physicochemical studies, amino acid sequences, X-ray diffraction, and electron microscopy suggest that the structure of a keratin filament might be similar to the model shown in Fig. 3. The general features are presumed to be characteristic of other intermediate filaments as well.

C. THE ASSEMBLY OF KERATINS INTO FILAMENTS in Vivo

Our present knowledge of intermediate filament assembly has left a number of major questions unanswered. (1) For the keratins, where two different proteins seem to be required for IF assembly, what is the fate of a single keratin polypeptide whose expression is introduced into a nonepithelial cell producing a single, but different IF network, e.g., vimentin? Is the keratin protein stable? Will it incorporate into the preexisting IF network? Can it form filaments on its own? (2) In cells expressing more than one pair of keratins, what, if anything, prevents the promiscuous association between any of the type I and type II keratins present? (3) Within a single cytoskeletal network, are there different keratin filaments each of which is composed of a single kind of tetramer?

To begin to investigate the answers to these questions, we have transfected a plasmid containing an SV40 enhancer-driven epidermal type I keratin gene encoding K14 (50 kDa) into fibroblasts and simple epithelial cells. Using a rabbit antibody specific for the epidermal type I keratins, we detected the expression of the transfected gene product by immunofluorescence. Using mouse monoclonal antibodies specific for either vimentin or the simple epithelial type I keratin K18 (Lane, 1982; this antibody does not cross-react with epidermal keratins), we detected the intermediate filament network endogenous to the transfected cell. Figure 4A reveals that the foreign expression of a type I keratin gene in a fibroblast leads to accumulation of aggregates of apparently unpolymerized keratin protein. This protein does not incorporate into the preexisting vimentin network, nor does it seem to disturb the vimentin network. Thus, keratin and vimentin do not copolymerize in vivo into 8- to 10-nm filaments, nor does a single keratin seem to be competent for filament formation in vivo. These results are consistent with previous in vitro studies (Steinert et al., 1976; Milstone, 1981; Franke et al., 1979; Kreis et al., 1983; Tolle et al., 1985).

When K14 is expressed in the simple epithelial cell line, PtK2, it readily incorporates into the endogenous keratin filament network (Fig. 4B and C). Since these cells express only a single type I keratin K18 and a single type II keratin K8, and since K14 by itself does not seem competent for filament assembly, it would appear that K14 has utilized the endogenous type II keratin K8 as a partner in filament

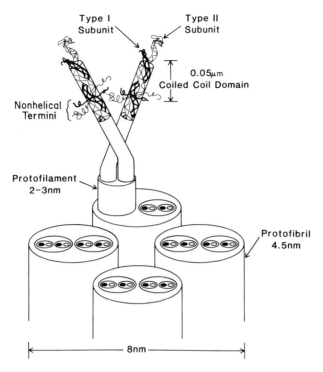

FIG. 3. A structural model for the 8-nm keratin filament. The model is based collectively on X-ray diffraction data (Crick, 1953; Pauling and Corey, 1953), physicochemical studies (Skerrow *et al.*, 1973; Steinert, 1978; Steinert *et al.*, 1983), chemical cross-linking data (Ahmadi and Speakman, 1978; Woods and Gruen, 1981), model building using keratin sequences (McLachlan, 1978), electron microscopy studies (Aebi *et al.*, 1983; Steven *et al.*, 1982), amino acid sequence data (Crewther *et al.*, 1980, 1984; Hanukoglu and Fuchs, 1982, 1983; Steinert *et al.*, 1983, 1984; Dowling *et al.*, 1983), and gene expression studies (Fuchs *et al.*, 1981; Moll *et al.*, 1982; Kim *et al.*, 1983; Roop *et al.*, 1983; Fuchs and Marchuk, 1983; Eichner *et al.*, 1984; Jorcano *et al.*, 1984a,b). The precise number of protofilaments per protofibril has not yet been unequivocally determined. Although the protofibrillar structures are shown as straight cylinders, they are most likely coiled in a left-handed helix with a periodicity of 21 nm (Milam and Erickson, 1982; Henderson *et al.*, 1982). The details of the structure of all intermediate filaments are thought to be similar with the major exception that in some cases, e.g., for the type III subunits, only a single subunit is necessary to form the coiled coil dimer of the protofilament (for review, see Geisler *et al.*, 1982).

formation. Moreover, since the presence of both type I keratins (K18 and K14) are detected throughout the filament network within the transfected PtK2 cell, it seems that no sorting out of keratins has taken place within the cell. Thus, the type II keratin K8 seems to be promiscuous in accepting a foreign type I keratin as a partner, even in

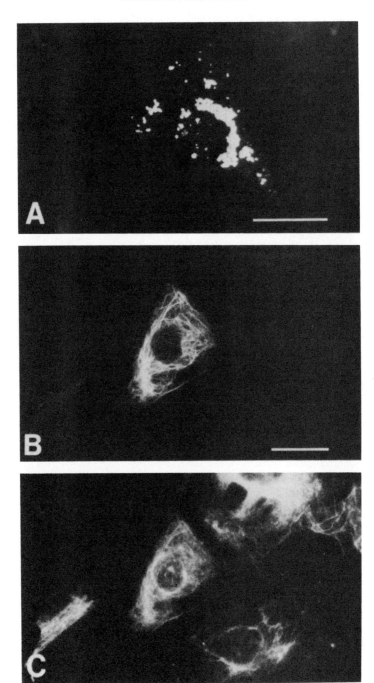

the presence of its "true" partner (as defined by Eichner *et al.*, 1984), keratin K18.

We do not yet know whether other keratins are promiscuous in cells expressing more than one set of type I and type II keratins. Keratin filaments containing only K14 and K5 have been isolated from epidermis (Eichner *et al.*, 1986). However, these filaments may have been present only in the basal cells, and not in the terminally differentiating cells that make additional keratins. Alternatively, since the strength of interaction between K14 and K5 is stronger than that between K8 and K18 (Hatzfeld and Franke, 1985), filaments containing only K14 and K5 may be able to assemble in cells containing several keratin pairs. Further studies will be necessary to determine the extent of homogeneity in the keratin filament network of complex epithelial cells.

D. THE FUNCTIONAL SIGNIFICANCE OF THE DIFFERENTIAL
EXPRESSION OF KERATIN FILAMENT SUBUNITS

The high degree of homology within the central helical domains of all keratins of a single type implies that the coiled coil structure of all pairs of type I and type II keratins is likely to be largely similar. If different pairs of keratins give rise to filaments with different properties and functions, then it is likely that the heterogeneous amino and carboxy termini are responsible for these differences. In the type I and type II keratins of wool, the amino and carboxy termini have cysteine-rich sequences, indicating the ability of the coiled coil dimers to form an extensively cross-linked 8- to 10-nm structure once the cellular membrane becomes permeable (Crewther *et al.*, 1980; Dowling *et al.*, 1983). Interestingly, during terminal differentiation in hair or wool, extensive interfilament disulfide bond cross-bridging occurs to yield masses of highly ordered and rigid 8- to 10-nm keratin filaments (macrofibrils). This entire process is most likely enhanced through the aid of several cysteine-rich matrix proteins (Powell *et al.*, 1983).

FIG. 4. The expression of a human epidermal keratin gene in transfected fibroblasts and simple epithelial cells. A human type I epidermal keratin gene encoding K14 was inserted into a bacterial plasmid containing an SV40 enhancer sequence. The vector was then transfected by the calcium phosphate method into either fibroblasts (A) or simple epithelial cells (B and C). Sixty-five hours after transfection, the cells were fixed and stained with either (A and B) a polyclonal antibody specific for epidermal type I keratins (Fuchs and Marchuk, 1983) or (C) a monoclonal antibody specific for keratin K18 (LE61, Lane, 1982). Note that the human K14 protein does not incorporate into the vimentin network of the transfected fibroblast, but it readily incorporates into the keratin network of the simple epithelial cells.

In contrast to the wool keratins, the termini of the type I and type II keratins of the basal epidermal layer are rich in glycine and serine (Hanukoglu and Fuchs, 1982, 1983; Steinert *et al.*, 1984; Jorcano *et al.*, 1984a,b; Tyner *et al.*, 1985; RayChaudhury *et al.*, 1986). Although the tertiary structures of these termini are unknown, the use of numerous glycines and serines in the terminal segments might be expected to give rise to a much more flexible cytoskeleton, a criterion that is most likely necessary for dividing and metabolically active epithelial cells (Fuchs and Hanukoglu, 1983).

During terminal differentiation in the epidermis, a shift to the synthesis of new and unusually large type I and type II keratins takes place (Fuchs and Green, 1980; Eichner *et al.*, 1984; Kim *et al.*, 1984a). These large keratins, which are not found in other tissues, seem to be similar to the basal epidermal keratins with the exception of their extended glycine- and serine-rich amino terminal domains (Steinert *et al.*, 1983; Johnson *et al.*, 1985). These excess sequences seem to protrude along the surface of the 8- to 10-nm filament, thereby coating the filament with glycine–serine-rich sequences (Steven *et al.*, 1982; Steinert *et al.*, 1983). Recently, Aebi and co-workers have shown that filaments reassembled *in vitro* from these large keratins form aggregates, whereas filaments composed of the basal epidermal keratins remain dispersed (Eichner *et al.*, 1986). A glycine–serine-rich matrix protein, filaggrin, may cause further bundling of the terminal differentiation-specific keratin filaments, thereby producing a flexible macrofibrillar structure (Dale *et al.*, 1978; Steinert *et al.*, 1985). If the choice of keratin subunits expressed by an epidermal cell is important in the aggregation and bundling of keratin filaments that takes place during terminal differentiation, then the expression of these large keratins may interfere with the ability of a cell to divide. Filaments consisting of different keratins may also differ in a number of other properties, e.g., stability, tensile strength, flexibility, and the ability to interact with other cytoplasmic proteins and organelles. By expressing different pairs of keratins, each epithelial cell may produce a cytoskeleton compatible with its structural and functional requirements.

III. The Keratin Genes: Structure, Evolution, and Regulation

A. The Structure of the Keratin Genes

Because the intermediate filament subunits are a family of very diverse polypeptides with extraordinarily similar and well-defined structures, they provide an excellent opportunity to investigate the evolutionary pressures of protein structure on gene structure in a sit-

uation where sequence conservation has provided only a minimal contribution. Recently, a number of clones containing the complete genes
for several type I and type II keratins have been isolated from various
mammalian genomic libraries (Marchuk *et al.*, 1984, 1985; Johnson *et
al.*, 1985; Tyner *et al.*, 1985; Krieg *et al.*, 1985; Jonas *et al.*, 1985;
Powell *et al.*, 1986; RayChaudhury *et al.*, 1986). In comparison with
previously determined cDNA sequence data, the sequences of these
genes have provided the complete amino acid sequences of the proteins, in addition to determining the overall structures of these genes.

The two types of keratin genes have remarkably similar structures.
Out of seven to eight introns in each of the two genes, six are nearly
identically positioned (Fig. 5). This is striking, considering that the
two types of keratins share only about 30% homology overall (Hanukoglu and Fuchs, 1983; Steinert *et al.*, 1984). Moreover, this gene
structure is virtually indistinguishable from that of the very distantly
related type III intermediate filament proteins, vimentin and desmin
(Quax *et al.*, 1983, 1985; Marchuk *et al.*, 1984). Thus, not only the
secondary structure of many of the IF proteins, but also the structural
skeletons of their genes, have been maintained throughout evolution.

Surprisingly, the number and placement of the introns in the type
IV neurofilament genes appear to be completely anomalous (Fig. 5;
Lewis and Cowan, 1986). Only three introns, none of which correspond
in position with introns in the type I, II, or III IF genes, are present in
the 68-kDa neurofilament gene. The similarities in gene sequence suggest that the neurofilament genes are derived from an ancestor gene
that is also common to the other IF genes. However, it seems that an
mRNA-mediated transposition event may have placed an intronless
cDNA sequence (made from a primordial neurofilament mRNA template) near an active promoter in the genome, thereby resulting in a
functional gene (Lewis and Cowan, 1986). If this was indeed the case,
then the three introns in the NF genes must have subsequently been
created through additional evolutionary events.

The sequences of the lamin genes have not yet been determined. If
the lamins play an integral role in the stabilization of the nuclear
envelope and if the evolution of the intermediate filament genes parallels the acquisition of their function, then the primordial lamin gene
might be expected to be the oldest IF gene. Although intermediate-like
filaments have been seen in single-cell eukaryotic organisms such as
yeast (Greer and Schekman, 1982), their relation (if any) to higher
eukaryotic IFs has not yet been established. In insects, only vimentin
filaments have thus far been identified (Walter and Biessmann, 1984).
Neurofilaments have been discovered in the annelid *Myxicola* (Lasek *et*

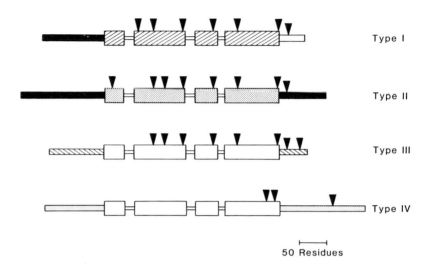

FIG. 5. The intron positions of the IF genes do not conform to the boundaries of the structural domains of the IF subunits. The secondary structures of the three IF proteins were determined from their amino acid sequences as described in the legend to Fig. 2. The complete amino acid sequences were obtained from the nucleic acid sequences of their genes: HK14 type I keratin gene (Marchuk *et al.*, 1984); HK6b type II keratin gene (Tyner *et al.* (1985); hamster vimentin type III gene (Quax *et al.*, 1983); and mouse neurofilament (68 kDa) type IV gene (Lewis and Cowan, 1986). The four sequences are aligned for optimal homology and drawn to scale, with the scale representing amino acid residue position. The thicker boxed regions indicate the four α-helical domains, and the thinner connecting lines indicate the presence of helix-disrupting sequences. The positions of the introns are shown by triangles. The positions of five of the introns, corresponding to introns 2–6 (left to right) of the K14 gene, are identical for the IF genes of types I–III. Intron 7 is shifted only three base pairs for the K14 gene and is identically positioned for the K6b and vimentin genes. Intron 2 for the vimentin and K6b genes has no counterpart for the K14 gene, and similarly, intron 1 for the K14 gene has no counterpart for the vimentin and type II keratin genes. Note that the placement of the introns in the neurofilament gene is completely different from that of the other IF genes.

al., 1979) and in several mollusks (Phillips *et al.*, 1983). Recently, the presence of keratin-like filaments has also been established in the mollusk (Bartnik *et al.*, 1985). However, even though these IFs present in lower eukaryotes are clearly related to the mammalian IFs, there seem to be major evolutionary differences between them (Fuchs and Marchuk, 1983; Spitzer *et al.*, 1984). Thus, it appears that several distant duplications led to the development of five different types of intermediate filament proteins. Numerous more recent duplications gave rise to multigene families encoding the multiple members of each of these classes.

The conservation of IF intron positions does not seem to have any strong correlation with the conservation of IF amino acid sequences. This can be demonstrated readily by comparing the amino acid sequences within the large exon of helical domain IV of the IF subunits of types I–III (corresponding to amino acid residues 352–424 of the 50-kDa keratin HK14 in Fig. 2). Whereas the residues in the first half of the exon are highly divergent, the residues in the second half of the exon are highly homologous. In some cases, the entire exon is highly homologous (see for example, the exon corresponding to amino acid residues 223–255 of HK14). In other cases, however, the entire exon is very different for different IF genes (see for example, the exon beginning in helical domain III and ending in helical domain IV, residues 309–350 of HK14). Therefore, the exons of the IF genes do not seem to have evolved as separate units.

B. The Positions of the Introns in the Keratin Genes Do Not Seem to Border the Structural Domains of the Protein

The remarkable conservation of intron position over millions of years of evolution must indicate that there are strict constraints against varying the lengths of the internal exons of the IF genes. This is perhaps best illustrated in Fig. 2, where it can be assessed readily that there are only two IF proteins (wool type II keratin and human lamin C) out of 11 shown for which a gap or insertion must be introduced in the alignment in order to obtain optimal homology within the central exons (corresponding to amino acid residues 174–440 in HK14). For the nuclear lamins, a large "insertion" of 42 amino acid residues occurs at amino acid residue 118 (Fig. 2). However, these 42 additional residues still maintain the heptad repeat characteristic of the coiled coil interaction of the helical domains of IF proteins.

If the primordial lamin gene was the oldest IF gene, then a deletion of the 42 residues must have taken place to give rise to a primordial gene encoding a cytoplasmic IF protein. It would seem that any deletion taking place during evolution would have to remove an integral number of heptads so that the formation of the coiled coil would not be perturbed. If the deletion of the six heptads took place through recombination, their sequences may have been similar at one time, suggesting the possibility that the central helical domains might have arisen through duplication of an integral number of heptads. Moreover, if a deletion of heptads gave rise to a gene coding for a cytoplasmic IF protein, the first cytoplasmic IFs would be predicted to be homopolymers: It is highly unlikely that a lamin protein and a cytoplasmic

IF protein could copolymerize to form proper 8-nm filaments, since the lengths of their coiled coils would be different.

It has been suggested that intron position may play an important role in demarcating the structural or functional domains of a protein (Gilbert, 1978; Artymiuk *et al.*, 1981). A number of examples relating intron position to these protein features have now been documented (Craik *et al.*, 1980; Efstradiatis *et al.*, 1980; Cochet *et al.*, 1979; Calame *et al.*, 1980; Wozney *et al.*, 1981; Nathans and Hogness, 1983; Blundell, 1983; Inana *et al.*, 1983). Despite the remarkable conservation of structure in the IF genes, the positions of the introns do not seem to correspond to the boundaries of the four α-helical domains of the molecules (see Fig. 5). In fact, the points at which introns are found in these genes do not seem to conform to any of the structural demarcations of the IF proteins. They are not found within the proline-containing segments interrupting the central helical regions, nor do they separate the unusual sequences in the amino termini from the rest of the polypeptide.

Even if the helical domains of the IF genes originated from duplication of heptad sequences, the positions of the exons do not seem to bear any resemblance to demarcations of the heptad units. There are no remnants of clues that might allow us to decipher how the IF genes could have evolved by a coupling together of exons. Rather, it appears that introns arose spontaneously and perhaps randomly throughout the primordial IF gene.

Regardless of the evolutionary origins of the IF introns, the conservation of exon length indicates that there are constraints on the design of the IF subunit that are likely to be relevant to filament assembly. Shifting the positions of the introns in multiples of three nucleotides would introduce (or delete) amino acid residues at an internal position in the protein which might disrupt the heptad repeat in a helical domain. For the keratins, where two distinct types of proteins are involved in the formation of the coiled coils, even altering the size of the helical domain by an integral number of heptads could prevent the coiled coil subunit structure from forming properly. Changing the size of the IF proteins by interfering with the size or positions of the α-helical domains of the polypeptide might have additional consequences for filament assembly: a small alteration in the coiled coil might perturb the lateral packing of the protofilaments, which would in turn be likely to influence the protofibrillar packing. Since the interactions of the coiled coil subunits are so complex, and since the IF introns are primarily dispersed throughout the segments encoding the helical domains of the polypeptide, little shifting in intron position would be expected to be tolerated.

C. THE REGULATION OF THE DIFFERENTIAL EXPRESSION OF THE KERATIN GENES

The evolution of the family of keratins has been by far the most complex of all of the classes of intermediate filaments. Most if not all of the more than 20 different keratin mRNAs that are differentially expressed in different epithelial tissues seem to have arisen from separate genes (Fuchs et al., 1981; Kim et al., 1983; Magin et al., 1983). All of the keratin genes characterized so far appear to encode a single transcript; each gene has a single transcription initiation site and a single polyadenylation site (Marchuk et al., 1985; Tyner et al., 1985; Krieg et al., 1985; Johnson et al., 1985; Rieger et al., 1985; RayChaudhury et al., 1986). For the reasons outlined above, conservation of intron position contributes further to the unlikelihood that differential splicing occurs within the internal intron sequences of any keratin RNA transcript (Marchuk et al., 1984). Finally, scanning the spacer region between two closely linked keratin genes has allowed us to rule out unequivocally the possibility of differential splicing within one keratin gene transcript (RayChaudhury et al., 1986).

There are at least 15–30 genes per keratin subfamily (Tyner et al., 1985). Earlier estimations based on reduced stringency hybridizations with type I and type II epidermal keratin cDNAs did not show cross-hybridization with all of the keratin genes, and therefore gave conservative predictions for these numbers (Fuchs et al., 1981; Fuchs and Marchuk, 1983). We have now demonstrated conclusively that at least for one keratin, a 56-kDa protein K6, there are at least two distinct K6 genes that are both expressed in epidermis (Tyner and Fuchs, 1986). There are most likely other cases where a number of recent gene duplications may have taken place to yield multiple genes coding for similar if not identical keratins (unpublished observations).

To ensure proper tissue-specific expression, the regulation of the keratin genes must be under strict control. In epidermis, there are two keratins, a type I (50-kDa) keratin K14 and a type II (58-kDa) keratin K5, which are expressed in the basal layer (Sun and Green, 1978; Fuchs and Green, 1980). During the course of terminal differentiation, new keratins of both the type I class (K10 and K11) and the type II class (K1 and K2) are induced (Fuchs and Green, 1980; Moll et al., 1982; Roop et al., 1983; Eichner et al., 1984). With the possible exception of K2 (Tyner and Fuchs, 1986), these changes in keratin expression take place at the level of mRNA, and they could be at the transcriptional level.

An unusual set of keratins (type I: K16 and K17; type II: K6) are only transiently expressed in epidermis during wound healing (Birgit Lane, personal communication). These keratins are also expressed in epidermal diseases of hyperproliferation and when epidermal cells are placed into tissue culture (Weiss *et al.*, 1984). Recently, we have discovered that although the hyperproliferation-associated keratins are not present in normal epidermis, their mRNAs are continuously expressed (Tyner and Fuchs, 1986). Although the levels of these keratin mRNAs increase during hyperproliferation, their levels in normal skin are nonetheless substantial. *In situ* hybridization of a radiolabeled cRNA probe specific for keratin K6 shows a uniform distribution of the K6 RNA throughout the living layers of the epidermis (Fig. 6A). In contrast, a radiolabeled cRNA probe specific for the basal keratin K14 shows predominant localization of this RNA in the basal epidermal layer (Fig. 6B). Considerable levels of K14 RNA are also present in the suprabasal layers, however, suggesting that the expression of K14 (and presumably its partner keratin K5) may not be shut off upon commitment of a cell to undergo terminal differentiation.

Nuclear run-off experiments will be necessary to determine whether the changes in keratin mRNA levels are truly at the transcriptional level, rather than at the level of mRNA stability. If the variations in mRNA levels prove to reflect changes in transcriptional activity of different keratin genes, then it would seem that the only major change in gene regulation taking place in the epidermis is a positive one, involving the induction of the genes encoding keratins K1, K10, and K11 that takes place during terminal differentiation. In tissue culture, the induction of these terminal differentiation-specific keratins can be mimicked by reducing the concentration of vitamin A in the culture medium (Fuchs and Green, 1981). This observation indicates an important role for the vitamin in regulating the differentiation process.

In the basal epidermal cell, approximately 30% of the total protein synthesis is devoted to making keratin, while the fully differentiated cell contains almost 85% of its protein as keratin (Sun and Green, 1978). The keratin mRNA levels are also very high in these cells (Fuchs and Green, 1980). The abundant expression of keratin mRNA indicates either that the mRNAs are unusually stable or, alternatively, that the level of keratin gene transcription is high. It is interesting to note that at three positions within 230 nucleotide residues 5′ upstream from the TATA box of the K14 gene, the sequence

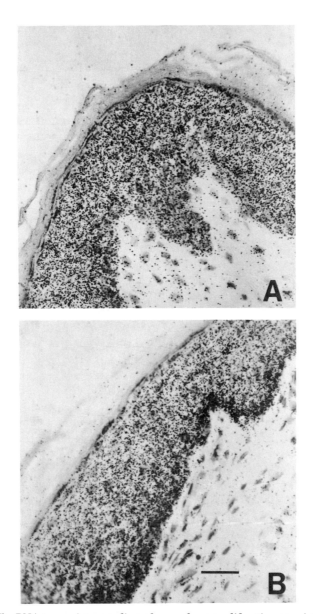

FIG. 6. The RNA transcripts encoding a human hyperproliferation-associated keratin are present in normal epidermis even though the protein is not. Tissues from human foreskin were fixed and sectioned (5 μm) as described by Tyner and Fuchs (1986). Hybridizations of ^{3}H-radiolabeled cRNA probes were followed by RNase treatment and autoradiography. Exposures were for 11 days. Probes were to (A) a 1415-bp DNA fragment encompassing a large portion of the coding region of a type II hyperproliferation-associated keratin (K6) mRNA; (B) a 1080-bp DNA fragment encompassing a large portion of the coding region of a type I basal keratin (K14) mRNA.

$T(G)_{1-3}AAAG$ is found (Marchuk *et al.*, 1985). This sequence is similar to the consensus enhancer sequence GTGGAAAG found in some viral and immunoglobulin genes expressed at high levels (Moreau *et al.*, 1981; Laimins *et al.*, 1982; Gillies *et al.*, 1983). These sequences are thought to be target sites for the binding of tissue-specific proteins that confer increased transcriptional rates to a gene (Laimins *et al.*, 1982; Gillies *et al.*, 1983; Scholer and Gruss, 1984). We have not yet tested whether the related sequences found in the type I K14 gene actually function as enhancers *in vivo*.

The sequences between the transcriptional and translational initiation sites of many eukaryotic genes have been shown to play an important role in the translational regulation of the encoded mRNA. The sequences within the first few hundred nucleotides 5' upstream from the TATA boxes have been shown to be involved in the transcriptional regulation of many eukaryotic genes. We have examined the 5' untranslated and the 5' upstream regulatory regions of several of the epidermal keratin genes for possible homologies, which might give us a clue to understanding how these genes are coordinately regulated in the epidermis. When the sequences located 5' upstream from the ATG translation initiation codons of the genes encoding K6, K14, and K17 are aligned for optimal homology, several stretches of sequence homology can be seen (Fig. 7; RayChaudhury *et al.*, 1986). Some of these homologies even exceed the similarities within the coding regions of the genes. In particular, the 5' untranslated leader sequences of these genes share substantial homology. In addition, a 60-bp segment of the two type I genes shows 90% homology, and a 30-bp stretch of the type II and the type I genes shares 69% homology. Interestingly, these homologies are not found when the corresponding sequences of the terminal differentiation-specific K1 gene (Johnson *et al.*, 1985) are compared with the three basally expressed keratin genes. As more genomic sequences for coexpressed sets of keratins become available, it should be possible to define more precisely candidate sequences in the 5' upstream regions that might play a role in regulating the tissue-specific expression of these genes and their transcripts. This will be an important prerequisite for identifying specific transcriptional or translational regulatory factors involved in activating the synthesis of different keratins in different epithelial tissues and at different stages of differentiation and development.

In addition to the tissue-specific expression of the keratins and to the variations in levels of keratins synthesized within a particular epithelial cell, there is also a profound influence on keratin expression which is exerted by a number of different extracellular regulators. For

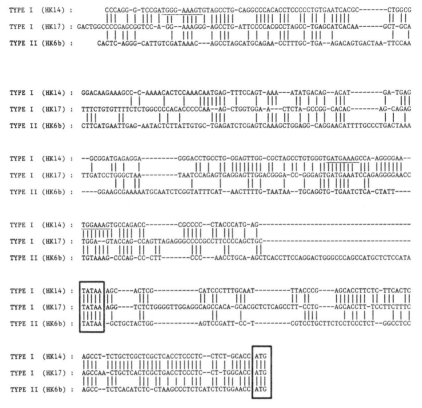

FIG. 7. Comparison of the nucleotide sequences 5′ upstream from the translation initiation codons of three genes that are coexpressed in epidermis and cultured human epidermal cells. The 5′ sequences of two coexpressed type I keratin genes, K14 (Marchuk *et al.*, 1984) and K17 (RayChaudhury *et al.*, 1986), and one coexpressed type II keratin gene, K6b (Tyner *et al.*, 1985), were aligned for optimal homology. Putative translation initiation codons and TATA boxes are outlined by boxes. The vertical lines indicate positions of sequence identity between the K14 and K17 sequences and the K17 and K6b sequences, respectively. The three squences of the K14 gene previously shown to share homology with the simian virus 40 core enhancer sequence (Marchuk *et al.*, 1985) are underlined.

example, not only has vitamin A been shown to suppress the expression of keratins K1, K2, K10, and K11, but it also causes the induction of two keratins, K13 and K19, which are not normally expressed in these cells (Fuchs and Green, 1981; Kim *et al.*, 1984b; Eckert and Green, 1984; Gilfix and Green, 1984). In contrast, some keratins, e.g., K5, K6, K14, and K17, do not seem to be influenced by the extracellular concentrations of the vitamin. We do not yet know whether vitamin A acts indirectly or directly to influence gene expression; however, different epithelial cells have different sensitivities to the vitamin, which may in part explain why some keratin patterns are different from others (Green and Watt, 1982; Kim et al., 1984b).

Epidermal growth factor (EGF) is another extracellular mediator known to have a marked effect on the expression of keratins (Wu et al., 1982). In the presence of EGF, human mesothelial cells suppress their expression of simple epithelial keratins (K7, K8, K18, and K19) and turn on the expression of vimentin. In conjunction with the biochemical changes, the shape of the cells changes from a simple epithelial to a fibroblast-like morphology. Although no such EGF-mediated changes have been observed for epidermal cells, it is interesting to note that the induction of the keratins K6, K16, and K17 during wound healing or growth of epidermal cells in tissue culture medium seems to be associated with a hyperproliferative, and possibly growth factor-related, response (Weiss et al., 1984; Tyner and Fuchs, 1986). Thus, there may be multiple factors, both intracellular and extracellular, which may be regulating the differential expression of different pairs of keratins in human epithelial tissues. The precise nature of the molecular mechanisms underlying this regulation must await further characterization of the keratin gene family.

ACKNOWLEDGMENTS

We would like to thank Dr. Tsuneo Fujita (Niigata University School of Medicine, Niigata, Japan) for lending us a scanning electron micrograph of the surface of human skin to use for publication. A special thank you goes to Ms. Grazina Traska, Ms. Margaret Eichman, Mr. Sean McCrohon, and Ms. Jennifor Javors for their expert technical assistance on many of the projects described in this review. We would also like to thank all of the other members of our laboratory who provided us with help, advice, and assistance wherever it was needed. Finally, we would like to thank Mr. Philip Galiga for his most capable artwork involved in the preparation of the figures. E. F. is the recipient of an NIH Career Development Award K04 AR00997 and an NSF Presidential Young Investigator Award. A. L. T. and M. R. are the recipients of Predoctoral Traineeships from the NIH. G. J. G. is a Postdoctoral Fellow funded by the NIH. This work was funded by grants from the NIH, The Cancer Research Foundation, and the Whirlpool Foundation.

REFERENCES

Aebi, U., Fowler, W. E., Rew, P., and Sun, T.-T. (1983). J. Cell Biol. 97, 1131–1143.
Aebi, U., Cohn, J., Buhle, L., and Gerace, L. (1986). Nature (London) 323, 560–564.
Ahmadi, B., and Speakman, P. T. (1978). FEBS Lett. 94, 365–367.
Artymiuk, P. J., Blake, C. C. F., and Sippel, A. E. (1981). Nature (London) 290, 287–288.
Bader, B. L., Magin, T. M., Hatzfeld, M., and Franke, W. W. (1986). EMBO J. 5, 1865–1875.

Balcarek, J. M., and Cowan, N. J. (1985). *Nucleic Acids Res.* **13**, 5527–5543.
Bartnik, E., Osborn, M., and Weber, K. (1985). *J. Cell Biol.* **101**, 427–440.
Blundell, T. (1983). *Nature (London)* **304**, 310–315.
Calame, K., Rogers, J., Early, P., Davis, M., Livant, D., Wall, R., and Hood, L. (1980). *Nature (London)* **284**, 452–455.
Chou, P. Y., and Fasman, G. D. (1978). *Adv. Enzymol.* **47**, 45–148.
Chou, P. Y., and Fasman, G. D. (1979a). *Biophys. J.* **26**, 367–383.
Chou, P. Y., and Fasman, G. D. (1979b). *Biophys. J.* **26**, 385–399.
Cochet, M., Gannor, F., Iten, R., Maroteaux, L., Perrin, F., and Chanbone, P. (1979). *Nature (London)* **282**, 567–574.
Craik, C. S., Buchman, S. R., and Beychok, S. (1980). *Proc. Natl. Acad. Sci. U.S.A.* **77**, 1384–1388.
Crewther, W. G., Dowling, L. M., and Inglis, A. S. (1980). *Proc. Quinquen. Int. Wool Test. Conf., 6th* **2**, 79–81.
Crewther, W. G.. Dowling, L. M., Steinert, P. M., and Parry, D. A. D. (1984). *Int. J. Biol. Macromol.* **5**, 267–274.
Crick, F. (1953). *Acta. Crystallogr.* **6**, 689–697.
Dale, B. A., Holbrook, K. A., and Steinert, P. M. (1978). *Nature (London)* **276**, 729–731.
Dowling, L. M., Parry, D. A. D., and Sparrow, L. G. (1983). *Biosci. Rep.* **3**, 73–78.
Dowling, L. M., Crewther, W. G., and Inglis, A. S. (1986). *Biochem. J.* **236**, 695–703.
Eckert, R. L., and Green, H. (1984). *Proc. Natl. Acad. Sci. U.S.A.* **81**, 4321–4325.
Efstradiatis, A., Posakony, J. W., Maniatis, T., Lawn, R. M., O'Connell, C., Spritz, R. A., DeRiel, J. K., Forget, B. G., Weissman, S. M., Slightom, J. L., Blechl, A. E., Smithies, O., Baralle, F. E., Shoulders, C. C., and Proudfoot, N. J. (1980). *Cell* **21**, 653–668.
Eichner, R., Bonitz, P., and Sun, T.-T. (1984). *J. Cell Biol.* **98**, 1388–1396.
Eichner, R., Sun, T.-T., and Aebi, U. (1986). *J. Cell. Biol.* **102**, 1767–1777.
Fisher, D. Z., Chaudhuary, N., and Blobel, G. (1986). *Proc. Natl. Acad. U.S.A.* **83**, 6450–6454.
Franke, W. W., Schmid, E., Winter, S., Osborn, M., and Weber, K. (1979). *Exp. Cell Res.* **123**, 25–46.
Franke, W. W., Schiller, D. L., Hatzfeld, M., and Winter, S. (1983). *Proc. Natl. Acad. Sci. U.S.A.* **80**, 7113–7117.
Frazer, R. D. B., MacRae, T. P., and Rogers, G. E. (1972). *In* "Keratins" (R. D. B. Frazer, T. P. MacRae and G. E. Rogers, eds.), pp. 56–82.
Fuchs, E., and Green, H. (1980). *Cell* **10**, 1033–1042.
Fuchs, E., and Green, H. (1981). *Cell* **25**, 617–625.
Fuchs, E., and Hanukoglu, I. (1983). *Cell* **34**, 332–334.
Fuchs, E., and Marchuk, D. (1983). *Proc. Natl. Acad. Sci. U.S.A.* **80**, 5857–5861.
Fuchs, E. V., Coppock, S. M., Green, H., and Cleveland, D. W. (1981). *Cell* **27**, 75–84.
Garnier, J., Osguthorpe, D. J., and Robson, B. (1978). *J. Mol. Biol.* **120**, 97–120.
Geisler, N., and Weber, K. (1981). *Proc. Natl. Acad. Sci. U.S.A.* **78**, 4120–4123.
Geisler, N., and Weber, K. (1982). *EMBO J.* **1**, 1649–1656.
Geisler, N., Kaufmann, E., and Weber, K. (1982). *Cell* **30**, 277–286.
Geisler, N., Kaufmann, E., Fischer, S., Plessmann, U., and Weber, K. (1983). *EMBO J.* **2**, 1295–1302.
Geisler, N., Kaufmann, E., and Weber, K. (1985). *J. Mol. Biol.* **182**, 173–177.
Gilbert, W. (1978). *Nature (London)* **271**, 501.
Gilfix, B. M., and Green, H. (1984). *J. Cell Physiol.* **119**, 172–174.
Gillies, S. D., Morrison, S. L., Oi, V. T., and Tonegawa, S. (1983). *Cell* **33**, 717–728.

Glass, C., Kim, K. H., and Fuchs, E. (1985). *J. Cell Biol.* **101**, 2366–2373.
Green, H., and Watt, F. M. (1982). *Mol. Cell. Biol.* **2**, 1115–1117.
Greer, C., and Schekman, R. (1982). *Mol. Cell. Biol.* **2**, 1270–1278.
Hanukoglu, I., and Fuchs, E. (1982). *Cell* **31**, 243–252.
Hanukoglu, I., and Fuchs, E. (1983). *Cell* **33**, 915–924.
Hatzfeld, M., and Franke, W. W. (1985). *J. Cell Biol.* **101**, 1826–1841.
Henderson, D., Geisler, N., and Weber, K. (1982). *J. Mol. Biol.* **155**, 173–176.
Hong, B.-S., and Davison, P. F. (1981). *Biochim. Biophys. Acta* **670**, 139–145.
Inana, G., Piatigorsky, J., Norman, B., Slingsby, C., and Blundell, T. (1983). *Nature (London)* **304**, 310–315.
Ip, W., Hartzer, M. K., Susana Pang, Y.-Y., and Robson, R. M. (1985). *J. Mol. Biol.* **183**, 365–375.
Johnson, L. D., Idler, W. W., Zhou, X-M., Roop, D. R., and Steinert, P. M. (1985). *Proc. Natl. Acad. Sci. U.S.A.* **82**, 1896–1900.
Jonas, E., Sargent, T. D., and Dawid, I. B. (1985). *Proc. Natl. Acad. Sci. U.S.A.* **82**, 5413–5417.
Jorcano, J. L., Franz, J. K., and Franke, W. W. (1984a). *Differentiation* **28**, 155–163.
Jorcano, J. L., Rieger, M., Franz, J. K., Schiller, D. L., Moll, R., and Franke, W. W. (1984b). *J. Mol. Biol.* **179**, 257–281.
Kim, K. H., Rheinwald, J. G., and Fuchs, E. V. (1983). *Mol. Cell. Biol.* **3**, 495–502.
Kim, K. H., Marchuk, D., and Fuchs, E. (1984a). *J. Cell Biol.* **99**, 1872–1877.
Kim, K. H., Schwartz, F., and Fuchs, E. (1984b). *Proc. Natl. Acad. Sci. U.S.A.* **81**, 4280–4284.
Knapp, A. C., Franke, W. W., Heid, H., Hatzfeld, M., Jorcano, J. L., and Moll, R. (1986a). *J. Cell. Biol.* **103**, 657–667.
Knapp, B., Rentrop, M., Schweizer, J., and Winter, H. (1986b). *Nucleic Acids Res.* **14**, 751–763.
Kreis, T. E., Geiger, B., Schmid, E., Jorcano, J. L., and Franke, W. W. (1983). *Cell* **32**, 1125–1137.
Krieg, T. M., Schafer, M. P., Cheng, C. K., Filpula, D., Flaherty, P., Steinert, P. M., and Roop, D. R. (1985). *J. Biol. Chem.* **260**, 5867–5870.
Laimins, L. A., Khoury, G., Gorman, C., Howard, B., and Gruss, P. (1982). *Proc. Natl. Acad. Sci. U.S.A.* **79**, 6453–6457.
Lane, E. B. (1982). *J. Cell Biol.* **92**, 665–673.
Lasek, R. J., Krishnan, N., and Kaiserman-Abramof, J. R. (1979). *J. Cell Biol.* **82**, 336–346.
Lazarides, E. (1980). *Nature (London)* **283**, 249–256.
Lee, L. D., and Baden, H. P. (1976). *Nature (London)* **264**, 377–379.
Lewis, S. A., and Cowan, N. J. (1986). *Mol. Cell. Biol.* **6**, 1529–1534.
Lewis, S. A., Balcarek, J. M., Krek, V., Shelanski, M., and Cowan, N. J. (1984). *Proc. Natl. Acad. Sci. U.S.A.* **81**, 2743–2746.
McKeon, F. D., Kirschner, M. W., and Caput, D. (1986). *Nature (London)* **319**, 463–468.
McLachlan, A. D. (1978). *J. Mol. Biol.* **124**, 297–304.
McLachlan, A. D., and Stewart, M. (1975). *J. Mol. Biol.* **98**, 293–304.
McLachlan, A. D., and Stewart, M. (1982). *J. Mol. Biol.* **162**, 693–698.
Magin, T. M., Jorcano, J. L., and Franke, W. W. (1983). *EMBO J.* **2**, 1387–1392.
Marchuk, D., McCrohon, S., and Fuchs, E. (1984). *Cell* **39**, 491–498.
Marchuk, D., McCrohon, S., and Fuchs, E. (1985). *Proc. Natl. Acad. Sci. U.S.A.* **82**, 1609–1613.
Mercer, E. H., and Matoltsy, A. G. (1969). *In* "Advances in Biology of Skin; Hair Growth" (W. Montagna and R. L. Dobson, eds.), Vol 9, p. 556.

Milam, L., and Erickson, H. P. (1982). *J. Cell Biol.* **94**, 592–596.

Milstone, L. M. (1981). *J. Cell Biol.* **88**, 317–322.

Moll, R., Franke, W. W., Schiller, D. L., Geiger, B., and Krepeer, R. (1982). *Cell* **31**, 11–24.

Moreau, P., Hen, R., Wasylyk, B., Everett, R., Gaub, M. P., and Chambon, P. (1981). *Nucleic Acids Res.* **9**, 6047–6068.

Nathans, J., and Hogness, D. S. (1983). *Cell* **34**, 807–814.

Parry, D. A. D., Crewther, W. G., Fraser, R. D., and MacRae, T. P. (1977). *J. Mol. Biol.* **113**, 449–454.

Parry, D. A. D., Steven, A. C., and Steinert, P. M. (1985). *Biochem. Biophys. Res. Comm.* **127**, 1012–1018.

Pauling, L., and Corey, R. B. (1953). *Nature (London)* **171**, 59–61.

Phillips, L. L., Autilio-Gambetti, L., and Lasek, R. J. (1983). *Brain Res.* **278**, 219–223.

Powell, B. C., Sleigh, M. J., Ward, K. A., and Rogers, G. E. (1983). *Nucleic Acids Res.* **11**, 5327–5346.

Powell, B. C., Cam, G. R., Fietz, M. J., and Rogers, G. E. (1986). *Proc. Natl. Acad. Sci. U.S.A.* **83**, 5048–5052.

Pruss, R. M., Mirsky, R., Raff, M. C., Thorpe, R., Dowding. A. J., and Anderton, B. H. (1981). *Cell* **27**, 419–428.

Quax, W., Egberts, W. V., Hendriks, W., Quax-Jeuken, Y., and Bloemendal, H. (1983). *Cell* **35**, 215–223.

Quax, W., van den Broek, L., Egberts, W. V., Ramaekers, F., and Bloemendal, H. (1985). *Cell* **43**, 327–338.

Quinlan, R. A., Cohlberg, J. A., Schiller, D. L., Hatzfeld, M., and Franke, W. W. (1984). *J. Mol. Biol.* **178**, 365–388.

RayChaudhury, A., Marchuk, D., Lindhurst, M., and Fuchs, E. (1986). *Mol. Cell. Biol.* **6**, 539–548.

Rieger, M., Jorcano, J. L., and Franke, W. W. (1985). *EMBO J.* **4**, 2261–2267.

Roop, D. R., Hawley-Nelson, P., Cheng, C. K., and Yuspa, S. H. (1983). *Proc. Natl. Acad. Sci. U.S.A.* **80**, 716–720.

Rudall, K. M. (1968). *In* "Comprehensive Biochemistry" (M. Florkin and E. H. Stotz, eds.), Vol 26B, p. 559.

Sauk, J. J., Krumweide. M., Cocking-Johnson, D., and White, J. G. (1984). *J. Cell Biol.* **99**, 1590–1597.

Scholer, H. R., and Gruss, P. (1984). *Cell* **36**, 403–411.

Singer, P. A., Trevor, K., and Oshima, R. G. (1986). *J. Biol. Chem.* **261**, 538–547.

Skerrow, D., Matoltsy, G., and Matoltsy, M. (1973). *J. Biol. Chem.* **248**, 4820–4826.

Sparrow, L. G., and Inglis, A. S. (1980). *Proc. Quinquen. Int. Wool Text. Res. Conf., 6th, Pretoria* **2**, 237–246.

Spitzer, R. H., Downing, S. W., Koch, E. A., Salo, W. L., and Saidel, L. J. (1984). *J. Cell Biol.* **98**, 670–677.

Steinert, P. M. (1978). *J. Mol. Biol.* **123**, 49–70.

Steinert, P. M., and Idler, W. W. (1975). *Biochem. J.* **151**, 603–614.

Steinert, P. M., Idler, W. W., and Zimmerman, S. B. (1976). *J. Mol. Biol.* **108**, 547–567.

Steinert, P. M., Zimmerman, S. B., Starger, J. M., and Goldman, R. D. (1978). *Proc. Natl. Acad. Sci. U.S.A.* **75**, 6098–6101.

Steinert, P. M., Rice, R. H., Roop, D. R., Trus, B. L., and Steven, A. C. (1983). *Nature (London)* **302**, 794–800.

Steinert, P. M., Parry, D. A. D., Racoosin, E. L., Idler, W. W., Steven, A. C., Trus, B. L., and Roop, D. R. (1984). *Proc. Natl. Acad. Sci. U.S.A.* **81**, 5709–5713.

Steinert, P. M., Steven, A. C., and Roop, D. R. (1985). *Cell* **42**, 411–419.

Steven, A. C., Wall, J., Hainfeld, J., and Steinert, P. M. (1982). *Proc. Natl. Acad. Sci. U.S.A.* **79,** 3101–3105.

Steven, A. C., Hainfeld, J. F., Trus, B. L., Wall, J. S., and Steinert, P. M. (1983). *J. Biol. Chem.* **258,** 8323–8329.

Sun, T.-T., and Green, H. (1978). *J. Biol. Chem.* **253,** 2053–2060.

Tolle, H.-G., Weber, K., and Osborn, M. (1985). *Eur. J. Cell Biol.* **38,** 234–244.

Tseng, S., Jarvinen, M. J., Nelson, W. G., Huang, J. W., Woodcock-Mitchell, J., and Sun, T.-T. (1982). *Cell* **30,** 361–372.

Tyner, A. L., and Fuchs, E. (1986). *J. Cell Biol.,* in press.

Tyner, A. L., Eichman, M. J., and Fuchs, E. (1985). *Proc. Natl. Acad. Sci. U.S.A.* **82,** 4683–4687.

Walter, M. F., and Biessmann, H. (1984). *J. Cell Biol.* **99,** 1468–1477.

Weber, K., Shaw, G., Osborn, M., Debus, E., and Geisler, N. (1983). *Cold Spring Harbor Symp. Quant. Biol.* **48,** 717–729.

Weiss, R. A., Eichner, R., and Sun, T.-T. (1984). *J. Cell Biol.* **98,** 1397–1406.

Woods, E. F., and Gruen, L. C. (1981). *Aust. J. Biol. Sci.* **34,** 515–526.

Wozney, J., Hanahan, D., Morimoto, R., Boedtker, H., and Doty, P. (1981). *Proc. Natl. Acad. Sci. U.S.A.* **78,** 712–716.

Wu, Y.-J., Binder, L. M., Beckett, M. A., Sinard, J. H., Griffiths, C. T., and Rheinwald, J. G. (1982). *Cell* **31,** 693–703.

CHAPTER 3

EXPRESSION AND MODIFICATION OF KERATINS DURING TERMINAL DIFFERENTIATION OF MAMMALIAN EPIDERMIS

P. E. Bowden, H.-J. Stark, D. Breitkreutz, and N. E. Fusenig*

INSTITUTE OF BIOCHEMISTRY
GERMAN CANCER RESEARCH CENTER (DKFZ)
D-6900 HEIDELBERG, FEDERAL REPUBLIC OF GERMANY

I. Introduction

Mammalian epidermis is a keratinized stratified squamous epithelium that undergoes many complex changes in morphology and related biochemical activity during the process of terminal differentiation (Matoltsy, 1976). Recently, attention has been focused on the molecular events that orchestrate the process of epidermal differentiation. Additional impetus for these studies has been provided by the need to understand the molecular basis of abnormal differentiation states in epithelial cells, which are known to be characteristic of several epidermal disorders. Also, keratinocytes are better suited than fibroblasts for the molecular studies related to tumor pathogenesis which now makes more knowledge of keratinocyte cell biology, biochemistry, and molecular biology a major research goal.

To date, many attempts have been made to culture epidermal cells (keratinocytes) in a way that completely preserves the "normal" program (as *in vivo*) of terminal differentiation (for review see Fusenig, 1986). Such an *in vitro* system would provide a controlled environment in which to study the molecular events involved. Several *in vitro* systems have been developed, but mainly due to the necessity for interplay between the epidermal keratinocytes and various underlying structures (e.g., basement membrane, dermal collagen architecture, and fibroblasts), it has been difficult to perfectly duplicate *in vivo* epidermis without the addition of variables such as living dermis (Fusenig, 1986). However, it is possible to elucidate some aspects of

* Present address: Dermatology Branch, National Cancer Institute, National Institutes of Health, Bethesda, Maryland 20892.

35

CURRENT TOPICS IN
DEVELOPMENTAL BIOLOGY, VOL. 22

molecular differentiation by comparison of the *in vivo* situation with the available culture systems.

In the present studies, we have examined keratin intermediate filament (IF) proteins in both epidermis (*in vivo*) and primary cultured keratinocytes, as the expression and modification of these proteins represent a major commitment of the keratinocyte to terminal differentiation (Brody, 1964; Green *et al.*, 1982). In particular, two aspects of epidermal keratin modification will be addressed, the differentiation-related proteolysis that is concomitant with formation of the stratum corneum and the posttranslational phosphorylation of keratins in the living epidermal cells. Details of the properties and expression of epidermal keratins (sometimes referred to as prekeratins) and comparison to the keratins of epidermal appendages (hair, nail, follicle, etc.) and other epithelia (cytokeratins or prekeratins) will be necessary, as will some discussion of keratin structure in the light of recent sequence data. However, more detailed aspects of these subjects appear elsewhere in this book (see Franke *et al.*, Fuchs *et al.*, Rheinwald *et al.*, Roop *et al.*, and Sun *et al.*, this volume).

Keratins are a complex group of differentiation-related IF proteins, which together with microtubules and microfilaments form the essential structural components of the epithelial cell cytoskeleton (for reviews see Anderton, 1981; Franke *et al.*, 1982; Lazarides, 1982; Steinert and Parry, 1985; Steinert *et al.*, 1985a). To date, 19 epithelial keratins have been identified in man (Moll *et al.*, 1982a; Quinlan *et al.*, 1985), and a similar number exist in mouse, rat, and cow (Franke *et al.*, 1981). Recently, several others which appear to be specific to hair (and nail) have been characterized (Lynch *et al.*, 1985; P. E. Bowden and H.-J. Stark, unpublished observations) and this has brought the recent work on IF proteins together with earlier work on wool and hair keratins (Steinert and Rogers, 1973; Dowling *et al.*, 1983; Crewther *et al.*, 1983; Weber and Geisler, 1984).

Keratins can be divided into two subfamilies (type I acidic and type II neutral-basic) according to their biochemical and immunological properties (Schiller *et al.*, 1982; Bowden *et al.*, 1984b; Eichner *et al.*, 1984) and by recent amino acid sequence data, both empirical and cDNA/genomic clone derived (Hanukoglu and Fuchs, 1983; Jorcano *et al.*, 1984; Steinert *et al.*, 1984, 1985a,b; Johnson *et al.*, 1985; Glass *et al.*, 1985; Bader *et al.*, 1986; Dowling *et al.*, 1986; Magin *et al.*, 1986; RayChaudhury *et al.*, 1986; Romano *et al.*, 1986). Type I keratins tend to be smaller (40–64 kDa) and more acidic (p*I* 4.8–5.7) while type II keratins tend to be larger (54–70 kDa) and more basic (p*I* 5.8–8.0). Both types are immunologically distinct (e.g., monoclonal antibody AE1 reacts with most type I and AE3 with most type II keratins; see

Sun *et al.*, 1985) and while there is about 60% sequence homology within each subfamily, only about 30% homology exists between subfamilies (Hanukoglu and Fuchs, 1983; Steinert *et al.*, 1985a; Fuchs *et al.*, 1985).

II. Keratins and Epidermal Differentiation

Although up to 30 individual epithelial keratins may exist, not all of them are expressed in any one epithelial cell type at any one time. Mouse and human epidermis express between two and eight major keratins depending on the stage of differentiation and anatomical location. The major ultrastructural changes that occur during terminal differentiation of mammalian epidermis are shown in Fig. 1. These data are based on an electron microscope study of neonatal mouse skin (Axel Bohnert) but the results are equally applicable to human epidermis. Important differentiation-related features to note are alterations in tonofilament density and organization, appearance of specialized organelles (keratohyalin granules, membrane-coating granules, lysosomes) in the stratum granulosum (granular layer), the generation of a cross-linked cell envelope prior to the removal of cellular organelles (Green *et al.*, 1982), and formation of the dead "horny layer" or stratum corneum (Brody, 1970; Matoltsy, 1976).

Changes in keratin expression and modification in mouse epidermis are also summarized in Fig. 1 and the underlying experimental details are presented below. This recent work has shown that previously observed differences between the keratin content of living epidermal cells and the stratum corneum (Fuchs and Green, 1980; Bowden and Cunliffe, 1981) result from the proteolytic modification of existing keratins. In addition, further evidence has been obtained in support of the finding that changes in keratin expression occur as living epidermal cells undergo differentiation (Skerrow and Skerrow, 1983; Bowden *et al.*, 1984b; Schweizer *et al.*, 1984). Similar findings have been made with human epidermis but the mouse data are more complete.

A. KERATIN EXPRESSION IN EPIDERMAL CELLS

Keratin IF proteins are very abundant in mammalian epidermis (25–35% of total protein), and the levels of keratin synthetic activity attained are dependent on the differentiation state of the keratinocyte. Levels are higher in suprabasal cells than basal cells but decline as cells reach the upper granular layer. An average contribution of keratins to the total protein profile can be obtained by extracting all SDS (sodium dodecyl sulfate)-soluble proteins (in the presence of a reducing agent such as β-mercaptoethanol) from a preparation of pure epidermis (see Bowden and Cunliffe, 1981; Bowden *et al.*, 1984b). Sam-

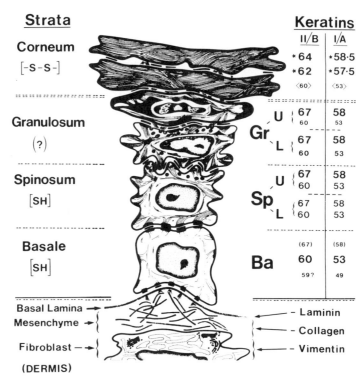

Fig. 1. Schematic of the major ultrastructural changes that occur during terminal differentiation of mouse (and human) epidermis. Successive layers from the inner stratum basale to the outer stratum corneum are shown on the left (SH, reducing, and S-S, oxidizing environment) and keratin expression in each layer on the right (the numbers designate relative molecular weight in thousands and size approximates to relative abundance). Keratins in left column (II/B) are type II basic-neutral and those in the right column are type I acidic (I/A). [Reproduced from Fusenig (1986) with permission of the publisher.]

ples of total mouse epidermal protein prepared in this manner were analyzed by SDS–polyacrylamide gradient (7.5–17.5%) slab gel electrophoresis (Fig. 2, lane 2). In addition to the keratins (40–70 kDa), the histidine-rich protein filaggrin (30 kDa; Dale *et al.*, 1985) and a group of histones (12–20 kDa) were also very prominent in neonatal mouse epidermis. A mixture of seven standard proteins (phosphorylase b, 94 kDa; bovine serum albumin, 68 kDa; pyruvate kinase, 58 kDa; L-glutamate dehydrogenase, 53 kDa; α-actin, 42 kDa; carbonic anhydrase, 29 kDa; and lysozyme, 14.3 kDa) were used to calibrate the gel (lane 1) for molecular mass determination.

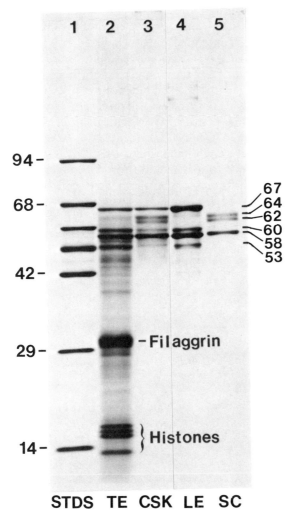

FIG. 2. SDS–polyacrylamide gradient (7.5–17.5%) slab gel electrophoresis of keratins isolated from mouse epidermis. Gels were calibrated with a mixture of seven standard (STDS) proteins (see text; lane 1, 14.3–94 kDa). Lane 2, total extract of whole epidermis (TE). Note that the keratins (40–70 kDa), filaggrin (30 kDa), and histones (12–20 kDa) were all major epidermal products. Lane 3, cytoskeletal (CSK) extraction of whole epidermis which considerably purified the keratins. Lane 4, CASC buffer preparation (see text) of whole epidermis which only extracts living epidermal cells (LE) and simplifies the keratin profile. Lane 5, Tris–urea–mercaptoethanol extract of pure stratum corneum (SC). Note that the keratins from these dead cells differ from those of living epidermal cells (LE).

Epidermal tonofilaments are composed of keratin IF proteins that are particularly resistant to nonionic detergents and 1.5 M salt, properties that have been exploited in the "cytoskeletal" (CSK) method of keratin purification (Bowden et al., 1984b; Breitkreutz et al., 1984). Cytoskeletal extracts of newborn mouse epidermis contained six major (67, 64, 62, 60, 58, and 53 kDa) and two minor (49 and 47 kDa) keratins (Fig. 2, lane 3). However, an alternative method of purifying keratins from living epidermis (prekeratins) with 0.1 M citric acid–sodium citrate (CASC) buffer, pH 2.65 (Matoltsy, 1964; Bowden and Cunliffe, 1981) indicated that only four keratins (67, 60, 58, and 53 kDa) were present in epidermal keratinocytes (Fig. 2, lane 4). Similar results were obtained with samples of human epidermis extracted by this procedure (Table I). These living cell keratins were also subjected to two-dimensional analysis (NEpHGE/SDS–PAGE, nonequilibrium pH gradient electrophoresis, pH 4.0–9.0; and IEF/SDS–PAGE, isoelectric focusing, pH 4.5–6.5) and the individual isoelectric points determined (Table I; see also Figs. 5 and 6).

Therefore, at least two major keratins in the CSK extracts of whole epidermis must originate from the stratum corneum, where they resist CASC buffer extraction. The other four major keratins (two type II and two type I) are truly representative of living epidermal cells (mouse and human). For reasons that will become clear later, these four keratins have been divided into two further subsets (A and B; see Table I).

TABLE I

MOUSE AND HUMAN EPIDERMAL KERATINS *in Vivo*[a]

	Number	Type	Subset	Mouse		Human	
				M_r	pI	M_r	pI
Living	1	II	A	67	8.0	68	7.8
epidermis	5	II	B	60	7.4	60	7.4
(LE)	10	I	A	58	5.5	57	5.5
	14	I	B	53	5.4	51	5.4
Stratum	1b	II	A*	64	7.0	65	7.0
corneum	1c	II	A*	62	6.6		
(SC)	10	I	A	58	5.5	57	5.5
	10a	I	A*	57.5	5.4	55	5.1

[a]For explanation of number, type, and subset see text. Relative molecular mass (M_r) is in kilodaltons (kDa) and the relative isoelectric point (pI) given is the pH of the most basic isoelectric variant as determined in 9.5 M urea. The SC keratins marked with an asterisk (*) are derived from existing gene products (see text).

B. KERATINS OF THE STRATUM CORNEUM

The corneocytes that make up the stratum corneum are very different from the underlying living keratinocytes (Matoltsy, 1976). They consist of a mass of highly organized keratin filaments embedded in a disulfide cross-linked matrix surrounded by a glutamyllysine cross-linked plasma membrane or envelope (Brody, 1970; Rice and Green, 1977; Matoltsy, 1980; Hennings *et al.*, 1981; Rothnagel and Rogers, 1984; Simon and Green, 1984). Efficient extraction of keratins from this material requires denaturing (SDS or urea) and reducing agents (dithioerythritol or β-mercaptoethanol). Extracts of stratum corneum (SC) keratin contain 60–85% of the total horny cell protein (Green *et al.*, 1982; Steinert, 1975). Analysis of these extracts revealed that several keratins were present, some of which differed from the keratins of living epidermal cells (Baden and Lee, 1978; Bowden and Cunliffe, 1981; Hunter and Skerrow, 1981; Breitkreutz *et al.*, 1984).

In the mouse for example, four major keratins (64, 62, 58, and 57.5 kDa) were found in the stratum corneum (Fig. 2, lane 5). The smaller pair of SC keratins were not well resolved in these gels but can be clearly separated on two-dimensional gels (IEF/SDS–PAGE; see Bowden *et al.*, 1984b). Three of these keratins were unique to the stratum corneum but the other (58 kDa) was also found in living keratinocytes. Results obtained with human stratum corneum were similar (Table I; also see Fig. 6b). As corneocytes have little or no metabolic activity, these distinct SC keratins must either arise as late synthetic products in the upper granular layer or be derived from preexisting keratins synthesized in the underlying spinous and lower granular cells.

In order to demonstrate a precursor–product relationship between keratinocyte and corneocyte IF proteins, individual keratins isolated from the living epidermis and the stratum corneum were compared by peptide mapping (Fig. 3; also see Bowden *et al.*, 1984b). It was concluded that the 64- and 62-kDa keratins (type IIA*) from mouse stratum corneum were derived from the 67-kDa keratin (type IIA) prominent in the living epidermal cells. This was also true for the mouse type IA keratin (58 kDa cleaved to 57.5 kDa), and both human type IIA (68 kDa cleaved to 65 kDa) and type IA (57 kDa cleaved to 55 kDa) keratins.

In addition, SC keratins were more acidic than their precursors (Table I; see also Figs. 5 and 6) but still displayed isoelectric variation. These findings are in agreement with recent data on terminal sequences of mouse and human epidermal keratins (Steinert *et al.*, 1983, 1985b) and with immunofluorescence data using antisera specific for

LE Keratin

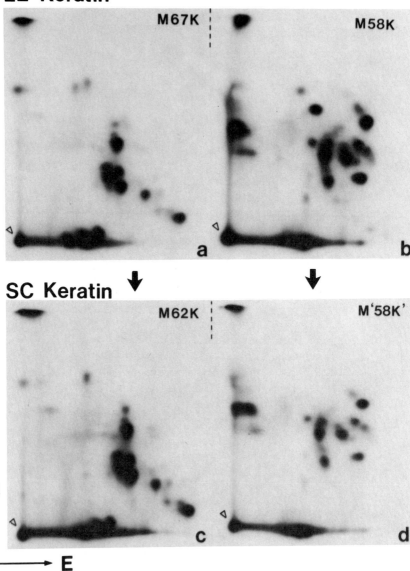

FIG. 3. Two-dimensional tryptic maps of individual mouse keratins isolated from extracts of living epidermal cells (a and b) or stratum corneum (c and d). Keratins were radioiodinated and trypsin digested, and the resulting labeled fragments separated in two dimensions by electrophoresis (E) and ascending chromatography (C) and visualized by autoradiography (arrowhead on lower left marks the origin). The 67-kDa keratin (M67K) of living epidermal cells (a) and the 62-kDa SC keratin (M62K) (c) had almost identical tryptic fingerprints. This was also true of the 58-kDa keratin (M58K) from granular cells and the 58/57.5-kDa keratins (M'58K') from stratum corneum.

keratin C-terminal sequences (Roop *et al.*, 1984). Together these results infer that basic terminal sequences are removed from the keratins as living cells differentiate and enter the stratum corneum. However, SC keratins still demonstrate isoelectric variation, so they presumably remain phosphorylated (see Section IV,A).

C. SEQUENTIAL EXPRESSION OF EPIDERMAL KERATINS

Analysis of keratins extracted from horizontal sections of human plantar epidermis (Fuchs and Green, 1980; Bowden and Cunliffe, 1981) indicated that alterations in keratin expression occurred sequentially during differentiation. Proteolytic modification of epidermal keratins in the later stages of differentiation has already been dealt with but the plantar epidermis data also indicated that changes occurred as living keratinocytes matured. Unavailability of the relevant monospecific keratin antisera made an immunocytochemical approach difficult but because certain keratin antisera showed differential staining of the basal and suprabasal cells (unpublished data), the keratin content of isolated epidermal cell fractions was examined.

Neonatal mouse epidermis was separated by trypsin treatment from the underlying dermis and both pieces labeled in medium containing [^{35}S]methionine. Epidermal cell fractions were prepared by filtration and Percoll density gradient centrifugation of cells scraped from the dermal and epidermal surfaces, and further by sequential removal of cells from the sheets of stratum corneum with 10 mM EDTA. Cell fractions were judged 80–90% pure by light microscopy (stained preparations and phase contrast) and immunofluorescence with keratin- and other epidermal cell-specific sera.

Extraction and SDS–PAGE analysis of basal, spinous, and granular cell fractions (Fig. 4a) showed that subset B keratins (60 and 53 kDa) that were major components in basal cell fractions declined in quantity as differentiation proceeded. The reverse was true of the subset A keratins (67 and 58 kDa), which steadily increased in relative quantity during differentiation such that these keratins were the major filament components in cells of the granular layer. The cells of the spinous layer were intermediate in keratin profile between basal and granular cells and represent an area in the epidermis where both subset B ("basal") and A ("suprabasal" or "differentiation-specific") keratins exist in approximately equal quantities. These results were in general agreement with recent monoclonal antibody studies of human epidermis (Woodcock-Mitchell *et al.*, 1982; Sun *et al.*, 1985) but provided a more quantitative evaluation.

Keratins from these cell fractions were also analyzed by two-dimensional electrophoresis (Fig. 5a,b) but no changes in the isoelectric

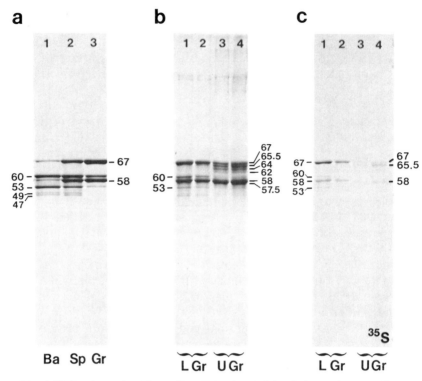

Fig. 4. SDS–polyacrylamide gradient (7.5–17.5%) slab gel electrophoresis of keratins extracted from isolated cell fractions of [³⁵S]methionine-labeled mouse epidermis by the cytoskeletal method. (a) Keratins from basal (Ba), spinous (Sp), and granular (Gr) cell fractions (lanes 1–3, respectively). Note a reciprocal change in the expression of subset B keratins (60 and 53 kDa; decrease during differentiation) and subset A keratins (67 and 58 kDa; increase). (b) Keratins from lower (LGr) and upper (UGr) granular layer fractions (lanes 1–4, respectively). Note the gradual disappearance of subset B ("basal cell") keratins (60 and 53 kDa) and in lanes 3 and 4, the appearance of a prominent intermediate (65.5 kDa) and the stratum corneum keratins (64, 62, and 57.5 kDa). (c) Fluorograph of b showing that methionine was incorporated mainly into subset A keratins in the granular layer and although the 65.5-kDa intermediate was labeled the stratum corneum keratins were not.

properties of individual keratins were apparent as cells differentiated. These results are similar to those of Schweizer and co-workers (1984) and in general agreed with the previous work on human epidermis (Skerrow and Skerrow, 1983). Furthermore, recent *in situ* hybridization experiments with riboprobes made from human and mouse keratin cDNA (D. R. Roop, personal communication) have confirmed our findings.

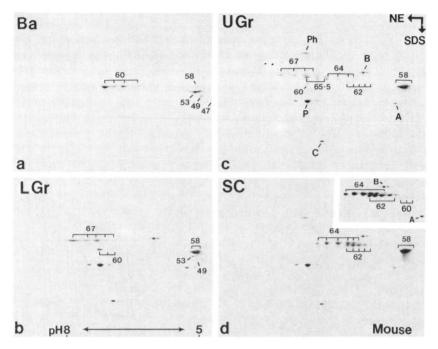

FIG. 5. Two-dimensional analysis (NEpHGE, pH 4–9 and SDS–PAGE) of keratins from mouse epidermal cell fractions (basal, spinous, and granular) and stratum corneum. Epidermis was labeled with [35S]methionine prior to fractionation and the labeled keratins were coelectrophoresed with standards (see text): Ph, phosphorylase b, 94 kDa, 7.5; B, bovine serum albumin, 68 kDa, 6.4; P, 3-phosphoglycerate kinase, 43 kDa, 7.4; A, α-actin, 42 kDa, 5.4; C, carbonic anhydrase, 29 kDa, 7.2). (a) Basal (Ba) cell fractions contained two type II (basic) keratins (60 kDa and trace amounts of 67 kDa) and four type I (acidic) keratins (53 kDa, major; 49 and 47 kDa, minor; 58 kDa, very minor). (b) Lower granular (LGr) cell fractions contained larger quantities of subset A ("suprabasal") keratins (67 and 58 kDa) than subset B ("basal cell") keratins (60 and 53 kDa). Trace amounts of the small keratins (49 and 47 kDa) were still present in these cells. (c) Upper granular (UGr) cell fractions showed evidence of sequential proteolysis which produced a "ladder" of smaller and more acidic products (65.5, 64, and 62 kDa) of the 67-kDa keratin. Small amounts of the 60-kDa keratin were still present but there was no trace of the smaller acidic keratins. (d) Extracts of pure stratum corneum (SC) contained two modified type II (A*) keratins (64 and 62 kDa) and two type I keratins (58 and 57.5 kDa). Minor amounts of another protein (60 kDa) were also observed when gels were heavily loaded (see inset). No traces of the 65.5-, 60-, 53-, 49-, or 47-kDa keratins were found.

D. KERATIN MODIFICATION IN THE GRANULAR LAYER

While fractionating mouse epidermis, separation of lower and upper granular cells was achieved as the latter adhere strongly to corneocytes of the stratum corneum. Analysis of keratins from these fractions (Figs. 4b and 5b,c) identified a new keratin (65.5 kDa), intermediate in both size and charge between the 67-kDa keratin and the SC keratins (64 and 62 kDa). Furthermore, this intermediate keratin was labeled with [^{35}S]methionine (Fig. 4c) while the SC keratins were not.

It is unclear at the moment whether the 65.5-kDa keratin is a product of de novo synthesis or proteolysis. The latter is more consistent with the present scenario but the answer must await further peptide mapping and *in vitro* translation experiments. Work on the analysis of granular cell fractions also showed that the levels of subset B (60 and 53 kDa) and smaller mouse epidermal keratins (49 and 47 kDa) progressively declined to zero during terminal differentiation. Thus, these keratins do not contribute to the filaments in the stratum corneum.

Finally, it would appear that further limited proteolysis of the SC keratins does occur, because a 60-kDa keratin different from that found in the basal cells was identified in two-dimensional gels of stratum corneum extracts (Fig. 5d). The blurry appearance of the 58- and 57.5-kDa complex, and occasional presence of smaller type I keratins not found in the living epidermal cells, would also support this conclusion. However, SC keratins, especially when bound up in the filament matrix found *in vivo*, are extremely resistant to attack by proteases and very insoluble, properties well suited to their position on the skin surface. This and other data on the sequential expression and modification of mouse epidermal keratins are summarized in Table II, and where possible the assigned keratin number is functionally equivalent in both species and the same as that in the human cytokeratin catalog (Moll *et al.*, 1982a).

E. KERATINS IN HUMAN PALMAR–PLANTAR EPIDERMIS

Epidermis that covers the palms, soles, and heels (palmar–plantar) is highly specialized. It not only differs dramatically in histology but also expresses a much more complex keratin profile (Fig. 6).

A direct comparison between heel (plantar) epidermis and epidermis from several other locations (scalp, back, arm, leg) was made. As already described in Section II,A, the living epidermal cells from back skin (Fig. 6a) contained four major keratins (68 and 60 kDa type II; and 57 and 51 kDa type I). The same profile was found in extracts of

TABLE II

EXPRESSION OF MOUSE EPIDERMAL KERATINS *in Vivo*[a]

Number	Type	Subset	M_r	pI	Epidermal cell fractions				
					Ba	Sp	LGr	UGr	SC
1	II	A	67	8.0	(+)	++	+++	++	
1a	II	A*	65.5	7.5			+	++	
1b	II	A*	64	7.2				++	+++
1c	II	A*	62	6.7				+	+++
1d	II	A*	60	6.3					+
5	II	B	60	7.4	+++	++	+	(+)	
10	I	A	58	5.3	(+)	++	+++	+++	++
10a	I	A*	57.5	5.4				+	++
14	I	B	53	5.4	+++	++	+	(+)	
15	I	?	51	5.4	(+)	(+)			
16	I	C	49	5.1	+	(+)			
17	I	?	47	4.8	+	+	(+)		

[a]Relative molecular mass (M_r) is in kilodaltons (kDa), and the relative isoelectric point (pI) given is the pH of the most basic isoelectric variant (in 9.5 M urea). Keratins marked A* are derived from the corresponding subset A gene product by proteolysis. Relative abundance of keratin in each layer (Ba, basal; Sp, spinous; LGr, lower granular; UGr, upper granular; and SC, stratum corneum) is shown as follows: +++, major; ++, moderate; +, minor; (+), very minor.

scalp, breast, arm, and leg epidermis (comparison not shown) but the profile was slightly modified in foreskin epidermis (Fig. 8c; it has an extra major type II keratin, 54 kDa). The living cells of heel epidermis contained four additional keratins (59 and 58 kDa type II; and 64 and 49 kDa type I). Different individuals appeared to express the 59- and 64-kDa keratins at variable levels but the other six keratins were consistently observed as major components (Moll *et al.*, 1982b; Knapp *et al.*, 1986).

The palmar–plantar epidermal keratins also undergo modification in the granular layer much the same as those in the other anatomical regions. However, due to the more complex pattern of keratin expression, extracts of heel stratum corneum (Fig. 6d) were considerably more complex than the corresponding non-palmar–plantar region (Fig. 6b). The principal changes were similar in that the smaller type II (60, 59, 58 kDa) and type I (51 and 49 kDa) keratins appeared to be progressively lost as differentiation proceeded. The larger keratins (68 kDa type II; and 64 and 57 kDa type I) were modified and produced at least eight products (67, 65, 64, 62, and 60 kDa type II; and 63, 55, and

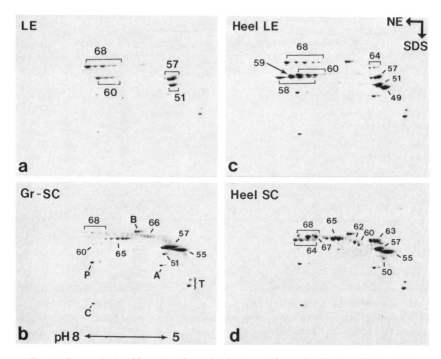

FIG. 6. Comparison of keratins from the living epidermal cells (a and c) or stratum corneum (b and d) of human back (a and b) and heel (c and d) skin. Keratins were separated by nonequilibrium pH gradient electrophoresis (NE, pH 4–9) and in the second dimension by SDS–polyacrylamide gel electrophoresis (SDS, 7.5–17.5% gradient gels). Standards were coelectrophoresed with the samples (see Fig. 5; T, tropomyosin, 33–37 kDa, 4.5). (a) CASC buffer (pH 2.65) extracts of human back skin [living epidermal (LE) cells] contained two type II (68 and 60 kDa) and two type I (57 and 51 kDa) keratins in approximately equal amounts. (b) Tris–urea–mercaptoethanol extracts of human back epidermis [upper granular layer and stratum corneum (Gr–SC) only]. Three keratins (65, 57, and 55 kDa) were present as major components together with minor amounts of keratins characteristic of living epidermal cells (68, 60, and 51 kDa). As in upper granular extracts of mouse epidermis (Fig. 5c) evidence of proteolysis was apparent. (c) CASC buffer extracts of human heel skin (living epidermal cells) (Heel LE) showed that keratin expression was more complex in this region (four type II keratins and four type I keratins). (d) Tris–urea–mercaptoethanol extracts of human heel stratum corneum (Heel SC) were also very complex. In addition to the 65-, 57-, and 55-kDa SC keratins found in other regions, plantar epidermis contained several others (67, 64, 63, 62, and 60 kDa) and traces of keratins (68. 60, 51, and 49 kDa) from the living cells below.

50 kDa type I), results which are in agreement with the limited published data (Fuchs and Green, 1980; Banks-Schlegel et al., 1981; Bowden and Cunliffe, 1981; Matoltsy et al., 1983).

Analyses were performed on several individuals of both sexes and considerably more variation was found in heel SC keratin profiles than in the corresponding living cell keratins. This variability in the extent of proteolytic modification between individuals is presumably because of differences in keratin expression and/or the structure (primary–secondary) of keratins or the enzymes that modify them. Genetic polymorphism could also contribute to such an effect but this is beyond the scope of the present work (see Wild and Miscke, 1986). A comparison of palm, heel, and sole stratum corneum samples from the same individual showed little variation in keratin profile (data not shown). Little variation was also found when serial horizontal sections through the stratum corneum of heel skin were made (data not shown), which showed that further extensive degradation of keratins does not occur, a consistent finding that differs from earlier published work (Steinert and Idler, 1979).

III. Keratins and Differentiation in Culture

Keratinocytes released from the epidermis with enzymes such as trypsin can be grown in primary epidermal culture (PEC). These cultures stratify and mimic some aspects of differentiation characteristic of epidermal keratinocytes *in vivo* (see Fusenig, 1986, and references therein). In particular, keratinocytes in primary culture can form cross-linked cell envelopes and squames mimicking stratum corneum formation *in vivo*. However, cells *in vitro* rarely produce keratohyalin granules and form fewer desmosomes than do keratinocytes *in vivo* (Breitkreutz et al., 1984). It was therefore of interest to examine keratin expression and modification in cultured keratinocytes and compare the findings to the epidermis (*in vivo*).

A. KERATIN EXPRESSION IN PRIMARY CULTURE

Keratin expression in primary epidermal culture followed the same principles in both species studied. In established confluent cultures (1–2 weeks after plating), differentiation-specific keratins (subset A) were absent or severely reduced while "basal cell" keratins (subset B) were present at high levels (Table III). Furthermore, these cells synthesized a third coexpressed pair (type II–type I) of keratins (subset C; 59 and 49 kDa in mouse and 58 and 49 kDa in human) which are not normally found in the epidermis (Table III; also see Fig. 8a). However, subset C keratins were present in normal human heel (plantar) epider-

TABLE III

KERATINS OF EPIDERMAL AND CULTURED KERATINOCYTES [a]

				Mouse			Human		
	Number	Type	Subset	M_r	pI	IEV	M_r	pI	IEV
Epidermis									
in vivo	1	II	A	67	8.0	6	68	7.8	6
	5	II	B	60	7.4	4	60	7.4	4
	10	I	A	58	5.5	6	57	5.5	6
	14	I	B	53	5.4	4	51	5.4	4
Primary culture (PEC)	5	II	B	60	7.4	4	60	7.4	4
	6	II	C	59	7.9	6	58	8.2	8
	14	I	B	53	5.4	4	51	5.4	4
	16	I	C	49	5.1	4	49	5.1	4

[a] For explanation of number, type, and subset see text. Relative molecular mass (M_r) is in kilodaltons (kDa), and the relative isoelectric point (pI) given is the pH of the most basic isoelectric variant as determined in 9.5 M urea (IEV, approximate number of isoelectric variants).

mis (see Fig. 6c), and the 49-kDa keratin (type IC) was found as a minor component in basal and spinous cell fractions of mouse epidermis (Fig. 5a,b). In addition, trace levels of type IC keratins could also be detected in extracts of whole epidermis (mouse and human) that had been labeled with [^{35}S]methionine or [^{14}C]glycine (see Bowden et al., 1987). These findings are in contrast to the normal rule of type II–type I coexpression, but absence of the type IIC keratins could be due to problems with detection of the small levels involved.

Subset C keratins are not degradation products of subset A or B keratins because they have unique V8 peptide maps (Fig. 7) and are among the mRNA translation products of cultured epidermal cells (Fuchs and Green, 1979; Roop et al., 1982; Kim et al., 1983). This is also substantiated by the limited primary sequence data available (Steinert et al., 1984; RayChaudhury et al., 1986; D. R. Roop, personal communication). In addition, cultured mouse cells expressed minor and variable amounts of another type I keratin (51 kDa; see Fig. 9,a–d) and could also conceivably express a type II equivalent (subset D?) in the 59- to 60-kDa region. However, clear evidence of another keratin in this region has not been found in mouse cultures even by the resolution obtained with two-dimensional electrophoresis, and a solution to this problem must await further investigation.

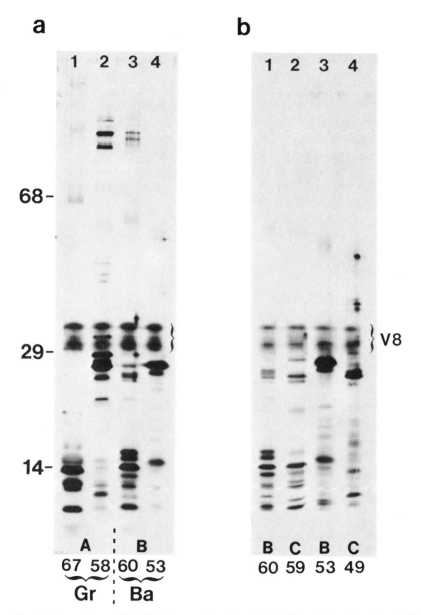

FIG. 7. Comparison of individual mouse keratins isolated from (a) epidermis and (b) primary culture by peptide mapping with V8 protease. Digested keratin fragments were analyzed by SDS–PAGE (10–20% gradient gel) and visualized by staining with silver. Although similarities were observed between all basic (67, 60, and 59 kDa) and all acidic (58, 53, and 49 kDa) keratins, the six mouse epidermal keratins all differed.

B. Variation in Keratin Expression

The keratin profile of mouse epidermal cell cultures was very consistent due to the use of back skin from age-matched (24–48 hours old) neonatal mice (C_3H strain) and established isolation and cultivation procedures (Fusenig and Worst, 1975). In contrast, methods for the isolation and culture of human keratinocytes were under development (different procedures and media) and the sources of skin were variable (anatomical site, age, sex). This gave rise to variable keratin expression in cultures of human keratinocytes (Fig. 8).

Cultures established from back, arm, leg, or breast skin epidermis were all similar in keratin profile (Fig. 8a), a finding consistent with the epidermal profiles (Section II,E). However, foreskin epidermal

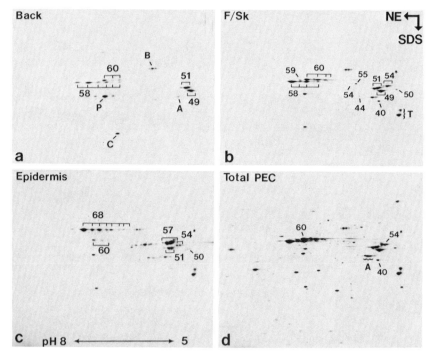

Fig. 8. Two-dimensional electrophoresis (NEpHGE/SDS) of keratins from primary keratinocyte cultures of human back skin (Back) (a) and foreskin (F/Sk) (b) and from foreskin epidermis (Epidermis) (c). Total proteins extracted from foreskin primary cultures (Total PEC) are shown in (d). Cultures of foreskin epidermis expressed a more complex pattern of keratins than cultures derived from other locations. The presence of two extra keratins (54 and 50 kDa) in foreskin epidermis (cf. Figs. 8a and 3a) provides a partial explanation (see text).

cultures expressed one major (54 kDa type I) and six minor (59, 55, and 54 kDa type II; and 50, 44, and 40 kDa type I) keratins in excess of the back skin profile (cf. Figs. 8a and b). These differences can in part be explained by the keratin profile of foreskin epidermis (Fig. 8c) which contained the extra 54- and 50-kDa type I keratins.

Although the other differences may be due to degradation of existing keratins, this is thought unlikely. Evidence from human heel epidermis (Fig. 6c) and mouse PEC (Bowden et al., 1985) would suggest that another type II keratin (59 kDa) exists. The other four extra keratins (55 and 54 kDa type II; and 44 and 40 kDa type I) are known to be present in cervical, bladder, and mesothelial cells (Moll et al., 1982a; Wu et al., 1982; Rheinwald and O'Connell, 1985) and could therefore represent outgrowth of minor cell populations. However, induction of these keratins in primary cultures of epidermal keratinocytes cannot be excluded and further work is required to clarify this point.

C. KERATIN MODIFICATION IN CULTURE

Although primary cultures of epidermal keratinocytes do express keratins as major differentiation products (Fig. 8d), the actual keratins expressed differ from those found in vivo (see Table III). These differences in keratin expression correlated with poor structural organization of these cultures (see Breitkreutz et al., 1984; Fusenig, 1986). Changes made in the culture systems ("organotypic" culture at air–liquid interface) did improve morphology but keratin expression was not altered significantly (data not shown). In particular, corneocytes produced on the surface of these cultures (mouse and human) did not show the ultrastructural organization typical of keratin filaments in vivo.

It has already been demonstrated that the stratum corneum (in vivo) consists exclusively of modified subset A keratins, yet cultured cells only synthesize these keratins in limited amounts under special circumstances (Fuchs and Green, 1981; Breitkreutz et al., 1984). It is therefore not possible for cultured keratinocytes to undergo the proteolytic modification of keratins that is characteristic of the epidermis (in vivo). In addition, cells in primary cultures have few if any keratohyalin granules, so it is not surprising that the corneocytes produced demonstrate poor structural organization. This would suggest either that tonofilaments made of subset B and C keratins differ significantly in their properties or that the poor structural organization results primarily from a lack of keratohyalin granules (Dale et al., 1985, and references therein). However, it was observed that long-term cultures which produce squames do experience some proteolysis of type IIB/IIC keratins (see Breitkreutz et al., 1984).

IV. Posttranslational Phosphorylation of Keratins

Posttranslational phosphorylation is a common feature of all IF proteins, and in most cases, serine appears to be the phosphate acceptor (Gilmartin et al., 1980; Eagles et al., 1981; Bladon et al., 1982; Gard and Lazarides, 1982; Shecket and Lasek, 1982; Steinert et al., 1982; Browning and Ruina, 1984). Mouse epidermal keratins (in vivo) appear to be phosphorylated mainly at serine residues in the terminal domains (Steinert et al., 1982, 1985b) and this also appears to be the case with human epidermal keratins (Bowden et al., 1984a; Gilmartin et al., 1984). Keratins are well phosphorylated and major products of terminal differentiation, so it is not surprising that they are among the most abundant phosphoproteins in the keratinocyte.

Modification by phosphorylation probably occurs immediately after synthesis and can occasionally be demonstrated in cell-free translation systems. It appears to be the major cause of charge heterogeneity but to date the dynamics of keratin phosphorylation have not been thoroughly investigated. It is possible that certain keratins, or even specific sites within the same keratin, are under different control (Vidrich et al., 1985) such that subtle differentiation-specific alterations in phosphate content could occur. Experiments with filament assembly have so far failed to elucidate a role for phosphorylation in this process (Steinert et al., 1982; Vidrich et al., 1985). However, changes in keratin phosphorylation have been found during mitosis (Celis et al., 1985). but again the functional significance is unknown. Thus the function of phosphate addition to keratin still remains a mystery and will be the subject of investigation for some time yet.

A. PHOSPHORYLATION OF EPIDERMAL KERATINS

Keratin phosphorylation was demonstrated in mouse and human epidermis by incubating thin whole skin slices in medium that contained [^{32}P]orthophosphate. The labeled epidermis was then separated from the underlying dermis (see Bladon et al., 1982) and keratins extracted by the two methods mentioned earlier (CASC buffer or cytoskeletal; see Section II).

Keratins were also labeled with [^{35}S]methionine, [^{14}C]glycine, and [^{14}C]serine, and comparison of orthophosphate and amino acid incorporation by two-dimensional electrophoresis showed that only the more acidic isoelectric variants contained phosphate (data not shown; see Bowden et al., 1987). This was true for basic (type II) and acidic (type I) keratins from both species. Thus, the most basic charge variant of each keratin contained no phosphate, and this represents the unmodified product of mRNA translation (Bladon et al., 1982). As several variants were labeled with [^{32}P]orthophosphate, they must represent the sequential addition of phosphate to each keratin up to a value of about 6 moles per mole (Steinert et al., 1982).

B. Keratin Phosphorylation in Culture

Cultured cells are particularly useful for studying keratin phosphorylation, and both the extent and structural location of phosphate addition appear to be similar to that found in vivo. Methionine, glycine, and serine labeled all keratin isoelectric variants (Fig. 9a,c,e,g). The methionine data (not shown) were similar to that for glycine and serine incorporation (see Bowden et al., 1987). Streaks found in the neutral region of some gels (NEpHGE/SDS), notably in cytoskeletal preparations, represent stable complexes between acidic and basic keratins (Franke et al., 1983).

All keratins from cultured epidermal cells were labeled with [^{32}P]orthophosphate and, as with the epidermis in vivo, the most basic isoelectric variants remained unlabeled (Fig. 9b,d,f,h). The mouse and human keratins studied had between four and eight isoelectric variants (see Table III), including the most basic unphosphorylated form. The minor 51-kDa keratin from mouse primary cultures was also phosphorylated in the same way. Overexposure of these autoradiographs, and of fluorographs of amino acid-labeled keratins, showed that phosphorylated keratin variants often existed that were not detectable by Coomassie staining. The extensive charge shift, especially prevalent with type II keratins, was presumably due to addition of large numbers of phosphates. However, this was not a common event as only a small percentage of the total keratin population existed in this state.

C. Location of Sites in Terminal Domains

The approximate molecular location of the phosphate was determined by comparative peptide mapping (V8 protease) of individual keratins labeled with either [^{32}P]orthophosphate, [^{35}S]methionine, or [^{14}C]glycine. Results for keratins from primary epidermal culture are presented in Fig. 10 and the in vivo data can be found elsewhere (Bowden et al., 1984a; 1987).

Comparison of the silver-stained gel (Fig. 10a) and the corresponding autoradiograph (Fig. 10b) showed that only some of the many small (10–20 kDa) keratin fragments produced by V8 protease (lanes

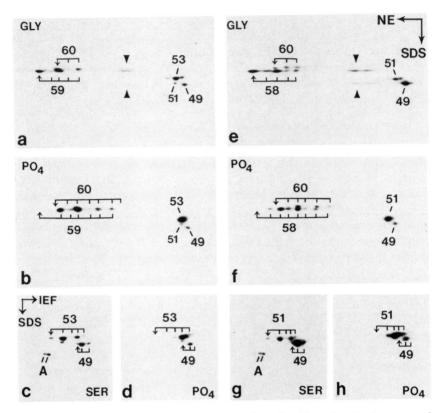

FIG. 9. Labeled keratins extracted from cultured epidermal cells (mouse, a–d; human, e–h) by the cytoskeletal method were analyzed by two-dimensional electrophoresis (NEpHGE/SDS for a, b, e, and f at pH 8.5–4.5 and IEF–SDS for c, d, g, and h at pH 6.0–4.5). While all keratin isoelectric variants were labeled with [^{14}C]glycine (GLY; a and e) and [^{14}C]serine (SER; c and g), only the more acidic variants (arrows mark most basic unphosphorylated variant) of each keratin were labeled with [^{32}P]orthophosphate (PO$_4$; b, f, d, and h). Streaks marked by arrowheads(a and e) represent stable complexes between basic and acidic keratins (see text) which migrate to neutral pH in the first dimension. Endogenous actin isomers (γ and β) were present in these cultures (abbreviated A in c and g).

10–17; 500 ng enzyme) were phosphorylated (13–15 kDa). This was most clearly demonstrated for the basic (type II) keratins because of the more resistant nature of acidic (type I) keratins to the enzyme. Thus it would appear that in all cases studied (mouse and human; *in vivo* epidermis and the derived primary cultures), phosphate is attached to a discrete part of the keratin molecule.

It has been known for some time that keratins are rich in glycine

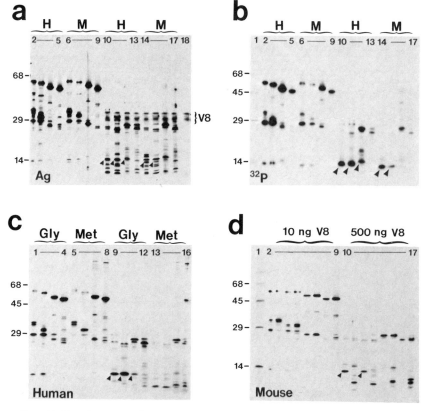

Fig. 10. One-dimensional peptide maps (V8 protease) of human (H) and mouse (M) keratins from primary cultures labeled with either [^{14}C]glycine, [^{35}S]methionine, or [^{32}P]orthophosphate and extracted by the cytoskeletal method. Gels were calibrated with standards (molecular mass in kilodaltons shown on left), and the keratins were run in groups of four (human: 60, 58, 51, and 49 kDa and mouse: 60, 59, 53, and 49 kDa). (a) Silver-stained gel (Ag) of keratins from human (lanes 2–5, 10–13) and mouse (lanes 6–9, 14–17) primary epidermal cultures digested with 10 ng (lanes 2–9) or 500 ng (lanes 10–17) of V8 protease. Lane 18 contains 500 ng V8 protease only and arrowheads mark the peptides that are particularly rich in glycine. (b) Autoradiograph of a showing [^{32}P]orthophosphate labeling (^{32}P) of specific 10- to 15-kDa fragments (arrowheads) in all basic (type II) keratins and some acidic (type I) keratins. Lane 1 contains labeled standards and lane 18 (V8 alone) is not shown. (c) Fluorograph of human keratins (Human) labeled in primary culture (Gly: lanes 1–4, 9–12 or Met: lanes 5–8, 13–16) and treated with 10 ng (lanes 1–8) or 500 ng (lanes 9–16) of V8 protease. Several differences between the glycine and methionine labeling profile were apparent especially at higher enzyme concentrations where some fragments were particularly rich in glycine (arrows). (d) Fluorograph of mouse keratins (Mouse) labeled in primary culture (Gly: lanes 2, 4, 6, ..., 16 and Met: lanes 3, 5, 7, ..., 17) showing the same phenomenon as in c above. In both species, phosphate labeling was associated with glycine-rich keratin fragments.

(Rowden and Budd, 1967; Steinert, 1975; Fuchs and Green, 1978; Bladon *et al.*, 1982), and recent sequence information (Hanukoglu and Fuchs, 1983; Steinert *et al.*, 1983, 1984, 1985b; Jorcano *et al.*, 1984; Marchuk *et al.*, 1985) has shown that while glycine and serine residues are abundant at the N and/or C terminus of most epidermal keratins, methionine is restricted to the central helical coiled coil regions. In comparing peptide maps of keratins labeled with [^{35}S]methionine or [^{14}C]glycine, it can be clearly seen that some peptides are rich in glycine and serine while being virtually free of methionine (Fig. 10c,d). Furthermore, it was glycine- and serine-rich keratin fragments that were phosphorylated in all cases (cf. Fig. 10b,c,d). Thus it would appear that all mouse and human epidermal keratins both *in vivo* and in primary culture (i.e., subsets A, B, and C) are modified by addition of phosphate to the serine residues in the terminal domains of the molecule. In addition, cyanogen bromide cleaves most epidermal keratins asymmetrically allowing the separation of N- and C-terminal fragments. Preliminary observations with the larger mouse and human suprabasal (subset A) keratins has indicated that phosphorylation occurs at both N- and C-termini (data not shown), but the precise locations are not yet known.

Two-dimensional tryptic maps of the phosphorylated keratins (data not shown; see Bowden *et al.*, 1987) indicated that between two and seven phosphopeptides existed, and the number for each keratin correlated well with the number of variants observed in two-dimensional gels (cf. Figs. 9 and 10; see also Table III) and the number of moles of phosphate typically found (Steinert *et al.*, 1982). In addition, the phosphorylated fragments all had similar properties and migrated in the same region of the tryptic maps. Furthermore, a greater similarity existed between keratins of similar size in different species than between the individual keratins within a species. Thus, it is likely that epidermal keratins are phosphorylated in several discrete terminal domains. In a recent publication by Vidrich and co-workers (1985), it was thought most likely that all the phosphorylation sites of a type I keratin (53 kDa) from a human cervical tumor cell line (ME 180) were located in the carboxy terminal half of the molecule, in contrast to our preliminary data on larger epidermal keratins. Thus, it is possible that different keratins are phosphorylated in different regions leading to a possible functional significance of this type of posttranslational modification. However, the exact number of sites and their precise molecular location are not yet known for any keratin and require further investigation in the light of present sequence information.

V. Keratins of the Hair and Nail

Early attempts at examining the keratins in hair and nail were variable in success due to the difficult nature of this modified and highly insoluble material. Experiments on sheep wool and other hard keratins relied on chemical modification by carboxymethylation in order to solubilize the keratins (Gillespie and Marshall, 1977; Marshall and Gillespie, 1977; Marshall, 1980; Rogers, 1985). Different methods were employed by others working on human hair and nail (Baden *et al.*, 1980) and the results that were obtained differed considerably. It was not until recent sequence information became available that the close similarity of low-sulfur "hard" keratins (wool, hair, etc.), "soft" epidermal keratins, and other IF proteins was recognized (Crewther *et al.*, 1983; Dowling *et al.*, 1983; Weber and Geisler, 1984).

This section contains a brief look at the keratins of human hair and nail and mouse hair in comparison to those of the epidermis and hair follicle (inner and outer root sheath). The upper hair follicle and interfollicular epidermis have a similar keratin profile (Bowden and Cunliffe, 1981) but deeper regions of the follicle, below the level of the sebaceous gland where the inner and outer sheath lie, differ (Lane *et al.*, 1985; Rogers, 1985). These cells express subset B and C keratins both in primary culture (Fig. 11a; cf Fig. 8a) and *in vivo* (Fig. 11b).

In addition, four keratins not previously observed (62 and 61 kDa type II; and 45 and 42 kDa type I) and not present in the human cytokeratin catalog (Moll *et al.*, 1982a) were found in extracts of lower follicle material that contained hair. When labled samples were analyzed (data not shown), radioactivity was only found in subset B and C keratins associated with follicle cells and not in these new keratins, which probably arose from the hair.

Initial attempts at removing keratins from mouse and human hair with buffered 8 *M* urea and 5% β-mercaptoethanol (β-ME) gave rise to two very diffuse bands on one-dimensional SDS gels (data not shown) similar to the earlier attempts of Baden and co-workers (1980). Application of cytoskeletal techniques or simply homogenizing the hair or nail in buffers containing 5% SDS and 5% β-ME improved the subsequent analysis. Four new keratins were identified in both mouse and human hair (H1–H4) and the same four keratins were also found in human nail (Fig. 11c,d). However, nail preparations also contained a variable amount of subset B and C keratins (Fig. 11d) which may relate to the number of nail bed cells adhering to the undersurface of the nail.

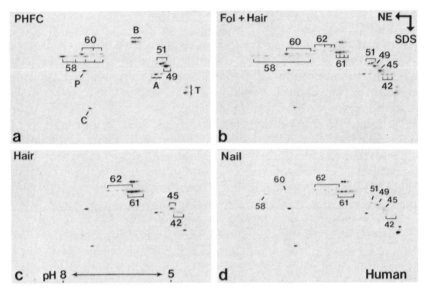

FIG. 11. Two-dimensional analysis of keratins extracted from human cultured hair follicle cells (a), isolated hairs with root sheath attached (b), pure hair (c), and nail (d). Keratins were extracted by the cytoskeletal method and separated by NEpHGE/SDS (pH range, 4–9) with coelectrophoresed standards (see Fig. 3). Primary cultures of isolated hair follicle root sheath cells contained four major keratins (60, 58, 51, and 49 kDa). The same four keratins were found in extracts of hair which contained follicle root sheath cells together with four other keratins (62, 61, 45, and 42 kDa) not previously identified. These latter keratins were found in extracts of hair and nail (c and d) and have been termed H1–H4.

Peptide mapping (V8 protease; data not shown) revealed that the hair keratins were not related to one another or to follicle keratins by degradation. Keratins H1–H4 are presumably synthesized in the hair bulb, possibly under dermal papilla influence, and have not yet been observed in cultures of isolated hair follicle keratinocytes. Whether they are synthesized in this form or modified from larger precursors, as is the case for stratum corneum keratins of the epidermis, has not yet been determined. It is also difficult to relate these findings to those of earlier work on human hair and nail (Gillespie and Marshall, 1977; Marshall, 1980) because the techniques employed were completely different. However, similar results have been reported recently (Lynch et al., 1985; Heid et al., 1986).

The expression of keratins so far described for human epidermis, hair follicle (inner–outer root sheath), hair, nail, and various cultured cells is summarized in Table IV. The relative two-dimensional electrophoretic mobility of these keratins in our system is also presented schematically (Fig. 12). Internal standard proteins are also shown (large stars) along with the position of vimentin (Vim), an IF protein from cells of mesenchymal origin that often contaminates primary keratinocyte cultures.

TABLE IV

KERATIN EXPRESSION IN HUMAN EPIDERMIS, EPIDERMAL APPENDAGES, AND CULTURED KERATINOCYTES[a]

Type II basic–neutral

Number		1	H1	H2	5	?	6	7	8
M_r		68	62	61	60	59	58	55	54
pI		7.8	6.8	6.5	7.4	7.7	8.0	6.0	6.2
Heel	LE	+++			+++	++	+++		
F/Sk	LE	+++			+++				
Back	LE	+++			+++				
HRS	LE				+++		+++		
Hair			++	+++					
Nail			++	+++	+		+		
F/Sk	PEC				+++	(+)	+++	+	(+)
Back	PEC				++	(+)	+++		
HRS	PFC				+++		+++		

Type I acidic

Number		9	10	13	14	15	16	H3	18	H4	19
M_r		64	57	54	51	50	49	45	44	42	40
pI		5.6	5.5	5.0	5.3	4.6	5.1	4.9	5.8	4.8	5.2
Heel	LE	++	+++		+++		+++				
F/Sk	LE		+++	++	+++	(+)	(+)				
Back	LE		+++		+++	(+)	(+)				
HRS	LE				+++		+++				
Hair								++		++	
Nail					+		+	++		++	
F/Sk	PEC			++	+++	+	+++		(+)		+
Back	PEC				+++	(+)	+++				
HRS	PFC				+++		+++				

[a]For details concerning keratin number, molecular mass, isoelectric point, and abundance see text and previous tables. F/Sk, Foreskin; LE, living epidermis; HRS, hair root sheath; PEC, primary epidermal culture; PFC, primary follicle culture.

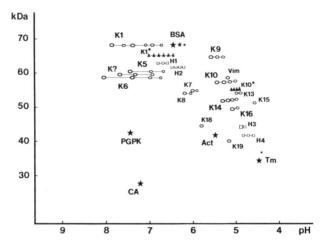

FIG. 12. Schematic summary of the two-dimensional analysis of keratins from human epidermis, epidermal appendages (hair, nail, and follicle), and various primary keratinocyte cultures. The keratins are labeled according to Moll *et al.* (1982a) except for the inclusion of K? between K5 and K6, the addition of modified SC keratins (K1* and K10*) and the hair and nail keratins (H1–H4). Vimentin is shown for comparison (Vim) and the position of coelectrophoresed standards are given as follows: BSA, bovine serum albumin; PGPK, 3-phosphoglycerate kinase; Act, α-actin; Tm, tropomyosin; CA, carbonic anhydrase.

VI. Keratins and Skin Disease

Keratin expression and modification are tightly linked to epidermal or hair follicle differentiation. Thus disruption of differentiation would lead to alterations in the keratin filaments. This has been shown to be the case in several skin disorders (psoriasis, seborrheic eczema, Darriers' disease) which exhibit abnormal keratin profiles (Baden *et al.*, 1978; Skerrow and Hunter, 1978; Bowden *et al.*, 1983; Weiss *et al.*, 1984; McGuire *et al.*, 1984; Sun *et al.*, 1985). However, the changes are not specific to each disease as reported earlier for psoriasis (Thaler *et al.*, 1978) but represent a general and variable response that reflects abnormal differentiation.

This response can be summarized in the light of present knowledge as a reduction in subset A keratins together with a reciprocal increase in subset C keratins. The epidermis in these conditions appears to be receiving signals for continuous proliferation rather than differentiation and could be said to be in a state of hyperproliferation characteristic of a wound healing response (see Weiss *et al.*, 1984). Such reasoning can also provide a possible explanation for the events which occur when keratinocytes are enzymatically removed from the epidermis and placed in primary culture (Section III; see Bowden *et al.*, 1985). In cases in which the reverse is true, the increase of subset A and decrease of subset C keratins characteristic of the response to vitamin A or transplantation onto syngeneic mice (Fuchs and Green, 1981; Breitkreutz *et al.*, 1984), keratinocytes probably proliferate more slowly and have a greater tendency to differentiate (see Fusenig, 1986).

In addition to changes in keratin expression, and possibly a consequence of them, some diseases of the epidermis (psoriasis for example) manifest a lack of keratin proteolytic modification. This again is a variable response depending on lesion severity and is not solely dependent on the quantity of suprabasal keratins (subset A) available as substrate (data not shown; see Bowden *et al.*, 1983). Thus, the stratum corneum (or scale) of psoriatic lesions contains variable amounts of unmodified keratins that are characteristic of living epidermal cells and unusually large amounts of subset B and C keratins. Although this may be a consequence of the increased transit time of epidermal cells that is characteristic of these conditions (not allowing time for keratin modification), defects in the modification process itself cannot be ruled out.

It is unlikely that abnormal epidermal differentiation is a direct result of defects in the coding regions of the keratin genes themselves. This is borne out by the observation that primary cultures of human keratinocytes isolated from psoriatic lesions and uninvolved skin have a keratin profile similar to normal cultures (Baden *et al.*, 1981; Bowden and Leigh, unpublished observations) and that uninvolved skin of the psoriatic has normal keratin expression (Bowden *et al.*, 1983). However, genetic defects in regulatory sequences of the keratin genes or in the genes coding for proteins which control the switch(es) between keratinocyte proliferation and differentiation cannot be ruled out.

Thus, the abnormal epidermis from various skin lesions might provide a suitable model for investigations into the molecular events that control sequential keratin expression and subsequent modification of specific keratin subsets. New techniques now available, such as *in situ* hybridization and the restriction enzyme mapping and sequencing of keratin genes and their intervening sequences, should improve our present knowledge of both normal and abnormal epidermal differentiation.

VII. Concluding Remarks

In this chapter, we have summarized our current and past studies on the expression and modification of keratins in relation to epidermal differentiation. Some of the molecular details that are collectively named terminal differentiation have been elucidated, but much work is still required before we obtain a more complete understanding of keratinocyte cell and molecular biology. Such knowledge is important not only in basic biology but also in medicine, where it will aid the understanding of pathogenic processes at play in several skin disorders and many epithelial carcinomas.

In particular, we have dealt with two aspects of keratin modification that are integral to the process of epidermal differentiation. We have shown that keratins are major phosphoproteins of the keratinocyte and that the addition of several moles of phosphate per keratin molecule is the probable cause of charge heterogeneity. The extent of phosphorylation varies depending on the keratin involved, and present data suggest that the phosphate is attached to serine residues in several N- and/or C-terminal domains. These domains are thought to project out from the filament (Steinert *et al.*, 1985b), placing the phosphorylation sites in the aqueous environment of the filament surface. The function of keratin phosphorylation remains unknown but it may form the basis of a mechanism that controls filament interactions.

We have shown that keratins are not synthesized uniformly across the epidermis but are sequentially expressed. The basal keratinocytes possess a characteristic keratin subset (B) which become progressively reduced in quantity as cell differentiation proceeds. These are replaced by another keratin subset (A) in suprabasal cells and by the time cells reach the upper granular layer, they consist almost entirely of these keratins. As the cells undergo preprogrammed death and cornification, the subset A keratins are modified by removal of terminal basic sequences. It is not yet clear whether this affects the terminal phosphorylation sites or not but as stratum corneum keratins also display charge heterogeneity, it is assumed that some sites are preserved.

This mechanism of differentiation-related keratin expression and modification is aberrant in diseased epidermis but present data would suggest that this is consequential rather than causal. The details of keratin expression and modification appear to vary with anatomical site, and human epidermis from both the palmar–plantar regions and foreskin are atypical in this respect. Keratin expression and modification in cultured keratinocytes, which are not the equivalent of but derived from epidermal basal cells, differ considerably from the situation *in vivo*. However, where the same keratins are synthesized, their properties are identical in both situations. The alterations therefore reflect a change in the control of keratin gene expression, a topic that is receiving much attention at present.

Finally, we have shown some preliminary data on hair and nail keratins which are sometimes termed "hard" keratins. They do not appear to be modified products of hair follicle keratin genes and must therefore represent another subset expressed specifically in cells of the hair bulb (or nail bed). Like the epidermal and hair follicle keratins, they are expressed as two subfamilies, one (type II) more basic than the other (type I). Thus, there are at least 24 human epithelial keratins and as it is possible that more than one gene exists for each of these keratins, the molecular biology of this multigene family of structural proteins will entertain us for some time to come.

ACKNOWLEDGMENTS

We thank our co-workers Axel Bohnert, Jurgen Hornung, Erika Herzmann, Petra Boukamp, and Charlotte Rausch for their important contributions to this work. We are grateful to Dr. Wolfgang Tilgen, University of Heidelberg Hautklinik, for providing human skin, Dr. Roy Quinlan, Institute of Cell and Tumor Biology, DKFZ, for help with two-dimensional analysis of tryptic peptides, and Dr. Dennis Roop for providing data prior to publication. We also thank Harry Schaefer for expert photographic assistance. Dr. Paul Bowden was in receipt of a DKFZ-Gastwissenschaftler Stipendium during the course of this work and the project was supported by the Deutsche Forschungs Gemeinschaft (Fu 91/2-1).

REFERENCES

Anderton, B. H. (1981). *J. Muscle Res. Cell Motil.* **2**, 141–166.
Baden, H. P., and Lee, L. D. (1978). *J. Invest. Dermatol.* **71**, 148–151.
Baden, H. P., McGilvray, N., Cheng, C. K., Lee, L. D., and Kubilus, J. (1978). *J. Invest. Dermatol.* **70**, 294–297.
Baden, H. P., McGilvray, N., Lee, L. D., Baden, L., and Kubilus, J. (1980). *J. Invest. Dermatol.* **75**, 311–315.
Baden, H. P., Kubilus, J., and MacDonald, M. J. (1981). *J. Invest. Dermatol.* **76**, 53–55.
Bader, B. L., Magin, T. M., Hatzfeld, M., and Franke, W. W. (1986). *EMBO J.* **5**, 1865–1876.
Banks-Schlegel, S. P., Schlegel, R., and Pinkus, G. S. (1981). *Exp. Cell Res.* **136**, 465–469.
Bladon, P. T., Bowden, P. E., Cunliffe, W. J., and Wood, E. J. (1982). *Biochem. J.* **208**, 179–187.
Bowden, P. E., and Cunliffe, W. J. (1981). *Biochem. J.* **199**, 145–154.
Bowden, P. E., Wood, E. J., and Cunliffe, W. J. (1983). *Biochim. Biophys. Acta* **743**, 172–179.
Bowden, P. E., Breitkreutz, D., and Fusenig, N. E. (1984a). *J. Submicrosc. Cytol.* **16**, 21–22.
Bowden, P. E., Quinlan, R. A., Breitkreutz, D., and Fusenig, N. E. (1984b). *Eur. J. Biochem.* **142**, 29–36.
Bowden, P. E., Stark, H.-J., Hornung, J., Breitkreutz, D., and Fusenig, N. E. (1985). *J. Cell Biol.* **101**, 22a.
Bowden, P. E., Breitkreutz, D., and Fusenig, N. E. (1987). *Biochem. J.* (submitted).

Breitkreutz, D., Bohnert, A., Herzmann, E., Bowden, P. E., Boukamp, P., and Fusenig, N. E. (1984). *Differentiation* **26,** 154–169.

Brody, I. (1964). *In* "The Epidermis" (W. Montagna and W. C. Lobitz, Jr., eds.), pp. 251–273. Academic Press, New York.

Brody, I. (1970). *J. Ultrastruct. Res.* **30,** 209–217.

Browning, E. T., and Ruina, M. (1984). *J. Neurochem.* **42,** 718–726.

Celis, J. E., Fey, S. J., Larsen, P. M., and Celis, A. (1985). *Ann. N.Y. Acad. Sci.* **455,** 268–281.

Crewther, W. G., Dowling, L. M., Steinert, P. M., and Parry, D. A. D. (1983). *Int. J. Biol. Macromol.* **5,** 267–275.

Dale, B. A., Resing, K. A., and Lonsdale-Eccles, J. D. (1985). *Ann. N.Y. Acad. Sci.* **455,** 330–342.

Dowling, L. M., Parry, D. A. D., and Sparrow, L. G. (1983). *Biosci. Rep.* **3,** 73–78.

Dowling, L. M., Crewther, W. G., and Inglis, A. S. (1986). *Biochem. J.* **236,** 695–703.

Eagles, P. A. M., Gilbert, D. S., and Maggs, A. (1981). *Biochem. J.* **99,** 101–111.

Eichner, R., Bonitz, P., and Sun, T.-T. (1984). *J. Cell Biol.* **98,** 1388–1396.

Franke, W. W., Schiller, D. L., Moll, R., Winter, S., Schmid, E., Engelbrecht, I., Denk, H., Krepler, R., and Platzer, B. (1981). *J. Mol. Biol.* **153,** 933–959.

Franke, W. W., Schmid, E., Schiller, D. L., Winter, S., Jarasch, E. D., Moll, R., Denk, H., Jackson, B. W., and Illmensee, K. (1982). *Cold Spring Harbor Symp. Quant. Biol.* **46,** 431–456.

Franke, W. W., Schiller, D. L., Hatzfeld, M., and Winter, S. (1983). *Proc. Natl. Acad. Sci. U.S.A.* **80,** 7113–7117.

Fuchs, E., and Green, H. (1978). *Cell* **15,** 887–897.

Fuchs, E., and Green, H. (1979). *Cell* **17,** 573–582.

Fuchs, E., and Green, H. (1980). *Cell* **19,** 1033–1042.

Fuchs, E., and Green, H. (1981). *Cell* **25,** 617–626.

Fuchs, E., Hanukoglu, I., Marchuk, D., Grace, M. P., and Kim, K. H. (1985). *Ann. N.Y. Acad. Sci.* **455,** 436–450.

Fusenig, N. E. (1986). *In* "Biology of the Integument" (J. Bereiter-Hahn, A. G. Matoltsy, and K. S. Richards, eds.), Vol. 2, pp. 409–442. Springer-Verlag, Heidelberg.

Fusenig, N. E., and Worst, P. K. M. (1975). *Exp. Cell Res.* **93,** 443–457.

Gard, D. L., and Lazarides, E. (1982). *Mol. Cell. Biol.* **2,** 1104–1114.

Gillespie, J. M., and Marshall, R. C. (1977). *Aust. J. Biol. Sci.* **30,** 401–409.

Gilmartin, M. E., Culbertson, V. B., and Freedberg, I. M. (1980). *J. Invest. Dermatol.* **75,** 211–216.

Gilmartin, M. E., Mitchell, J., Vidrich, A., and Freedberg, I. M. (1984). *J. Cell Biol.* **98,** 1144–1149.

Glass, C., Kim, K. H., and Fuchs, E. (1985). *J. Cell Biol.* **101,** 2366–2373.

Green, H., Fuchs, E., and Watt, F. (1982). *Cold Spring Harbor Symp. Quant. Biol.* **46,** 293–302.

Hanukoglu, I., and Fuchs, E. (1983). *Cell* **33,** 915–924.

Heid, H. W., Werner, E., and Franke, W. W. (1986). *Differentiation* **32,** 101–119.

Hennings, H., Steinert, P. M., and Buxman, M. M. (1981). *Biochem. Biophys. Res. Commun.* **102,** 739–745.

Hunter, I., and Skerrow, D. (1981). *Biochim. Biophys. Acta* **674,** 155–159.

Johnson, L. D., Idler, W. W., Zhou, X.-M., Roop, D. R., and Steinert, P. M. (1985). *Proc. Natl. Acad. Sci. U.S.A.* **82,** 1896–1900.

Jorcano, J. L., Franz, J. K., and Franke, W. W. (1984). *Differentiation* **28,** 155–163.

Kim, K. H., Rheinwald, J. G., and Fuchs, E. V. (1983). *Mol. Cell. Biol.* **3,** 495–502.

Knapp, A. C., Franke, W. W., Heid, H., Hatzfeld, M., Jorcano, J. L., and Moll, R. (1986). *J. Cell Biol.* **103,** 657–667.

Lane, E. B., Bartek, J., Purkis, P. E., and Leigh, I. M. (1985). *Ann. N.Y. Acad. Sci.* **455,** 241–258.

Lazarides, E. (1982). *Annu. Rev. Biochem.* **51,** 219–250.

Lynch, M. H., Hardy, C. L., Mak, L., and Sun, T.-T. (1985). *J. Cell Biol.* **101,** 21a.

McGuire, J., Osber, M., and Lightfoot, L. (1984). *Br. J. Dermatol.* **111,** 27–37.

Magin, T. M., Jorcano, J. L., and Franke, W. W. (1986). *Differentiation* **30,** 254–264.

Marchuk, D., McCrohon, S., and Fuchs, E. (1985). *Proc. Natl. Acad. Sci. U.S.A.* **82,** 1609–1613.

Marshall, R. C. (1980). *J. Invest. Dermatol.* **75,** 264–269.

Marshall, R. C., and Gillespie, J. M. (1977). *Aust. J. Biol. Sci.* **30,** 389–400.

Matoltsy, A. G. (1964). *Nature (London)* **201,** 1130–1131.

Matoltsy, A. G. (1976). *J. Invest. Dermatol.* **67,** 20–25.

Matoltsy, A. G. (1980). *In* "The Skin of Vertebrates" (R. I. C. Spearman and P. A. Riley, eds.), Vol. 9, pp. 57–66 (Linnean Society Symposium Series). Dorset Press, UK.

Matoltsy, A. G., Matoltsy, M. N., and Cliffel, P. J. (1983). *J. Invest. Dermatol.* **80,** 185–188.

Moll, R., Franke, W. W., Schiller, D. L., Geiger, B., and Krepler, R. (1982a). *Cell* **31,** 11–24.

Moll, R., Franke, W. W., Volc-Platzer, B., and Krepler, R. (1982b). *J. Cell Biol.* **95,** 285–296.

Quinlan, R. A., Schiller, D. L., Hatzfeld, M., Achtstatter, T., Moll, R., Jorcano, J. L., Magin, T. M., and Franke, W. W. (1985). *Ann. N.Y. Acad. Sci.* **455,** 282–306.

RayChaudhury, A., Marchuk, D., Lindhurst, M., and Fuchs, E. (1986). *Mol. Cell. Biol.* **6,** 539–548.

Rheinwald, J. G., and O'Connell, T. M. (1985). *Ann. N.Y. Acad. Sci.* **455,** 259–267.

Rice, R. H., and Green, H. (1977). *Cell* **11,** 417–422.

Rogers, G. E. (1985). *Ann. N.Y. Acad. Sci.* **455,** 403–425.

Romano, V., Hatzfeld, M., Magin, T. M., Zimbelmann, R., Franke, W. W., Maier, G., and Ponstingl, H. (1986). *Differentiation* **30,** 244–253.

Roop, D. R., Hawley-Nelson, P., Cheng, C. K., and Yuspa, S. H. (1982). *Proc. Natl. Acad. Sci. U.S.A.* **80,** 716–720.

Roop, D. R., Cheng, C. K., Titterington, L., Meyers, C. A., Stanley, J. R., Steinert, P. M., and Yuspa, S. H. (1984). *J. Biol. Chem.* **259,** 8037–8040.

Rothnagel, J. A., and Rogers, G. E. (1984). *Mol. Cell. Biochem.* **58,** 113–120.

Rowden, G., and Budd, G. C. (1967). *J. Invest. Dermatol.* **48,** 571–586.

Schiller, D. L., Franke, W. W., and Geiger, B. (1982). *EMBO J.* **1,** 761–769.

Schweizer, J., Kinjo, M., Furstenberger, G., and Winter, H. (1984). *Cell* **37,** 159–170.

Shecket, G., and Lasek, R. J. (1982). *J. Biol. Chem.* **257,** 4788–4795.

Simon, M., and Green, H. (1984). *Cell* **36,** 827–834.

Skerrow, D., and Hunter, I. (1978). *Biochim. Biophys. Acta* **537,** 474–484.

Skerrow, D., and Skerrow, C. J. (1983). *Exp. Cell Res.* **143,** 27–36.

Steinert, P. M. (1975). *Biochem. J.* **149,** 39–48.

Steinert, P. M., and Idler, W. W. (1979). *Biochemistry* **18,** 5664–5669.

Steinert, P. M., and Parry, D. A. D. (1985). *Annu. Rev. Cell Biol.* **1,** 41–65.

Steinert, P. M., and Rogers, G. E. (1973). *Biochem. J.* **135,** 759–771.

Steinert, P. M., Wantz, M. L., and Idler, W. W. (1982). *Biochemistry* **21,** 177–183.

Steinert, P. M., Rice, R. H., Roop, D. R., Trus, B. L., and Steven, A. C. (1983). *Nature (London)* **302,** 794–800.

in vivo (Knapp and Sawyer, 1983; Bunn *et al.*, 1985; Knapp *et al.*, 1985b); and (5) are organized in characteristic arrangements in cells which can be easily recognized by immunocytochemistry or other techniques (Sun and Green, 1978; Sun *et al.*, 1979; Franke *et al.*, 1978, 1982; Knapp *et al.*, 1983a,b; Horwitz *et al.*, 1981).

C. SIGNIFICANCE

Keratins are found in nearly all epithelial tissue types in vertebrates, and in many cases keratins constitute the majority of the proteins produced (e.g., skin and its derivatives; see Lane *et al.*, 1985). Their organization in the cytoplasm of epithelial cells has elevated them to prominence as fundamental elements of the cytoskeleton and established them as part of a much larger, interrelated group of polymer-forming proteins which give rise to intermediate filaments (Osborn *et al.*, 1982; Lazarides, 1982; Steinert and Parry, 1985). Experimental manipulation of epithelial cells provides a means by which these proteins and the filaments formed by them can be better understood both in the context of basic cell biology and with regard to their importance in the clinical diagnosis of disease (Osborne *et al.*, 1985; Virtanen *et al.*, 1985).

We present results and interpretations from two experimental approaches in which the expression and/or organization of keratins has been altered (Knapp *et al.*, 1983a,b, 1985a,b; Bunn *et al.*, 1985). The first involves the analysis of drug-induced alterations of cytokeratin in cultured epithelial cells. The second focuses on the analysis of clonal variations in keratin filament expression by human somatic cell hybrids.

II. Alterations of Cytokeratin Organization in Epithelial Cells

A. NORMAL DISTRIBUTION OF KERATIN FILAMENTS AND OTHER CYTOSKELETAL ELEMENTS

The structure, function, and organization of the vertebrate cytoskeleton reflects the presence and interactions of microfilaments, microtubules, and intermediate filaments (IF). The ubiquitous presence of microtubules and microfilaments in cells of all tissue types contrasts with the restricted, tissue- and cell type-specific appearance of the various classes of intermediate filaments (Steinert and Parry, 1985; Osborne *et al.*, 1982). Lazarides (1980) has suggested that IF are involved in the organization and mechanical integration of the cytoplasm. Each of the five major groups of IF (see Steinert and Parry, 1985, for reviews) is undoubtedly expressed and organized to perform

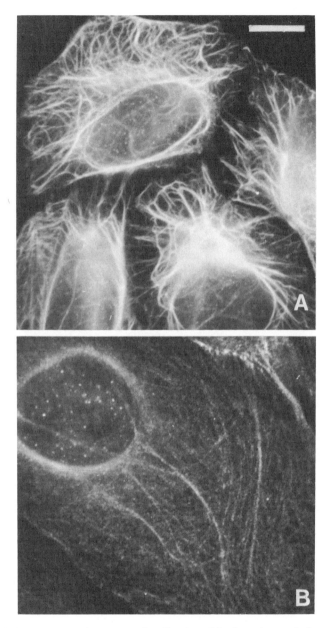

FIG. 1. Indirect immunofluorescence localization of the keratin cytoskeleton of HeLa cells (A) and KLN 205 squamous cell carcinoma cells (B). Bar, 8 μm.

specialized functional or structural role(s) in the cells or tissues in which they appear, although these roles have not as yet been completely determined. The most complex group of IF proteins are the keratins. Keratin filaments are the primary IF of epithelial cells. Their cytoplasmic organization appears to be dependent on the interactions they have with the other cytoskeletal elements and with the cell and nuclear membranes (Knapp et al., 1983a,b, 1985a,b; Celis et al., 1984; Keski-Oja and Alitalo, 1985; Franke et al., 1981; Denk et al., 1985). This organization has also been shown to be remarkably stable in a great variety of epithelial cell types in culture. We will restrict our discussion of keratins to those organized as a cytoskeleton in tissue culture cells. Cytokeratins are also found in epithelial cells in intact tissues, though such arrangements may be complicated by the presence of other forms of noncytoskeletal keratins and keratin-associated proteins (Sawyer and Borg, 1979; Sawyer et al., 1984; Dale et al., 1985).

The cytokeratins of cultured cells are found in anastomosing bundles of filaments which are distributed throughout the cytoplasm and are capable of forming and maintaining stable associations with the cell membrane and possibly the nuclear envelope (Jones et al., 1985). The keratin cytoskeletons of two representative cell types used in the work presented here are shown in Fig. 1. Both these cell types, HeLa and KLN 205, are transformed and are essentially immortal in culture. We have also used primary cultures of fetal mouse epidermal (FME) cells, which have limited life-span, and immortal PtK2 cells. Coexisting in the cytoplasm of these cells are structurally, biochemically, and immunologically distinct microfilament and microtubule systems, constructed principally of actin and tubulin, respectively, which have their own characteristic cytoskeletal arrangements. Figure 2 illustrates the four types of cytopolymers observed in HeLa cells. This includes vimentin, which is another of the IF types coexpressed by HeLa as well as many other transformed and culture-adapted epithelial cells (Lazarides, 1982; Osborne et al., 1982). It is against these standards of cytoskeletal organization that we will compare and dis-

---

FIG. 2. Indirect immunofluorescence localization of HeLa cell cytoskeletal elements. Untreated control cells are represented in (A)–(D) and cells treated with colchicine and cytochalasin D for 2 hours are represented in (E)–(H). Characteristic differences in cytoskeletal organization are compared for keratin (A and E), actin (B and F), tubulin (C and G), and vimentin (D and H) in the absence and presence of inhibitors. N, Nucleus. Arrows in (E) indicate focal sites for keratin filaments. Bars, 10 μm. [From Knapp et al. (1983b). Reproduced from The Journal of Cell Biology, 1983, **97**, 1788–1794 by copyright permission of The Rockefeller University Press.]

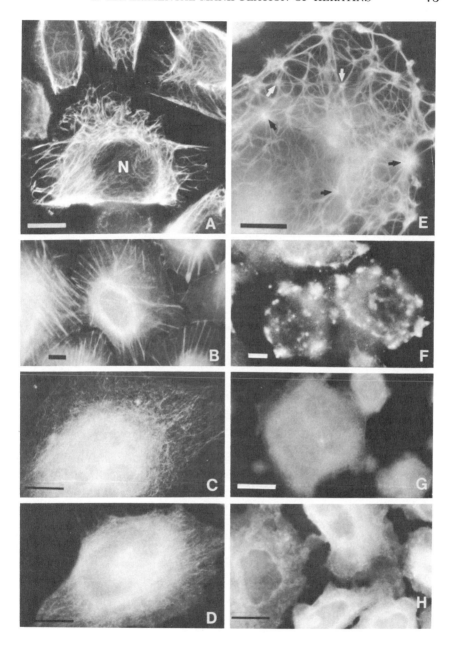

cuss the significance of alterations induced by specific experimental manipulations.

B. ALTERATIONS IN THE ORGANIZATION OF THE KERATIN CYTOSKELETON: DRUG STUDIES

The organization of the keratin cytoskeleton in many types of cultured epithelial cells can be extensively rearranged by simultaneous treatment with a combination of antimitotic drugs (Fig. 2A and E; Knapp *et al.*, 1983a,b, 1985a). The disruption of microfilaments and microtubules by cytochalasin B or D and colchicine induces the conversion of the keratin cytoskeleton from a branching, even distribution to an arrangement best described as a series of starlike structures whose radiating filaments appear to be maintained by multiple membrane-attachment sites. The capability to induce such changes in a large percentage of treated cells has provided a way to study the relationships among the various cytoskeletal elements, some of which are directly affected by these compounds (microfilaments and microtubules) and some of which are only indirectly affected by them (keratin and vimentin IF). Microinjection of antikeratin antibodies has been shown to directly and selectively alter the organization of the keratin cytoskeleton (Eckert *et al.*, 1982; Klymkowski *et al.*, 1983), but relatively few cells in a given population can be manipulated and analyzed by this technique. Also, the cytokeratins, when affected by microinjected antibodies, appear to be "disorganized" as opposed to the "reorganization" which follows drug treatment. Information from both approaches is helping to define keratin organization in epithelial cells.

Disruption of either microfilaments with cytochalasins (Sun and Green, 1978; Knapp *et al.*, 1983a) or microtubules with colchicine derivatives (Franke *et al.*, 1979; Knapp *et al.*, 1983a) does not significantly alter the inherent organization of the keratin cytoskeleton in HeLa cells (Fig. 3). This is also true for KLN 205 squamous cell car-

---

FIG. 3. Indirect immunofluorescence localization of keratin in HeLa, KLN 205, and fetal mouse epidermal (FME) cells. An untreated HeLa cell control for keratin IF is represented in A. HeLa cells were treated with colchicine (B) or cytochalasin D (C) alone. HeLa cells in D represent cells arrested in mitosis by colchicine treatment. Keratin is in the form of spheroidal bodies. The FME cell represented in E is treated with colchicine and cytochalasin D and shows keratin–membrane focal sites immunostained with antikeratin antiserum. The apposed KLN 205 cells in F demonstrate cell–cell contact sites (arrows) with respect to keratin distribution. The HeLa cell in G has been treated with colchicine and cytochalasin D and should be compared to A–C. N, Nucleus. Bars, 10 μm. [E and F are reproduced from Knapp *et al.* (1983a). *Science* **219,** 501–503. Copyright 1983 by the AAAS.]

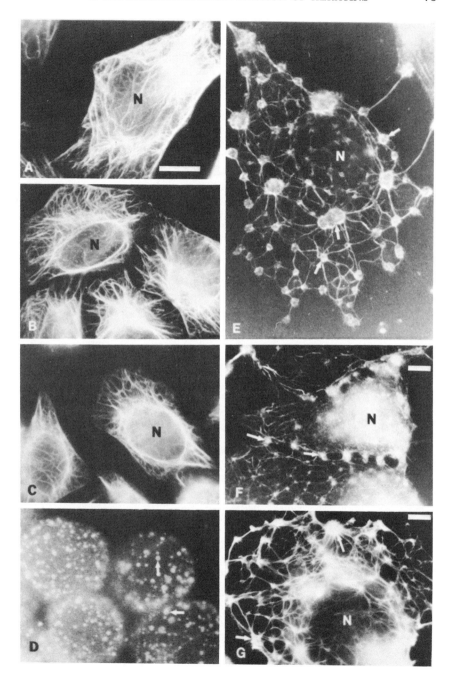

cinoma cells, PtK2 rat kangaroo kidney epithelial cells, and FME cells. However, as previously described, combinations of these two types of drugs (Table I) induces dramatic rearrangements of keratin filament organization in all cell types tested (Fig. 1, A and H, and Fig. 3, E–G). Figure 2 (E–H) illustrates the effects of a combination of cytochalasin D and colchicine on the organization of HeLa keratin IF, microfilaments, microtubules, and vimentin. Microfilaments, which appear as stress fibers in untreated HeLa cells (Fig. 2B), are disrupted completely (Fig. 2F). Indirect immunofluorescence demonstrates intense staining of nonfilamentous actin-positive material which is distributed in patches in the cytoplasm (Fig. 2F). Microtubules are also lost (Fig. 2, C and G), but there is no apparent redistribution of tubulins as observed for actin. Vimentin IFs are not obviously affected

TABLE I

EFFECT OF CYTOSTATIC DRUGS ON KERATIN
CYTOSKELETON ORGANIZATION[a]

| | Microfilament inhibitors | | |
Microtubule inhibitors	Cytochalasin B	Cytochalasin D	None
Colchicine	+	+	0
Colcemid	+	+	0
Vinblastine sulfate	+	+	0
Lumicolchicine	nt	0[a]	0
None	0[b]	0[b]	0

[a]Drug-induced changes in cytokeratin organization in HeLa, FME, KLN 205, and PtK2 cells were tested with various microtubule- or microfilament-inhibiting compounds. A dose–response for each microtubule or microfilament inhibitor was tested either alone or in binary combination over a 2-hour period. Colchicine, demecolcine, vinblastine, and β-lumicolchicine alone were ineffective in eliciting changes in cytokeratin organization (0) over a concentration range of 10^{-6} to 10^{-3} M. Cytochalasin B (0.5–25 μg/ml) or cytochalasin D (0.05–5 μg/ml) in 1% DMSO elicited a variable and limited response, restricted to the cell periphery (0[b]). Combination of β-lumicolchicine and cytochalasin D (0[a]) resulted in a cytokeratin configuration indistinguishable from that of cytochalasin D controls (0[b]). β-Lumicolchicine with cytochalasin B was not tested (nt). Combinations of inhibitors at low concentrations (10^{-6} M microtubule inhibitors with either cytochalasin D, 0.05 μg/ml, or cytochalasin B, 0.5 μg/ml) were ineffective in eliciting changes in cytokeratin organization. A graded increase in the degree of cellular response was observed up to dosages of 10^{-4} M for microtubule inhibitors with cytochalasin D, 0.5 μg/ml, or cytochalasin B, 10 μg/ml (+). Higher concentrations of binary drug combinations elicited not only alterations in cytokeratin organization but also excessive retraction of spread cells, as well as rounding up and release of cells from the substratum.

after combined drug treatment, and regardless of any subtle effects on their organization which we may not able to resolve by immunofluorescence, they do not codistribute with keratin IF under these conditions (Fig. 2, D and H).

Treatment of cells with colchicine alone has long been known to disrupt the organization of vimentin filaments and to result in their redistribution into perinuclear whorls (Franke et al., 1978, 1979). However, in order to affect vimentin organization cells must be treated extensively (20 hours or more) with any of a number of microtubule inhibitors, including colchicine. It is not clear why such long treatments are needed to disrupt vimentin IF since microtubules are disrupted rapidly in treated cells. By comparison, combined drug treatments with cytochalasin D and colchicine, which are needed for optimal effect in the cells we have examined, alter keratin IF within minutes and have little or no effect on vimentin (Knapp et al., 1983b). Thus, there are clear differences in response between keratin and vimentin IF in HeLa cells with regard to the nature of the timing and the reorganization induced by selective drug treatment. This suggests that these different IF types are associated in different ways with other elements of the cytoskeleton. Vimentin organization is apparently not affected by keratin rearrangement under these conditions. However, from these experiments it was not clear whether the presence of vimentin was necessary for keratin IF rearrangement to occur. In order to test the response of keratin IF to drug treatments independent of vimentin, primary cultures of FME cells were used. These cells had no demonstrable vimentin, yet the responses to the combination of antimitotic drugs was essentially the same as that elicited in HeLa, KLN 205, and PtK2 cells (Fig. 3). This supports the argument that keratin IF organization can be largely independent of vimentin IF even when vimentin is present in cells as a second IF system. While vimentin organization is influenced by microtubule inhibitors, keratin IF organization is codependent on microtubules and microfilaments. Indeed, in all the cell types tested it is necessary for both microtubules and microfilaments to be disrupted to induce the maximum degree of reorganization of keratin filaments (Knapp et al., 1983a,b).

Recent work by Celis et al. (1984) with monkey kidney epithelial TC7 cells provides evidence of differences in the sensitivity of keratin organization to single drug treatments. These cells, when treated with cytochalasin for 1 hour, or demecolcine or nocodazole for 20 hours, form rearrangements of keratin filaments similar to those reported for HeLa, FME, KLN 205 (Fig. 3), and PtK2 (Keski-Oja and Alitalo, 1985) cells following combined drug treatment. TC7 cells also demonstrate codistribution of vimentin with keratins under these conditions. These intriguing findings reinforce the suggestion that different cell types organize or maintain keratin and vimentin filament systems in different ways. Establishing the organizational relationships among filament systems in different cell types which react differently to antimitotic drugs may provide needed insight into the functional role(s) of cytokeratins.

In addition, Celis *et al.* (1984) have reported that following cyto-chalasin-induced depolymerization actin tends to concentrate at focal sites shared or coincident with keratin. Keski-Oja and Alitalo (1985) have reported similar findings in PtK2 cells. This is a condition which we have also observed in HeLa (Fig. 2F), as well as KLN 205 and FME cells. The cell membrane-associated sites in HeLa, KLN 205, and FME cells which are involved in the maintenance of the keratin filament lattice are thought to be predominantly desmosomal in nature (Knapp *et al.*, 1983a, 1985a). It is clear that the filaments radiate from and are maintained by multiple membrane-attachment sites. This stable array of keratin IF emanates from either basal cell surface hemidesmosomes or functionally related substratum attachment plaques (Knapp *et al.*, 1983a; Fig. 3). There is also a periodic distribution of attachment sites observed between apposed cells (Fig. 3F). Indirect immunofluorescence microscopy using antiserum against desmosomal proteins shows that they colocalize with the focal centers of the starlike structures of keratin (and actin) in treated KLN 205 cells (Fig. 4,B–D). During the progress of rearrangement of keratin filaments, which takes only minutes to complete, there is a dramatic change in the distribution and staining density of desmosomal proteins (Fig. 4,A and C). The normal distribution of these structures in KLN 205 cells (Fig. 4A) corresponds to a similar distribution reported by Franke *et al.* (1981) for basal cell surface desmosomal proteins and correlates with fine structural evidence showing tonofilament (keratin filaments) associations with desmosomes and hemidesmosomes (Overton, 1975; Kelly, 1966; Staehelin, 1974; Skerrow and Matoltsy, 1974; Denk *et al.*, 1985; Pirbazari and Kelly, 1985; Geiger *et al.*, 1983). The mechanism by which these molecules and/or molecular complexes are rearranged is not yet known, but one possibility is that these entities are mobile in the plane of the membrane and may be translocated in response to tensional forces induced by the keratin IF system as a result of the loss of microtubules and microfilaments (Knapp *et al.*, 1983a,b). Similar mobility of desmosomes has been reported for cells whose keratin filament organization has been disrupted by microinjection of antikeratin antibodies (Klymkowski *et al.*, 1983). It is interesting to note that PtK2 cells,

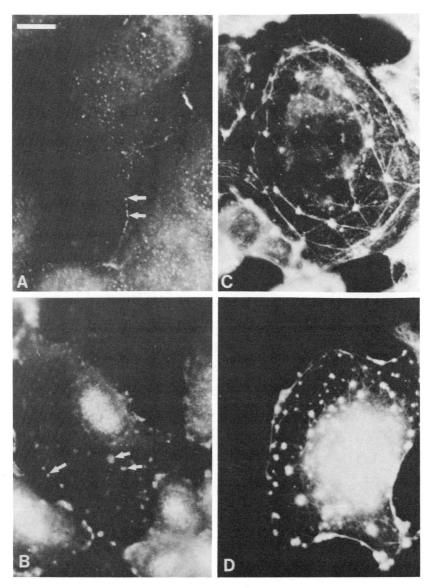

FIG. 4. Indirect immunofluorescence localization of keratin, desmosomal polypeptides, and actin is shown in KLN 205 cells. Punctate distribution of desmosomal polypeptides (A) is observed at the margins of apposed cells in untreated cultures (arrows). Variably sized plaques (arrows) are stained by antidesmosomal antiserum in cells treated for 2 hours with a combination of cytochalasin D and colchicine (B). Indirect immunofluorescence localization of keratin following combined drug treatment is shown in C and localization of actin, which appears to colocalize at sites of keratin and desmosomal polypeptide concentration, is shown in D. Bar, 12 μm. [A and B are reproduced from Knapp *et al.* (1985a), by copyright permission of the New York Academy of Sciences.]

which apparently lack desmosomes, still have membrane-associated sites at which keratin IF appear to be integrated. Under the appropriate conditions of drug treatment the keratin cytoskeleton of these cells forms the lattice arrangement of filaments characteristic of other cell types examined (Knapp and O'Guin, unpublished observations; Keski-Oja and Alitalo, 1985). Both cytochalasin and colchicine are needed to fully induce these rearrangements. It would appear that the associations that keratins establish with the membrane or membrane-related structures (including but not exclusive to desmosomes) are a necessary part of the basic mechanism by which the keratin cytoskeleton is maintained both before and after treatment with cytostatic drugs.

C. Cell Cycle-Dependent Alterations in Keratin Organization

Keratins are not the static, imperturbable structures which they were originally thought to be. They undergo a naturally occurring rearrangement in many, but not all, types of cultured epithelial cells during the mitotic phase of the cell cycle (Horwitz *et al.*, 1981; Franke *et al.*, 1982; Celis *et al.*, 1983). Under these circumstances keratin filaments are reorganized into condensed noncytoskeletal forms (Horwitz *et al.*, 1981; Franke *et al.*, 1982), which appear to be distributed in the cytoplasm as condensed, spheroidally shaped structures. The mechanism for this transition is not known, but the phenomenon may be of considerable importance in working out some of the special relationships that exist among IF, microtubules, microfilaments, and other cytoplasmic or membranous structures during the cell cycle. We have approached this problem by asking whether there are any relationships between the formation of spheroidal bodies during mitosis and the rearrangements in keratin IF in interphase cells induced by microfilament and microtubule inhibitors. The configurations of cytokeratins in HeLa and other cell types induced by combined drug treatment appear to have some features in common with the cell cycle-dependent alterations.

The first is that keratin reorganization is coordinated with changes in the organization and distribution of microtubules and microfilaments. Rearrangement of both cytoskeletal elements, which occurs in many cultured vertebrate cells during mitosis, may be involved in keratin IF rearrangements. For instance, if both microfilaments and microtubules act as scaffolding for the keratin filaments, their removal, either by drug treatment or by cytoplasmic cues responsible for microtubule and microfilament reorganization during mitosis, could trigger the rearrangements of keratin observed. Many epithelial cell types, particularly transformed cells, may utilize this type of mechanism in order to be able to circumvent possible cytoplasmic constraints imposed by the interphase cytoskeletal organization of cytokeratins. By altering cytokeratin filaments into packets of condensed noncytoskeletal material during mitosis and redistributing them throughout the cytoplasm they not only are removed from potential interference with spindle function and cytokinesis but are localized for partition into daughter cells (Knapp *et al.*, 1983b).

Combined antimitotic drug treatment directly interferes with the integrity of the microfilament–microtubule systems. One consequence of the loss of microfilaments and microtubules is that there appears to be an increased concentration of keratin-positive material at the focal sites (Fig. 4C). These sites may represent "partial" condensed, spheroidal keratin bodies. Electron microscope studies of these structures should establish whether or not they are similar in fine structure.

Changes in phosphorylation of keratin polypeptides during mitosis have been demonstrated (Celis *et al.*, 1983). Though it is not clear how such changes might affect keratin filaments and their organization, these findings suggest that biochemical alterations involving phosphorylation or other modifications may be related in some way with keratin rearrangement. Analysis of phosphorylation of the keratins of drug-treated cells in comparison to untreated cells has not yet been carried out but may be of importance in establishing the physiological basis for these two phenomena. It is possible, then, that drug-induced changes may mimic part of a complex physiological process observed in the normal sequence of cell cycle events, events which can go to completion (i.e., form spheroidal bodies) only with other, as yet unknown cytoplasmic cues. The fact that not all cell types undergo cell cycle-dependent changes in keratin arrangement provides a basis for comparison between cell types in determining the factors involved in the process. Simply releasing the keratin filaments from membrane and nuclear associations, as observed following microinjection of selected antikeratin antibodies, does not result in formation of spheroidal bodies or any other organized keratin filament array. A coherent view of the role(s) of cytokeratins in epithelial cells is obscured by the fact that cells in which keratin has been disrupted by microinjection of antikeratin antibodies are not obviously altered in morphology or other cellular activities (Klymkowski *et al.*, 1983). Conversely, the morphology of cells treated with microtubule and microfilament inhibitors appears to be maintained solely by the rearranged, but persistent, lattice of keratin filaments (Knapp *et al.*, 1983a,b).

The dynamics of the process of keratin IF rearrangement can be followed in living cells. Once the characteristic response of keratin organization to antimitotic drugs has been established for a given cell type (usually by indirect immunofluorescence), comparison with results from other techniques of microscopy is possible. Differential interference and phase microscopy of living cells demonstrates that corresponding structural alterations in cytoplasmic organization occur following drug treatment (Fig. 5,A and B). Observation of live cells at short intervals following the addition of cytochalasin D and colchicine has shown that the first clearly visible effects occur after 15–20 minutes (Knapp and O'Guin, unpublished observations). The image produced by phase microscopy depicts primarily "asterisk"-shaped structures that appear to be the focal sites of the keratin IF (Fig. 5B). The differential interference image resolves not only the focal sites but also some of the larger keratin filament bundles arising from them which appear to interconnect focal centers (Fig. 5A). The indirect immunofluorescence images visualized using antikeratin (Fig. 5C) and antidesmosomal (Fig. 4B) antiserum clearly show the similarity in distribution of these sites when they are compared to the cytological structures seen in living cells (Fig. 5,A and B). Studies of these manifestations in living cells provide a valuable experimental approach by which progressive and continuous changes in cytoplasmic organization can be monitored in single cells as well as in populations of cells.

The unperturbed organization and potential for rearrangement of the cytokeratins in HeLa are representative of the majority of cell types so far studied. However, not all epithelial cell types continuously maintain a keratin cytoskeleton during interphase even though keratins are present in these cells. For example, the keratins of mouse embryonic epithelial cells (MMC-E cells) are organized in condensed structures which have been shown to be capable of undergoing redistribution into a filamentous network in response to epidermal growth factor (Keski-Oja et al., 1981). Although this situation is, so far, unique to this cell type, it serves to point out that keratin organization in epithelial cells does not always fit into a single category represented by a cytoskeletal array of keratin filaments. It also suggests that there is diversity in the types of signals (exogenous and/or endogenous) utilized by cells which are capable of influencing this state of keratin organization. In some fish epithelial cells, low temperature (0°C) has been shown to induce rearrangement of keratins from a cytoskeletal network to condensed structures within the cytoplasm (Schliwa and Euteneuer, 1979). Drug-induced perturbation of the organization of keratins in the cells of intact epithelial tissues, which has yet to be examined, may prove to be of considerable value in

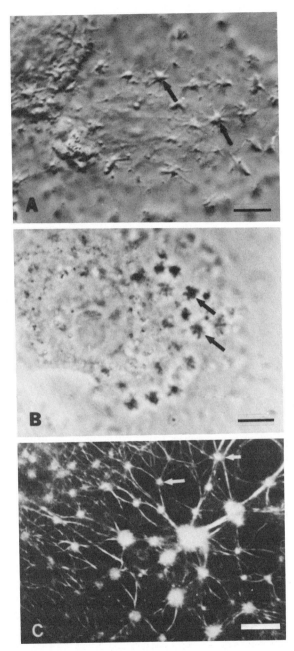

FIG. 5. Differential interference (A), phase (B), and indirect immunofluorescence microscopy utilizing antikeratin antiserum (C) is depicted in KLN 205 cells treated with a combination of colchicine and cytochalasin D. Bars, 10 μm for A and B; 5 μm for C.

determining how keratin organization is influenced by the extra-cellular matrix and as a result of cell–cell interactions (Hay, 1981; Ben-Ze'ev, 1985). The alteration of keratin organization in cells that are apposed to one another in culture (Fig. 3F) demonstrates that cell surface interactions occurring at special sites correspond to the keratin–membrane focal centers. Since many of these sites are desmosomal in nature, their number and distribution between cells of different tissues may provide insight into intercellular influences on keratin organization. Obviously much more needs to be known about the ways in which keratin filaments are assembled and disassembled *in vivo* and about the manner in which they interact with the membrane as well as with other elements of the cytoskeleton (Hatzfeld and Franke, 1985).

D. Applications

There are several ways for the techniques of drug-induced keratin filament alterations to be used in the study of the function(s) of the cytoskeleton. One involves using these conditions, which result in a uniform response in a given population of epithelial cells, to monitor the distribution of noncytoskeletal cytoplasmic components associated with the cytokeratins. This includes organelles, as well as cytoplasmic molecules whose distributions may be influenced by association with keratin IF. The existence of such associations would clearly implicate the keratin filaments in establishing or maintaining functional asymmetry of the cytoplasm. Keski-Oja and Alitalo (1985) have reported that the distribution of a protein known as p36, which is a major substrate for tyrosine kinase in PtK2 cells, is associated with the keratin filaments of these cells. They demonstrated that treatment of PtK2 cells with a combination of cytochalasin D and colchicine brought about not only the characteristic reorganization of the keratin cytoskeleton but redistribution of p36, which colocalized with the keratins. In addition these authors showed that actin also colocalized with the keratin–membrane focal sites under these conditions, as has been observed in other cell types (Fig. 4D). Treatment of PtK2 cells with either colchicine or cytochalasin D alone did not elicit rearrangement of either the keratin IF or the distribution of p36. The demonstration of this association was dependent upon the ability to experimentally manipulate the organization of the cytokeratins, by combined drug treatment. The possibility that other kinds of cytoplasmic molecules may be associated, either transiently or permanently, with keratin filaments is of fundamental importance in the cell biology of cytokeratins and other intermediate filament types.

Another application of this technique for manipulating the cytokeratins is a diagnostic one. Drug-induced alterations of the organization of keratin IF, particularly in cells whose IF organization is not obvious or is in some way ambiguous, allows the establishment and/or verification of the presence of these elements. One such application will be discussed later in this chapter in reference to human somatic cell hybrids constructed by fusion of keratin-positive and keratin-negative parental cell types and in which the expression and organization of keratins are important predictors of cell behavior (Bunn *et al.*, 1985; Knapp *et al.*, 1985b).

This approach may also be useful in defining the conditions under which cells are able to respond to antimitotic drugs that perturb cytokeratin organization. With respect to the cell cycle and the reorganization of keratin filaments, any epithelial cell which undergoes cytokeratin alterations during mitosis can be used to study the changes that occur in the physiology of cells that bring about keratin reorganization. Changes in the susceptibility of cells to drug-induced alterations in keratin organization should be of value in determining the timing and spatial relationships among the filament systems during the progress of mitosis. The structural relationships among keratin filaments, microtubules, microfilaments, and the cell membrane revealed by application of this technique are providing critical new information on the nature of the interactions of polymer-forming elements of the cytoplasm.

III. Experimental Manipulation of Keratin Expression and Organization in Human Somatic Cell Hybrids

A. KERATIN EXPRESSION AND ORGANIZATION

Somatic cell hybridization has been a useful technique in the study of the expression of differentiated functions in mammalian cells (Ringertz and Savage, 1976). Hybrids have been constructed using one parental cell that expresses a differentiated function and another cell that does not express that function, the "undifferentiated" parent. These studies have generally attempted to distinguish between three possible states of genes for differentiated functions, namely (1) autonomous expression of structural genes, (2) continuous activation of structural genes by some activator, or (3) continuous expression as the result of the cessation of action of a repressor gene product present in the undifferentiated cell (Davis and Adelberg, 1973).

Two kinds of fusions have been performed in these investigations, and each provides different information on gene regulation. Each type of experiment has its advantages and disadvantages. In heterokaryon experiments, fused cells are examined before nuclei of the two parental cells fuse and become a hybrid (or synkaryon). A large number of heterokaryons can be examined without the need for selective conditions, and all parental chromosomes are assumed to be present. However, some activator or repressor molecules, even if present, may not pass the nuclear membranes. Furthermore, heterokaryons can only be examined for 1–3 days, which may not be sufficient time for the action of activators or repressors to be expressed. This may be particularly true for experiments examining IF, which have relatively long half-lives. Indeed, Laurila *et al.* (1982) have examined heterokaryons of human fibroblasts and amnion epithelial cells and found that both vimentin and keratin IF were coexpressed up to 3 days from fusion. In similar experiments, Laurila and Virtanen (1985) described the coexpression of three IF types. This result may suggest autonomous expression of these different types of IF genes, but the limitations of heterokaryon experiments mentioned above make such an interpretation difficult.

The first description of keratin expression in proliferating human hybrids was that of Peehl and Stanbridge (1981), who reported the loss of keratin IF expression in HeLa (D98) × fibroblast hybrids. In our laboratory, we have fused the HeLa-derived cell line HEB 7A, which is epithelial in origin, and a normal human diploid fibroblast, GM 2291. In fact, hybrids from this fusion show a range of expression and organization of keratin IF (Knapp *et al.*, 1985b). These parental cell lines differ from one another in growth pattern and tissue origin (Bunn and Tarrant, 1980) and in IF composition. HeLa cells produce keratins and organize them into a typical cytoskeletal arrangement (Fig. 1), while GM 2291 cells do not express keratins. Both cell types produce vimentin. The complementary recessive genetic markers of HEB 7A allow selection of proliferating hybrids in HAT medium (Littlefield, 1964).

The advantages of using proliferating hybrids for the study of IF gene expression are apparent. The two parental genomes are free to interact in a single nucleus, and the maintenance of hybrids in selective medium over a long period enables the detection of rare clones. Furthermore, as these are intraspecific fusions, the affinities of putative activators or repressors should be the same as in the parental cells (Davis and Adelberg, 1973).

Initially, five independently isolated hybrid clones, H-8, H-12, H-13, H-18, and H-19, were examined for morphology and for keratin IF expression by indirect immunofluorescence (Fig. 6). These five hybrids were also analyzed for the presence of keratin and vimentin polypeptides by sodium dodecyl sulfate–polyacrylamide gel electrophoresis (SDS–PAGE) (Fig. 7).

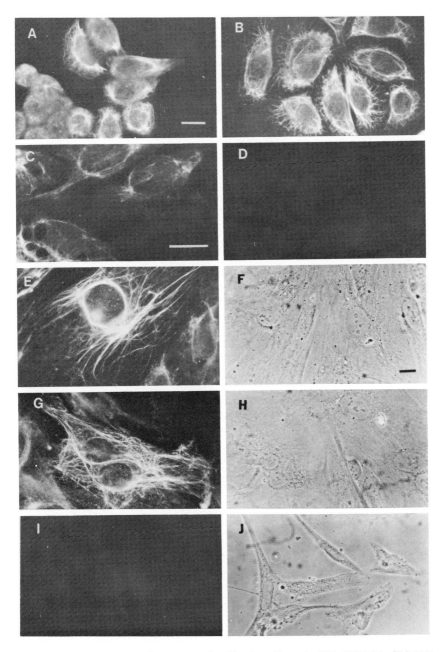

FIG. 6. Indirect immunofluorescence localization of keratin IF in HEB 7A, GM 2291, and hybrids derived from their fusion. Epifluorescence microscopy using antikeratin antiserum was carried out on (A) H-19, (B) HEB 7A, (C) H-13, (D) GM 2291, (E) H-8, (G) H-18, and (I) H-12. Phase microscopy of (F) H-8, (H) H-18, (J) H-12 is presented in conjunction with their immunofluorescently stained counterparts. Bars, 20 μm. (Reproduced from Knapp *et al.*. 1985b, by copyright permission from Academic Press.)

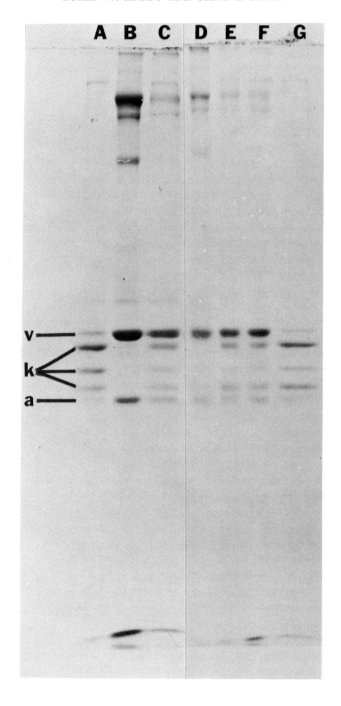

The chromosome numbers (not shown) and the presence of glucose-6-phosphate dehydrogenase heteropolymers shown by starch gel electrophoresis (Fig. 8) confirm that these are true hybrids. Based on immunocytochemical and biochemical criteria (Figs. 6 and 7) there are three general categories of IF expression in hybrids. In the first, cells have well organized keratin filaments and produce the major keratin polypeptides (H-8, H-18, H-19). In the second, keratin is less abundant and not as well organized, though characteristic keratin polypeptides are present in gels (Fig. 7, H-13). In the third, hybrids contain no detectable keratin as shown by both immunofluorescence and SDS–PAGE (H-12). The extinction of keratin IF expression from some hybrids suggests that fibroblasts contain a repressor of keratin IF.

However, this conclusion that keratin IF genes are inactivated in some hybrids is subject to two requirements. It must be established that the keratin genes are present, and that keratin proteins are not being masked even though transcription and translation are occurring. Chromosome loss does occur in intraspecific hybrids, although it is much slower than interspecific hybrids (Bengtsson et al., 1975; Stanbridge et al., 1982). Indeed, the different chromosome numbers of D98 used by Peehl and Stanbridge (1981) and HEB 7A in our laboratory may account for the different results. (It should also be established that the parental nuclei are not repressing each other's gene activities nonspecifically, for these results to be significant for keratin IF expression. The expression of other genes in hybrids is discussed below.)

Detailed karotypes are very difficult to perform in these intraspecific fusions. However, we have isolated relatively rare clones from proliferating keratin-negative hybrids which reexpress keratin (see below and Table II). This strongly suggests that the genes for HeLa keratins were present and suppressed in the keratin-negative hybrids. It is also possible that silent fibroblast keratin genes have been reactivated in these rare hybrids. If a restriction fragment length polymorphism (RFLP) can be found which distinguishes between the two parental cell sets of keratin genes, this possibility can be investigated. Probes for keratin genes are available (Fuchs et al., 1981), and these can be used to screen for an RFLP. Northern analysis may also dis-

---

FIG. 7. SDS–PAGE pattern of cytoskeleton-enriched cell extracts stained with Coomassie brilliant blue. Polypeptides insoluble in Triton X-100/1.5 M KCl were prepared from cultures of (A) HEB 7A, (B) GM 2291, (C) H-8, (D) H-12, (E) H-13, (F) H-18, (G) H-19 and run on a 10% gel. The major polypeptides present are vimentin (v), keratins (k), and actin (a). (Reproduced from Knapp et al., 1985b, by copyright permission from Academic Press.

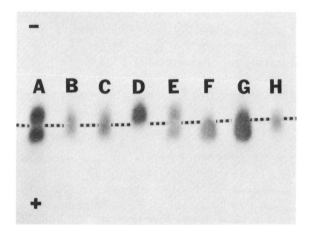

FIG. 8. Starch gel electrophoresis of glucose-6-phosphate dehydrogenase (G6PD) isozymes. Lanes A and E are 1:1 mixtures of parental isozyme variants. The more anodal form is from HEB 7A (lane F); the more cathodal is from GM 2291 (lane D). Cell extracts for H-8 (B), H-18 (C), H-19 (G), and H-13 (H) were run concurrently with controls on a 12% starch gel. Heterodimers are indicated by dotted line.

tinguish the parental keratins expressed, if differences in the mRNA transcripts can be detected. The level of keratin gene repression, whether transcriptional or translational, can also be shown by Northern analysis.

The absence of keratin polypeptides in SDS–PAGE analysis of keratin-negative hybrids indicates that our negative immunocytochemical results are not the result of masking of antigenic determinants. The hybrids which do express keratin IF show heterogeneity of keratin content and organization, suggesting that several genes are responsible for their synthesis, organization, and regulation. It is interesting to note that although the keratin polypeptides found in these hybrids are always expressed together, there is quantitative variation among the individual polypeptides (Fig. 7). There are also differences in the relative abundance of keratin and vimentin, which coexist in all the keratin-positive hybrids examined. Two-dimensional gel electrophoretic analysis of the keratin polypeptides produced by the different hybrid clones should further resolve the number and kinds of keratins present as categorized by Moll *et al.* (1982), and allow us to compare cytoskeletal keratin organization with keratin content.

It is clear that fusion has introduced variation in the expression and organization of keratins in these hybrids. Other genes whose expression and function may be linked to keratin IF can be examined.

For example, the organization, expression, and localization of desmosomal proteins can be detected by indirect immunofluorescence with antidesmosomal antiserum. Susceptibility of hybrids to treatments with antimitotic drugs could reveal whether the organization of cytokeratins can be altered as they can be in the parental HeLa cells (Fig. 2H; Knapp et al., 1983b). Since desmosomes and their associated keratin IF are present only in the HeLa parental cells, their appearance or nonappearance in these hybrids offers an opportunity to investigate the coordinated expression of separate but functionally related families of genes.

B. KERATIN IF EXPRESSION AND LIFE-SPAN POTENTIAL

A further property of these HEB 7A × GM 2291 hybrids has been examined. Strain GM 2291, a human diploid fibroblast, shows a limited life-span in culture similar to that of fibroblasts used in aging studies (Hayflick, 1980). HEB 7A, in common with tumor-derived cells, can be propagated indefinitely. We have previously described that the majority of hybrids formed from HEB 7A × GM 2291 fusions show a limited life-span in culture (Bunn and Tarrant, 1980). Variant transformed cells occur only at two times. About 1–10% of hybrids formed at the time of fusion proliferate indefinitely. Also, at the end of the life-span, clones of rapidly dividing cells appear at a frequency of about 1 in 10^5 hybrid cells in some hybrid clones (Bunn and Tarrant, 1980; Muggleton-Harris and DeSimone, 1980; Pereira-Smith and Smith, 1981). These rapidly dividing cells are also "immortal," and can be propagated indefinitely.

These two classes of hybrids, which we call limited life-span and "transformed," have been examined for keratin IF expression and the possession of certain characteristics of transformed cell growth (Table II). Of 11 limited-life-span hybrids, all were keratin negative. Of eight immortal hybrid clones, all were keratin positive. Furthermore, two of these eight immortal hybrids had arisen "late" as colonies in limited-life-span, keratin-negative hybrids. Thus, the correlation between keratin expression and growth potential was highly significant (p less than 0.0001; Bunn et al., 1985).

These 19 hybrid clones in Table II include the five described above which were analyzed with SDS–PAGE. The keratin-positive hybrids show a range of quantitative expression of individual keratin polypeptides. Thus, hybrids H-10 and H-13 (moderate levels of keratin) and H-8, H-18, and H-19 (high levels of keratin) are all keratin positive and immortal. Also, some limited-life-span hybrid cultures have weak, disorganized keratin expression in a small number (<5%) of cells of

TABLE II

KERATIN EXPRESSION AND LIMITED LIFE-SPAN IN HUMAN CELL HYBRIDS[a]

Cell	Keratin expression[b]	Life-span[c] (PD)	Density-dependent inhibition[d]	Plating efficiency[d]	
				Soft agar	Low serum
HEB 7A	4+	I	−	+	+
GM 2291	−	24.9–38.9	+	−	−
H-3	−	30.1	+	−	−
H-12	−	34.0	+	ND	ND
H-16	−	22.7	+	ND	ND
H-1B3	−	24.0	+	−	−
H-1C3	−	23.8	+	−	−
H-1F	−	34.2	+	−	−
H-2A4	−	29.1	+	−	−
H-2B5	−	26.2	+	ND	ND
H-2C3	−	27.0	+	−	−
H-2C5	−	24.4	−	−	−
H-2D6	−	32.8	+	−	−
H-4	2+	I	−	+	+
H-8	4+	I	−	+	+
H-10	2+	I	−	+	+
H-13	3+	I	−	+	+
H-18	4+	I	−	+	+
H-19	4+	I	−	+	+
H-3a	2+	I	−	ND	+
H-1B3a	2+	I	−	ND	+

[a]Adapted from Bunn et al. (1985). Each independently isolated hybrid clone from the fusion of HEB 7A and GM 2291 is denoted by an "H" prefix. Clones H-3a and H-1B3a are transformed hybrids arising in limited-life-span hybrids H-3 and H-1B3, respectively, at the end of their life-span.

[b]Keratin cytoskeletal elements were detected by indirect immunofluorescence: 4+ denotes abundant and well-organized keratins; 3+ and 2+, abundant but less well organized; −, keratin filaments absent. This scale is based on analysis of cells similar to those in Fig. 6.

[c]The life-span attained by each limited-life-span culture, hybrid, or parental cell, is shown as population doublings (PD) from the time of fusion, compared with six clones of parental GM 2291. I denotes an immortal or transformed culture.

[d]Assays for density-dependent inhibition of growth (+), the ability to form colonies (plating efficiency) in soft agar (+), and the ability to form colonies in low (2%) serum (+) have been described (Bunn and Tarrant, 1980). (−) Absence of these properties; ND, not determined.

the population. This low level of keratin expression may be transient, or it may be related to the minor species of keratin-like IF reported in some fibroblasts, or it may be contamination (Zackroff *et al.*, 1984; Cooper *et al.*, 1985). The correlation reported here is between growth potential and *well-organized, abundant* keratin IF, detected by indirect immunofluorescence.

The transformed growth properties of HEB 7A cells, namely anchorage independence, low serum dependence, and loss of density-dependent inhibition, were also examined in these hybrids. All immortal hybrids possessed the transformed growth properties of HEB 7A. All limited-life-span hybrids lacked these properties (Table II). We have found only one exception to this: a limited life-span hybrid which is keratin negative but lacks density-dependent inhibition (H-2C5, Table II).

Thus, the expression of limited life-span in hybrids is associated with the suppression of the IF type of the tumor cell parent, and transformation is associated with the expression of that IF type. The expression of keratin IF proteins in these hybrids therefore constitutes a marker for proliferative activity other than proliferation itself. Furthermore, indirect immunofluorescence allows the examination of large numbers of single cells, whose life-span can now be predicted. Morphological criteria used previously were unreliable, as morphology varies with cell density and culture conditions.

The identification of genes whose expression correlates with changes in growth potential may suggest mechanisms by which these changes occur. Keratin genes can be grouped into two classes each consisting of about 10 separately transcribed genes whose sequences do not cross-hybridize with members of the other class (Fuchs and Green, 1979; Fuchs *et al.*, 1981). At least one protein member of each of these classes is present in all human epithelial cells (Kim *et al.*, 1984; Steinert and Parry, 1985). Thus, one or more keratin genes may be coexpressed with some HeLa protooncogene which is activated when transformation occurs. The frequency and timing of "escape from senescence" or transformation in these hybrids suggest that this event may be associated with loss or inactivation of the fibroblast gene or chromosomal segment responsible for repression of HeLa keratin genes. The identification of more biochemical markers whose loss or retention correlates with life-span potential, and whose chromosomal locations are known, may point to the chromosomal regions involved in the determination of keratin gene regulation. At the present time, the chromosomal locations of keratin genes are not known, although mapping studies are in progress (E. Fuchs, personal communication). Other HeLa cell-specific markers such as desmosomal proteins (described above), chorionic gonadotropin (Stanbridge *et al.*, 1982), and fibroblast cell-specific markers such as type I collagen (Peehl and Stanbridge, 1981), as well as isozyme markers specific for each parental cell, can be assayed in these hybrids. In addition, the two-dimensional gel electrophoresis analysis of keratins expressed in these hybrids described above may identify which keratins are implicated in these growth patterns. Such experiments may suggest a wider role for keratin IF beyond cell shape definition and organelle positioning (Lazarides, 1982; Steinert and Parry, 1985).

These intraspecific fusions can be performed between any cells differing in IF type and in growth potential, and the expression of IF and other differentiated function genes can be followed similarly to the keratin IF described above. The combination of immunocytochemical analysis, which allows assays to be performed at the single-cell level and which shows both the expression and the organization of these proteins, with the techniques of molecular biology which probe at the gene and transcriptional level should help elucidate the coordinated regulation and organization of these gene families. The generation of a defined set of somatic cell hybrids with differently and stably expressed IF should facilitate this study.

ACKNOWLEDGMENTS

Special thanks to Dr. W. M. O'Guin for his participation in much of the work presented here. Thanks also to Debra Chavis for typing the manuscript. This research was supported by ACS Grant IN107G, NSF Grants PCM8011745 and PCM83-09068, NIA Grant AG02664, and NIH Grant 1 R01 HD18129-01.

REFERENCES

Bengtsson, B. O., Nabholz, M., Kennett, R., Bodmer, W. F., Povey, S., and Swallow, D. (1975). *Som. Cell Genet.* **1**, 41–64.

Ben-Ze'ev, A. (1985). *Ann. N.Y. Acad. Sci.* **455**, 597–613.

Bunn, C. L., and Tarrant, G. M. (1980). *Exp. Cell Res.* **127**, 385–396.

Bunn. C. L., White, F. A., O'Guin, W. M., Sawyer, R. H., and Knapp, L. W. (1985). *In Vitro* **21**, 716–720.

Celis, J., Larsen, P., Fey, S., and Celis, A. (1983). *J. Cell Biol.* **97**, 1429–1434.

Celis, J., Small, J., Larsen, P., Fey, S., DeMey, J., and Celis, A. (1984). *Proc. Natl. Acad. Sci. U.S.A.* **81**, 1117–1121.

Cooper. D., Schermer, A., and Sun, T. T. (1985). *Lab. Invest.* **52**, 243–256.

Dale, B., Resing, K., and Lonsdale-Eccles, J. (1985). *Ann. N.Y. Acad. Sci.* **455**, 330–342.

Davis, F. M.. and Adelberg, E. A. (1973). *Bacteriol. Rev.* **37**, 197–214.

Denk, H., Weybora, W., Ratschek, M., Sohar, R., and Franke, W. (1985). *Differentiation* **29**, 88–97.

Eckert, B., Daley, R., and Parysek, L. (1982). *Cold Spring Harbor Symp. Quant. Biol.* **46**, 403–412.

Franke, W., Schmid, C., Osborne, M., and Weber, K. (1978). *Proc. Natl. Acad. Sci. U.S.A.* **75**, 5034–5038.

Franke, W., Schmid, E., Weber, K., and Osborn, M. (1979). *Exp. Cell Res.* **118**, 95–109.

Franke, W., Schmid, E., Grund, C., Miller, H., Engelbrecht, I., Moll, R., Stadler, J., and Jarasch, E. D. (1981). *Differentiation* **20**, 217–241.

Franke, W., Schmid, E., Grund, C., and Geiger, B. (1982). *Cell* **30**, 103–113.

Fuchs, E., and Green, H. (1979). *Cell* **17**, 573–582.

Fuchs, E., Coppock, S. M., Green, H., and Cleveland, D. W. (1981). *Cell* **27**, 75–84.

Fuchs, E., Hanukoglu, I., Marchuk, D., Grace, M., and Kim, K. (1985). *Ann. N.Y. Acad. Sci.* **455**, 436–450.

Geiger, B., Schmid, E., and Franke, W. (1983). *Differentiation* **23**, 189–205.

Hatzfeld, M., and Franke, W. (1985). *J. Cell Biol.* **101**, 1826–1841.

Hay, E. (1981). *J. Cell Biol.* **91**, 205S–223S.

Hayflick, L. (1980). *Mech. Ageing Dev.* **14**, 59–79.

Horwitz, B., Kupfer, H., Eshhar, Z., and Geiger, B. (1981). *Exp. Cell Res.* **134**, 281–290.

Jones, J., Goldman, A., Yang, H.-Y., and Goldman, R. (1985). *Ann. N.Y. Acad. Sci.* **455**, 695–698.

Kelly, D. (1966). *J. Cell Biol.* **28**, 51–72.

Keski-Oja, J., and Alitalio, K. (1985). *Exp. Cell Res.* **158**, 86–94.

Keski-Oja, J., Lehto, V.-P., and Virtanen, I. (1981). *J. Cell Biol.* **90**, 537–541.

Kim, K., Rheinwald, J., and Fuchs, E. (1983). *Mol. Cell. Biol.* **3**, 494–502.

Kim, K., Marchuk, D., and Fuchs, E. (1984). *J. Cell Biol.* **99**, 1872–1877.

Klymkowski, M., Miller, R., and Lane, E. (1983). *J. Cell Biol.* **96**, 494–504.

Knapp, L. W., and Sawyer, R. H. (1983). *Trans. Am. Microsc. Soc.* **102**, 60–67.

Knapp, L. W., O'Guin, W. M., and Sawyer, R. H. (1983a). *Science* **219**, 501–503.

Knapp, L. W., O'Guin, W. M., and Sawyer, R. H. (1983b). *J. Cell Biol.* **97**, 1788–1794.

Knapp, L. W., O'Guin, W. M., and Sawyer, R. H. (1985a). *Ann. N.Y. Acad. Sci.* **455**, 758–761.

Knapp, L. W., O'Guin, W. M., Sawyer, R. H., Mitchell, D., and Bunn, C. L. (1985b). *Exp. Cell Res.* **156**, 359–366.

Lane, B., Bartek, J., Purkis, P., and Leigh, I. (1985). *Ann. N.Y. Acad. Sci.* **455**, 241–250.

Laurila, P., and Virtanen, I. (1985). *Ann. N.Y. Acad. Sci.* **455**, 741–743.

Laurila, P., Virtanen, I., Lehto, V.-P., Vartio, T., and Stenman, S. (1982). *J. Cell Biol.* **94**, 308–315.

Lazarides, E. (1980). *Nature (London)* **283**, 249–252.

Lazarides, E. (1982). *Annu. Rev. Biochem.* **51**, 219–250.

Littlefield, J. W. (1964). *Science* **145**, 709–710.

Moll, R., Franke, W. W., Schiller, D. L., Geiger, B., and Krepler, R. (1982). *Cell* **31**, 11–24.

Muggleton-Harris, A. L., and DeSimone, D. W. (1980). *Som. Cell Genet.* **6**, 689–698.

Osborne, M., Geider, N., Shaw, G., Sharp, G., and Weber, K. (1982). *Cold Spring Harbor Symp. Quant. Biol.* **46**, 413–429.

Osborne, M., Altmannsberger, M., Debus, E., and Weber, K. (1985). *Ann. N.Y. Acad. Sci* **455**, 649–668.

Overton, J. (1975). *Curr. Top. Dev. Biol.* **10**, 1–34.

Peehl, D. M., and Stanbridge, E. J. (1981). *Int. J. Cancer* **17**, 625–635.

Pereira-Smith, O. M., and Smith, J. R. (1981). *Som. Cell Genet.* **7**, 411–421.

Pirbazari, M., and Kelly, D. (1985). *Cell Tissue Res.* **241**, 341–351.

Quinlan, R., Schiller, D., Hatzfeld, M., Achtstätter, T., Moll, R., Jorcano, J., Magin, T., and Franke, W. (1985). *Ann. N.Y. Acad. Sci.* **455**, 282–306.

Ringertz, N. R., and Savage, R. E. (1976). "Cell Hybrids." Academic Press, New York.

Roop, D., Hawley-Nelson, P., Cheng, C., and Yuspa, S. (1983). *Proc. Natl. Acad. Sci. U.S.A.* **80**, 716–720.

Sawyer, K., and Borg, T. (1979). *J. Morphol.* **161,** 111–122.

Sawyer, R. H., O'Guin, W. M., and Knapp, L. W. (1984). *Dev. Biol.* **101,** 8–18.

Schliwa, M., and Euteneuer, U. (1979). *Exp. Cell Res.* **122,** 93–101.

Skerrow, C., and Matoltsy, A. G. (1974). *J. Cell Biol.* **63,** 520–530.

Staehelin, A. (1974). *Int. Rev. Cytol.* **39,** 191–283.

Stanbridge, E. J., Der, C. J., Doersen, C.-J., Nishimi, R. Y., Peehl, D. M., Weissman, B. E., and Wilkinson, J. E. (1982). *Science* **215,** 252–259.

Steinert, P. M., and Parry, D. A. D. (1985). *Annu. Rev. Cell Biol.* **1,** 41–65.

Sun, T. T., and Green, H. (1978). *Cell* **14,** 469–476.

Sun, T. T., Shih, H., and Green, H. (1979). *Proc. Natl. Acad. Sci. U.S.A.* **76,** 2813–2817.

Sun, T. T., Tseng, S., Huang, A., Cooper, D., Schermer, A., Lynch, M., Weiss, R., and Eichner, R. (1985). *Ann. N.Y. Acad. Sci.* **455,** 309–329.

Virtanen, I., Miettinen, M., Lehto, V.-P., Kariniemi, A.-L., and Paasivuo, R. (1985). *Ann. N.Y. Acad. Sci.* **455,** 635–649.

Zackroff, R. V., Goldman, A. E., Jones, J. C. R., Steinert, P. M., and Goldman, R. D. (1984). *J. Cell Biol.* **98,** 1231–1237.

CHAPTER 5

PATTERNS OF KERATIN EXPRESSION DEFINE DISTINCT PATHWAYS OF EPITHELIAL DEVELOPMENT AND DIFFERENTIATION

W. Michael O'Guin, Sharon Galvin, Alexander Schermer,
and Tung-Tien Sun

DEPARTMENTS OF DERMATOLOGY AND PHARMACOLOGY
NEW YORK UNIVERSITY SCHOOL OF MEDICINE
NEW YORK, NEW YORK 10016

I. Introduction

Keratins are of particular interest to developmental biologists because they provide convenient markers of differentiation for all vertebrate and potentially certain invertebrate epithelia and their derivatives (Bartnik *et al.*, 1985; Franke *et al.*, 1981a; Lazarides, 1982; Osborn *et al.*, 1981; Steinert *et al.*, 1984; Sun *et al.*, 1984). During the past decade or so, keratin polypeptides have been subjected to an intense scrutiny which has resulted in the elucidation of a wealth of information on the physical, biochemical, immunological, and molecular properties of the products of this multigene family. These studies indicate that there are a number of characteristics unique to keratin polypeptides which make them especially valuable for studies dealing with epithelial determination and differentiation. Keratins are produced by virtually all epithelia and their expression is specifically restricted to epithelia and epithelial derivatives (Franke *et al.*, 1978, 1979; Sun and Green, 1978b; Sun *et al.*, 1979). They are expressed very early in development, concomitantly with the primary delineation of an epithelium (e.g., mammalian trophectoderm) (Jackson *et al.*, 1980; Lehtonen *et al.*, 1983). They demonstrate specific, coordinately regulated patterns of expression throughout embryogenesis which eventually reflect the stabilization of adult programs of epithelial differentiation (Banks-Schlegel, 1982; Dale *et al.*, 1976, 1985; Moll *et al.*, 1984). Individual keratin polypeptides are expressed in a differentiation-specific manner (Franke *et al.*, 1981b; Sun *et al.*, 1984) and also exhibit specific patterns of distribution in different layers of a given (stratified) epi-

97

thelium (Fuchs and Green, 1980; Woodcock-Mitchell *et al.*, 1982). This tissue distribution of particular keratins is a function of the degree of differentiation or maturation of the individual cells as they express the phenotypic characteristics of their particular program of differentiation. Also, the polypeptide composition of keratin varies with disease (Moll *et al.*, 1982, 1984; Tseng *et al.*, 1984; Weiss *et al.*, 1984), transformation (Hronis *et al.*, 1984), and growth environment of epithelial cells (Eichner *et al.*, 1984).

Studies from this laboratory using monoclonal antibodies raised against human keratins have helped to establish definitive patterns of expression of keratin polypeptides within many epithelia of human origin (for review see Cooper *et al.*, 1985; Sun *et al.*, 1985; also see Moll *et al.*, 1982). That is, these mammalian keratins exist as two distinct subclasses of polypeptides which are distinguished by their reactivity with the AE-1 and AE-3 monoclonal antibodies and their charge characteristics as determined by two-dimensional polyacrylamide gels (Eichner *et al.*, 1984). These classes are composed of the basic (AE-3 positive) subfamily and the generally smaller, acidic (AE-1 positive) subfamily. This differential classification was consistent with information derived at the gene level by cDNA clones which distinguished subclasses of mRNA corresponding to the acidic and basic polypeptide subfamilies (Fuchs *et al.*, 1981). This resulted in the designation of type I and type II keratin genes which code for the acidic and basic subfamilies of polypeptides, respectively. Further, it has been determined by using one- and two-dimensional polyacrylamide gel electrophoresis in conjunction with monoclonal antibodies that frequently one member of the acidic subfamily and one member of the basic subfamily are coordinately regulated and expressed as a coupled "pair" of polypeptides in a differentiation-specific manner (Sun *et al.*, 1984). The realization of this "pair concept" of keratin polypeptides, as defined by coexpression, has allowed for the establishment of direct correlations between particular programs of epithelial differentiation and the synthesis of specific keratin pairs (Cooper *et al.*, 1985; Tseng *et al.*, 1982). These associations indicate that the expression of particular keratin polypeptides in an individual cell or tissue provides useful information on its program of epithelial differentiation, its relative degree of differentiation, and its potential to express other keratin polypeptides under various morphological and environmental conditions.

It has become increasingly obvious from these studies that valuable information concerning the mechanism(s) controlling epithelial determination and differentiation may be obtained through the analysis of keratin expression during the developmental divergence and maturation of the various epithelial cell lineages, as well as through the examination of pathological and experimentally manipulated conditions. We will summarize the current information regarding the expression of differentiation-specific keratins under a variety of conditions and will discuss the implications of their existence toward our understanding of epithelial differentiation in general. However, the great majority of these studies have involved human tissues and cell types. Therefore, it is not entirely clear that these properties will be common to all mammals, much less whether they are ubiquitous among all higher vertebrates. Since it is not practical to perform extensive developmental studies designed to determine the nature of factors involved in regulating epithelial differentiation using tissue derived from human sources, it is essential to establish an equivalent set of standards for keratin expression in experimental systems which more readily lend themselves to convenient developmental analysis. Therefore, using the well-established concepts associated with human keratins as a model, we will also present data which demonstrate that the pair concept of keratin expression and the theory of differentiation-specific keratins are equally applicable to a range of mammalian as well as to at least one nonmammalian (e.g., avian) species which are more amenable to developmental analysis.

II. Differentiation-Specific Keratin Pairs

A. Human Keratin Pairs Defined by Coexpression

It has by now become well established that human keratins are composed of roughly 20 distinct polypeptides, the majority of which have been shown to be distinct translational products. All of the known human keratins have been compiled into a catalog which assigns an empirical numerical value (1–19) to each polypeptide in order to provide a standard system of nomenclature (Moll *et al.*, 1982). Further, by examining a large number of normal and abnormal tissues and cell types, it was described that specific acidic and basic polypeptides form "pairs" which came to be associated with particular programs of epithelial differentiation (Sun *et al.*, 1984; Tseng *et al.*, 1982). The 56.5K acidic and 65–67K basic keratins (keratins number 10 and 1–2, respectively, in the Moll *et al.* nomenclature) are usually found in association with keratinized stratified squamous epithelia of all types (Moll *et al.*, 1982; Tseng *et al.*, 1982, 1984). The 55K acidic and 64K basic keratins (keratins 12, 3) are found mainly in association with corneal epithelium in humans, and the 51K acidic and 59K basic keratins (keratins 13, 4) are found in most other nonkeratinized stratified squamous epithelia (Moll *et al.*, 1982; Sun *et al.*, 1984). In addition, the 50/58K (keratins 14, 5) pair of keratins is found to be present in variable quantities in all keratinocytes (which are defined as being the major cell type in all stratified epithelia) but is not expressed in simple epithelial cells, whereas the 48/56K (keratins 15, 6) pair is found only in "hyperproliferative keratinocytes" (Moll *et al.*, 1982; Sun *et al.*, 1984; Weiss *et al.*, 1984). There are also a number of additional keratins which are mainly restricted to simple epithelia or pseudostratified epithelia. These pairs, which were defined by coexpression, are probably the result of a combination of specialized functional characteristics of the polpeptides which dictate their differential expression and the fact that keratin filament formation requires an equimolar ratio of acidic to basic components (Hatzfeld and Franke, 1985).

B. KERATIN PAIRS DEFINED BY COEXPRESSION IN NONHUMAN EPITHELIA

As in the case of human keratins, the keratins from cow, rabbit, and chicken can also be subclassified into acidic and basic subfamilies based on both their isoelectric points and their reactivity with AE-1 and AE-3 (Figs. 1–11). Also, Pruss *et al.* (1981) have produced a broadly reactive monoclonal antibody (aIF) which recognizes most intermediate filament polypeptides. This antibody, used in conjunction with AE1 and AE3 on two-dimensional immunoblots, allows for the identification of most keratin polypeptides (Cooper *et al.*, 1984).

In bovine epithelia, Schiller *et al.* (1982) and Cooper and Sun (1986) have shown that the basic subfamily consists of about eight polypeptides ranging in molecular weight from 55K to 67K. The acidic subfamily also consists of eight polypeptides which range in molecular weight from 41K to 56.5K (Cooper and Sun, 1986). Cooper and Sun (1986) have also shown that bovine acidic and basic polypeptides show

---

FIG. 1. Keratin extracted from representative chicken tissues and subsequently separated by SDS–PAGE and blotted to nitrocellulose. (a) Fast Green-stained (FG) blot of protein from (1) middorsal epidermis, (2) corneal epithelium, (3) esophageal epithelium, (4) ventricular (gizzard) epithelium, and (5) intestinal epithelium. (b and c) Blots similar to a except that they have been immunostained by the peroxidase–antiperoxidase (PAP) procedure with AE3 (b) and AE1 (c) monoclonal keratin antibodies. The pattern seen in middorsal epidermis (lane 1) is identical to that found in epidermis taken from comb, scutate scale, and reticulate scale skin. The epithelium from the tongue and crop produces the same keratin profile as that seen in esophagus (lane 3) and the proventriculus (fore stomach) produces the same keratins as the ventriculus.

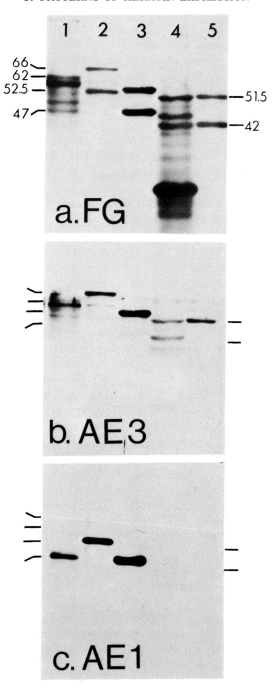

specific patterns of coexpression similar to human keratin. In cows, the 56.5 acidic keratin and the 62–65K keratins form a pair which is restricted to keratinized stratified squamous epithelia such as skin and hoof and are therefore functionally equivalent to the human 56.5/65–67 pair. The bovine 56K acidic and 66K basic keratins form a pair which is mainly found in corneal epithelium, making them equivalent to the human 55/64K cornea pair. The 43K acidic and 58'K basic keratin polypeptides of cow are found in all nonkeratinized stratified squamous epithelia (other than cornea) such as esophagus and are therefore equivalent to the human 51/59K pair. The 50/58K keratinocyte marker in humans is represented by the 50/58K cow keratins and is found in most stratified epithelia as well as cultured epithelia derived from stratified epithelia. Hyperproliferative bovine keratinocytes produce a 46/57K pair which is equivalent to the human 48/56K pair. The remaining cow keratins are found in varying amounts among simple and pseudostratified epithelia (Cooper and Sun, 1986; Franke et al., 1981a; Schiller et al., 1982).

The analysis of chicken keratin has so far yielded two subfamilies of keratin polypeptides composed of six major basic and six acidic keratins (Figs. 1 and 2). Of these keratins, the 59K and 62K keratins are found only in keratinized stratified squamous epithelia including epidermis from skin, comb, scutate, and reticulate scales and are therefore equivalent to the human 56.5/65–67K pair (Fig. 3). The chick 52.5/66K pair is found in corneal epithelium (Figs. 1 and 4) and the 47/55.5K pair is restricted to all other nonkeratinized stratified squamous epithelia including esophagus, crop, and tongue (Figs. 1 and 5). The chick 47/60K pair appears to be the keratinocyte-specific marker although the 60K polypeptide is more easily detected. Due to the lack of availability of cultured chicken epithelia or hyperproliferative diseased epithelia, a marker for hyperproliferative keratinocytes from chick has not been determined. The remaining keratins are found in various combinations in simple and pseudostratified epithelia such as intestine, trachea, proventriculus (fore stomach), and ventriculus (gizzard) (Figs. 1, 6, and 7).

A very similar situation is found in rabbits. The rabbit keratins may be divided into acidic and basic subfamilies consisting of about eight polypepties each (Figs. 8 and 9). Based on their distribution and patterns of coexpression we have determined that all keratinized stratified squamous epithilia express the 56.5/63.5K keratin pair (Figs. 8 and 9). The cornea pair is represented by the 55/64K pair, and most other nonkeratinized stratified squamous epithelia express the 46/59K pair (Figs. 8 and 9). All rabbit keratinocytes express the 50/58K

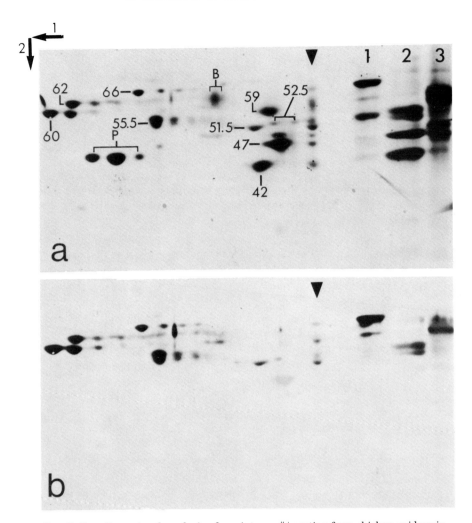

FIG. 2. Two-dimensional analysis of a mixture of keratins from chicken epidermis, cornea, esophagus, and intestine. The first dimension (1) separation was achieved by nonequilibrium pH gradient gel electrophoresis (NepHGE) and the second dimension (2) was SDS–PAGE. This figure allows direct evaluation of the relative position of the majority of chicken keratin polypeptides which are indicated by approximate molecular weight ($\times 10^{-3}$). Arrowhead indicates aggregated polypeptides not entering the first dimensional gel. Side lanes are (1) cornea keratins, (2) a mixture of esophageal and intestinal keratins, and (3) epidermal keratins. a is stained with Fast Green and b is the same blot after staining with aIF. Note that all of the basic keratins are stained but only a subset of the acidic keratins are stained. This pattern is frequently observed when using aIF (Cooper *et al.*, 1984). Bovine serum albumin (B) and 3-phosphoglycerate kinase (P) are included as standards.

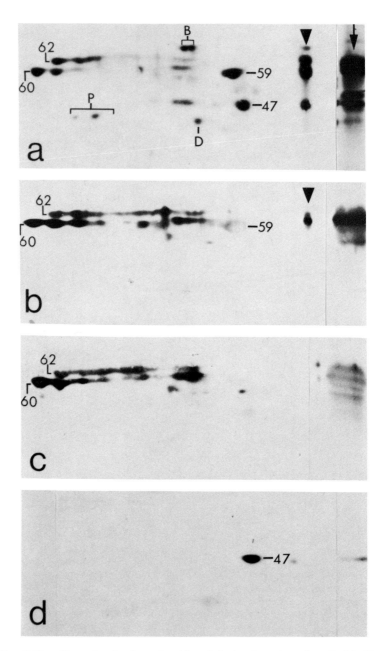

Fig. 3. Two-dimensional polyacrylamide gel electrophoresis as described in Fig. 2 of keratins extracted from chicken epidermis. Arrowheads indicate the location of aggregated material not entering the first dimensional gel and the arrow indicates a one-dimensional side lane provided for comparison. (a) Fast Green-stained blot with the major epidermal keratins indicated by molecular weight ($\times$ 10^{-3}). Standards included on the gel were bovine serum albumin (B), 3-phosphoglycerate kinase (P), and deoxyribonuclease (D). (b–d) Immunoblots of gels similar to a stained with (b) aIF mono-

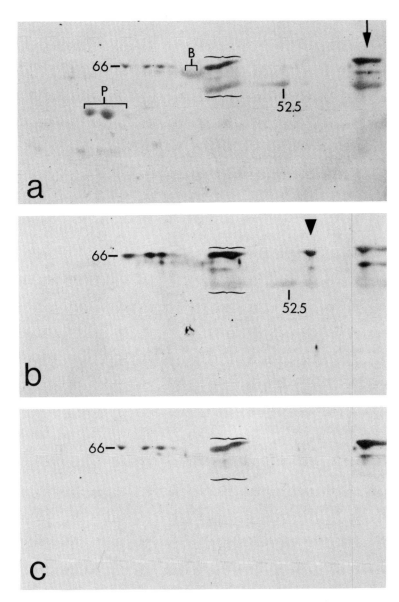

FIG. 4. Two-dimensional gel analysis, as described for Fig. 2, of chicken corneal epithelial keratin. (a) Fast Green-stained blot, with the major keratin polypeptides indicated by molecular weight ($\times 10^{-3}$). The brackets indicate the presence of a strong complex of corneal 66K and 52.5K keratin not dissociated in the first dimension. (b) Immunoblot of corneal keratin using the aIF antibody; (c) immunoblot with AE3.

clonal antibody which recognized most intermediate filament proteins, (c) AE3 mono-clonal antibody which recognizes all basic keratin polypeptides, and (d) AE1 monclonal antibody which recognizes most acidic keratin polypeptides.

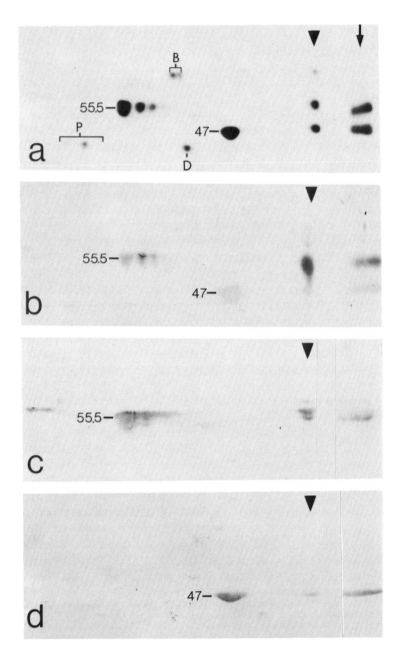

FIG. 5. Two-dimensional analysis of chicken esophageal keratins as described in Fig. 2. (a) Fast Green staining pattern; (b–d) immunoblots. (b) aIF staining pattern of esophageal keratin. Note the weak staining of the 47K polypeptide. This is frequently seen in aIF stains of various acidic keratins (see Cooper *et al.*, 1984). The acidic (47K) and basic (55.5K) polypeptides are well distinguished by AE3 (c) and AE1 (d).

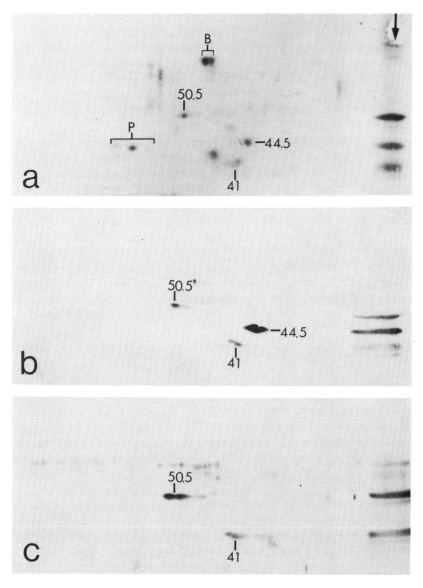

Fɪɢ. 6. Two-dimensional immunoblot analysis of chicken ventriculus (gizzard) keratins. (a) Fast Green-stained proteins blotted onto nitrocellulose as described in Fig. 2; (b) shows that all of the keratins are recognized by aIF; (c) shows the reactivity of AE3 with these keratins. AE1 does not recognize any keratin from the ventriculus.

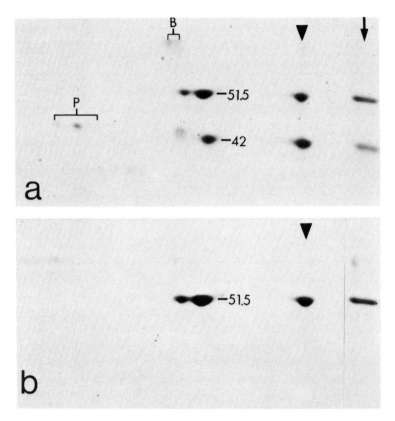

Fig. 7. Two-dimensional immunoblot analysis of a cytoskeletal preparation from chicken intestinal epithelium which has been separated by two-dimensional gel electrophoresis. (a) Fast Green staining pattern. (b) The staining pattern of AE3 on intestinal keratin shows strong reactivity with the 51.5K polypeptide; the same pattern was also seen with aIF (not shown). AE1 does not stain any intestinal polypeptide.

pair while those keratinocytes undergoing hyperproliferation additionally express a 48/56K pair (Figs. 8 and 9). The remaining polypeptides are found in a variety of nonstratified epithelia (Fig. 10).

C. SPECIES DIFFERENCES IN KERATIN PAIRS

It becomes obvious from the above comparisons that both the patterns of keratin expression and their reactivity with AE-1, AE-3, and aIF are highly conserved over a wide range of species. There are a few notable differences in the characteristics of the human keratin pairs and those from other species (Table I). One difference is that the molecular weight difference of 8–11K between the acidic and basic members of most human keratin pairs is much more variable among the

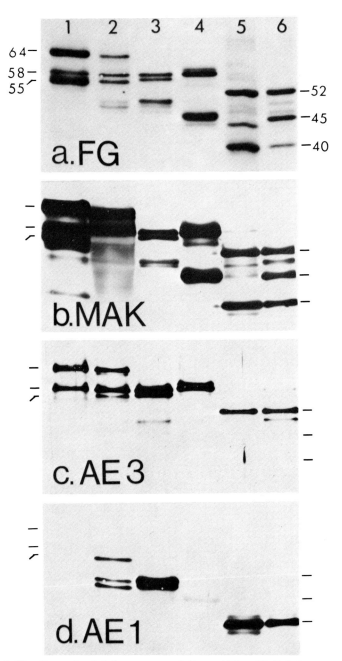

FIG. 8. Keratins extracted from representative rabbit epithelial tissues and separated by SDS–PAGE. (a) Fast Green blot of proteins from (1) cornea, (2) epidermis, (3) epidermal cells cultured *in vitro,* (4) esophagus, (5) intestine, and (6) bladder. (b–d) Immunoblots of the same samples in a using (b) a mixture of monoclonal antibodies (AE1, AE3, aIF, and CA-20) which recognize almost all keratins or (c) AE3 alone and (d) AE1 alone.

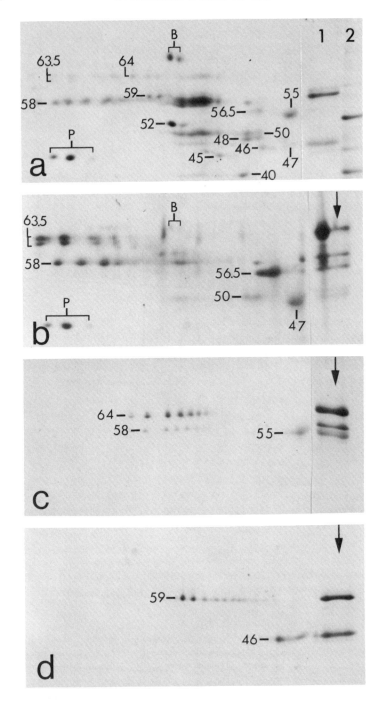

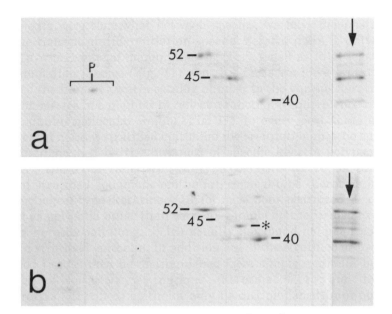

FIG. 10. Fast Green-stained two-dimensional gels of simple epithelial keratins from rabbit bladder (a) and intestinal (b) epithelium. Arrows indicate one-dimensional side lanes for reference and asterisk (*) indicates the presumptive location of actin.

other species, especially the cow 43/58K pair and the chick 52.5/66K pair. The significance of this divergence is not clear at this time but it does seem that the molecular weight difference between members within a keratin pair is not as stringent as the human results would seem to indicate (Sun et al., 1985). Another notable difference lies in the fact that the highest molecular weight basic keratin of humans is a member of the skin-type differentiation pair but in cow, rabbit, and chicken this polypeptide is found in the corneal-type differentiation pair. These differences serve to emphasize the problems associated with assigning functional equivalence of keratin polypeptides based solely on charge and molecular weight similarities.

While the actual molecular weight and isoelectric points of the

FIG. 9. Fast Green-stained profiles of rabbit keratins from representative tissues separated by two-dimensional PAGE and transferred to nitrocellulose. (a) Combination of keratins from the six tissues described in Fig. 8. The one-dimensional side lanes are (1) esophageal keratin and (2) bladder keratin. This combination presents virtually all of the known rabbit keratins. (b) Epidermis and epidermal cells cultured in vitro; (c) corneal epithelium; (d) esophageal epithelium. Arrows locate one-dimensional side lanes of each respective tissue.

B. INTRINSIC VERSUS EXTRINSIC REGULATION
OF KERATIN EXPRESSION

Regardless of the starting tissue, when cells from stratified epithelia are grown *in vitro,* they cease expressing their respective differentiation-specific keratins, but continue to produce the keratinocyte marker (5/14) (Doran *et al.,* 1980; Eichner *et al.,* 1984). A frequent response to cell culture conditions is the induction of significant amounts of the hyperproliferative marker (6/16) (Eichner *et al.,* 1984). Standard tissue culture conditions are not generally favorable for the expression of normal patterns of epithelial differentiation. In many cases, these cells fail, at least initially, to reexpress the differentiation-specific markers. It is usually not until such cultures form stratified colonies that they may produce the differentiation-specific keratins, although stratification alone is insufficient to elicit their expression. If, however, these cells are injected subcutaneously into athymic mice, they all resume a normal pattern of differentiation and express the specific keratin markers typical for their tissue of origin (Banks-Schlegel and Green, 1980; Doran *et al.,* 1980). These studies clearly demonstrate that adult epithelial cells are determined to preferentially express a single, intrinsically regulated program of differentiation and readily do so in the permissive *in vivo* environment. Simple epithelial cells grown in culture, however, usually demonstrate relatively minor changes in their patterns of keratin expression (Denk *et al.,* 1982; Franke *et al.,* 1981a; Moll *et al.,* 1982).

C. PHENOTYPIC VERSUS LINEAGE MARKERS

It should be emphasized that these so-called skin-type, corneal-type, and esophageal-type differentiation markers are not necessarily tissue specific. In fact, no keratin has been shown to be totally specific for a single tissue. They are, however, specific for the program of differentiation most frequently associated with the tissues for which they are named. For example, any keratinized, stratified squamous epithelium will express the skin-type differentiation marker regardless of the origin of the epithelium (e.g., Hassall's corpuscles of the thymus or vitamin A-deficient cornea). But not all adult epithelial cells possess equal capacity to enter a particular, alternate pathway of differentiation.

Interestingly, Hronis *et al.* (1984) have shown that when cultured human epidermal keratinocytes are stably transformed by SV40 they lose their capacity to stratify or synthesize precursor molecules of the cornified envelope. This loss of differentiative potential, typically expressed by normal skin keratinoctyes, indicates that these virally transformed cells have taken on characteristics of cultured simple epithelia. Accordingly, the analysis of keratins expressed in these fully transformed cells demonstrated a complete loss of all normal epidermial keratinocyte keratins, including the 5/14 (50/58K) keratinoctye marker associated with the potential to stratify (Nelson and Sun, 1983) and the 6/16 (48/56K) pair found in hyperproliferating keratinoctyes. In fact, these cells were only expressing keratin polypeptides found in simple epithelia. This clearly shows that at least certain virally transformed cell lines can fail to demonstrate any of the characteristic keratins associated with their tissue of origin.

Patterns of keratin synthesis also vary with disease. For example. Weiss *et al.* (1984) have shown that in addition to their normal keratin complement, areas of human epidermis involved in hyperproliferative disorders (e.g., psoriasis, actinic keratoses, etc.) synthesize significant amounts of keratins 6/16 (the 48/56K hyperproliferative keratinocyte marker) (also see McGuire *et al.,* 1984; Moll *et al.,* 1984). Several nonhyperproliferative epidermal disorders failed to produce these markers.

Under various other pathological and experimental conditions. epithelia may express differentiation-specific keratins which are not typical for their tissue of origin, but rather are typical for the program of differentiation being expressed in responding to these unique conditions. For example, in cases of vitamin A deficiency both corneal and esophageal epithelia present atypical regions of overt keratinization. Under these conditions, both the cornea and the esophagus express the keratin markers which specifically indicate the presence of skin-type differentiation (i.e., the 1–2/10 pair) (Fuchs and Green, 1981; Tseng *et al.,* 1984). To date, the expression of the differentiation-specific markers appears to be in agreement with the phenotypic organization of the epithelium rather than with absolute tissue specificity.

A similar extension of this logic has significant clinical implications. Carcinomas, whether of primary or metastatic origin, may be reliably differentiated from other types of nonepithelial neoplasms based on their continued synthesis of keratin (reviewed by Osborn and Weber, 1983). However, do carcinoma cells continue to express keratins which are typical of the state of differentiation of their progenitor cell or do their patterns of expression reflect merely the degree of histological organization within the neoplasm? Investigators from several groups have analyzed keratins in hundreds of individual carcinomas representing a wide range of classification. The most striking result lies in the tremendous heterogeneity of the keratin polypeptide composition among neoplasms derived from closely related tissues. For example, both Moll *et al.* (1984) and Nelson *et al.* (1984) have examined a range of human squamous cell carcinomas which are derived from stratified squamous epithelia. They found that some of the tumors synthesize the skin-type keratinization markers, almost all synthesize the keratinocyte markers, and some synthesize only simple epithelial keratins which are not normally found in significant amounts in stratified epithelia. As in the case of SV40-transformed cells (Hronis *et al.*, 1984), the fact that even a small number of tumors derived from a stratified epithelium express only simple epithelial-type keratin serves to emphasize that the presense of a particular differentiation-specific keratin pair in an epithelial cell is much more conclusive evidence for the tissue type of origin than its absence. This also shows that the expression of simple epithelial keratins in a carcinoma does not prove that the tumor is of simple epithelial orgin. Thus it becomes obvious that not only is there a considerable heterogeneity among keratin synthesis in tumors of a common cellular origin, there is also no indication of the presence of a specific profile of keratin synthesis typical for a single class of carcinoma. No histopathological information was described for these tumors, but the differences are more than likely due to the heterogeneity in the degree of differentiation found among tumors of the same carcinoma type. While keratins remain a valuable tool to pathologists for the distinction of a carcinoma from other types of neoplasm, the variability in keratin expression among individual carcinomas is probably more an accurate reflection of the degree of differentiation found within the tumor, rather than the intrinsic program of differentiation in the original neoplastic progintor cell. In any case, the concept of differentiation-specific keratins is equally applicable to diseased epithelia.

D. ADULT VERSUS EMBRYONIC PATTERNS OF KERATIN EXPRESSION

Up to this point we have primarily restricted our discussion of keratins as markers for differentiation relative to patterns of expression observed in adult cells and tissues. What, then, is the relationship between patterns of keratin synthesis in embryonic epithelia to those derived from adult cells and tissues? Initially, all embryonic epithelia are simple epithelia. As development proceeds those epithelia which are destined to become stratified become progressively multilayered and eventually express histotypical patterns of differentiation. Accordingly, at least in the limited number of systems examined, the patterns of keratin synthesis show a parallel progression. In the very early embryo, where perspective stratified epithelia exist as a single layer of cells, only the simple-epithelial-type keratin markers are expressed. Later, shortly before the acquisition of a multilayered phenotype the keratinocyte markers are expressed. The expression of the keratinocyte marker is, therefore, unlinked to the actual event of stratification, but reflects the potential of a cell or tissue to become stratified. Then finally the differentiation-specific markers are expressed at about the same time that morphologically mature cells are detected in the apical regions of the epithelium (Banks-Schlegel, 1982; Dale et al., 1976, 1985; Moll et al., 1984). Simple epithelia, on the other hand, initially express the simple epithelial markers and maintain a relatively constant pattern of keratin expression throughout embryogenesis. This clearly indicates that the expression of specific markers for various degrees of epithelial differentiation are closely coordinated with the morphological pattern of embryonic epithelial organization. Further, Regauer et al. (1985) have recently demonstrated that areas of normal human amnion present localized regions of stratification and keratinization in an otherwise nonstratified epithelium. These workers have shown that the skin-type differentiation markers are expressed in these keratinized patches but are absent in the "less differentiated" regions of the amnion which nevertheless express the keratinocyte markers.

These findings are in agreement with two points associated with the pair concept of keratin expression. First, even extraembryonic epithelia express the "correct" differentiation-specific markers associated with their morphological characteristics of differentiation and, second, since all of the cells apparently expressed the keratinocyte markers whether or not they were actually stratified, the expression of the keratinocyte markers only indicates a potential for those cells to stratify and come to express a particular pattern of terminal differentiation (Nelson and Sun, 1983). Thus, the concept of keratin pairs as markers for epithelial differentiation, originally derived from the analysis of adult epithelia, is consistent with both embryonic and extraembryonic patterns of keratin synthesis when considered with reference to morphological features of differentiation.

Adult epithelia have always provided a particularly attractive model system for the study of cell maturation due to the fact that they possess a permanent "stem cell" or germinal population which continually produces differentiating cells. Because of the sequential pattern of keratin synthesis described for cells within a stratified epithelium as they progress through the various stages of terminal differentiation, it has been proposed that it is likely that the patterns of keratin synthesis in adult epithelia represent a continuous, vertical recapitulation of embryonic patterns of synthesis (Banks-Schlegel, 1982). However, this concept needs modification since normal, stratified epithelia do not express the simple epithelial keratins seen in early embryonic epithelia.

IV. Conclusions and Perspectives

It is apparent that the precise localization of particular keratin polypeptides will eventually enable one to subclassify both embryonic and adult epithelial cells and tissues with respect to their relative degree of differentiation. This capacity should be exceptionally useful in studying the various aspects of epithelial differentiation. These localization studies will be largely dependent upon immunological procedures involving monoclonal antibodies. While a great deal has been learned about the biochemical and immunological properties of keratin polypeptides through the use of broadly cross-reacting monoclonal antibodies such as AE-1 and AE-3, they are of limited usefulness in the tissue localization of individual keratins within various epithelia. Any studies using conventional or monoclonal antibodies which recognize multiple keratin polypeptides must always be performed in conjunction with immunochemical analysis of the keratins recognized in a given tissue before conclusions may be made about their localization.

The current "state of the art" monoclonal antibody studies on keratin localization involve highly selective antibodies (usually recognizing a single keratin polypeptide) which demonstrate an extraordinary degree of keratin specificity. It is important to note, however, that we have screened more than a dozen of these second-generation monoclonal antibodies, some to each of the known differentiation-specific pairs of mammalian keratins, as well as others to simple epithelial keratins, by immunoblotting against the chicken keratins extracted from their respective "specific" tissues. These antibodies include AE-2 (recognizing keratins 1,2/10), AE-5 (keratin 3), AE-8 (keratin 13), AE-9 (keratin 13), RGE53 (keratin 18), 10.11 (keratins 18/8), 6.11 (keratin 18), and BE-14 (keratin 5). We have found that without exception they fail to recognize the equivalent avian keratins. In fact, the majority fail to react at all. This, unfortunately, suggests that specific keratin antibody probes may have to be individually prepared for use in the analysis of the fine characteristics of keratin polypeptide distribution in tissues from unrelated species and, potentially, between closely related species.

Despite the relative absence of comprehensive studies on the precise tissue localization of individual keratin polypeptides, the apparent ubiquity of the keratin pair concept and the theory of differentiation-specific pairs is so uniformly consistent that one could conceivably be able to accurately predict the total keratin polypeptide composition of any epithelial tissue given only the species of origin and its histological characteristics. However, one of the remaining major questions concerning keratin distribution cannot be directly answered based on current knowledge. That question is, *why?* Why are the patterns of keratin synthesis so complex in both composition and distribution within stratified epithelia and relatively trivial in simple epithelia and in poorly differentiated derivatives of stratified epithelia (e.g., certain carcinomas and transformed cell lines)? Why do cultured epithelial cells derived from fully differentiated tissues fail to maintain, at least initially, the expression of differentiation-specific markers typical of their tissue of origin? Why does the synthesis of differentiation-specific keratins seem to be restricted to the more mature cells of the epithelium?

Clearly, the complex heterogeneity of keratin composition may be ascribed intuitively to the specific functional requirements of various epithelia and the compatibility of individual keratin polypeptide characteristics with fulfilling those requirements. In this manner, the diversity of differentiation-specific markers is linked to the variations in epithelial cell function. Also, the properties of the keratins expressed in a given cell must reflect the specialized functional organization of that tissue. That is to say, the germinal or proliferative cells of a given tissue must express only products which are compatible with continued cell division while the more mature cells which are not directly involved in tissue renewal must provide the bulk of tissue-specific synthesis. If one accepts the possibility that the high molecular weight, differentiation-specific keratin pairs of stratified epithelia are incompatible with significant levels of epithelial proliferation, then it becomes possible to explain their patterns of synthesis under most of the conditions described above.

To date, most differentiation-specific keratins which have been localized *in vivo* show a suprabasal pattern of immunological staining. While the possibility of antigenic "masking" cannot be totally ruled out, it would appear that the germinal population of the epithelia do not express significant amounts of the differentiation-specific keratins. Certainly the *in vitro* studies show that the true basal population does not synthesize these keratins while the suprabasal cells do (Schermer et al., 1986). Therefore, in normal statified epithelia, the expression of the high molecular weight, differentiation-specific keratins apparently occurs only in cells with little or no proliferative potential. In simple epithelia, presumably all of the cells have significant proliferative potential and subsequently must express only keratins which are compatible with continued mitosis. The patterns of synthesis described for embryonic epithelia are also consistent with this idea. During early embryogenesis, when no differentiation-specific keratins are being expressed, the entire embryonic epithelium displays proliferative activity. It is not until a time closely linked to the initial appearance of morphologically mature, amitotic cells in the tissue that differentiation-specific markers are detected.

The patterns of keratin synthesis by tissue culture cells may also be explained on the basis of proliferative potential. The initial failure of epithelial cells cultured *in vitro* to sustain production of differentiation-specific keratins can be related to the selection of the proliferative subpopulation of cells dissociated from the differentiated epithelium. The fact that these cells grow in culture demonstrates that they had proliferative potential *in vivo* and therefore, would not be expected to express significant amounts of a differentiation-specific keratin. It is not until these cultured epithelial cells organize into stratified colonies with amitotic cells or reorganize into mature stratified epithelia when injected *in vivo* that they may express the differentiation-specific keratins. Similarly, the presence of nonproliferative, differentiated cells in a tumor is prerequisite to the expression of differentiation-specific keratins. Those carcinomas which are poorly differentiated possess no significant amitotic subpopulation and therefore do not synthesize specialized, differentiation-related keratins.

Therefore, it would seem that in order to accommodate the expression of highly specialized, differentiation-specific keratins, a structural organization of epithelia which is compatible with both proliferative and specialized, nonproliferative cells is required. In this way, the complex patterns of keratin expression and localization in stratified epithelia may be explained.

Thus, it may be true not only that selective environmental and physiological pressures placed upon primitive epithelia have resulted in the evolutionary advancement of epithelial function, but also that the evolution of highly specialized keratin polypeptides in partial response to those demands has played an important role in directing the structural organization of the epithelia themselves by imposing proliferative constraints on the cells which come to express them.

PERSPECTIVES

The keratins certainly represent the most highly characterized family of polypeptides which exhibit differential expression among the various epithelia derived from a wide range of species. Regardless of the actual mechanism, it is clear that all epithelial cells are probably bound by a common set of structural/functional constraints which dictate their potential to express specific keratin polypeptides. Therefore, the value of keratin analysis in studies of epithelial differentiation is twofold. First, the analysis of the keratin polypeptide composition and distribution within a given tissue provides reliable information about its program of differentiation and its relative degree of differentiation. Second, the predictable patterns of differential gene expression presaged by the morphological features of the tissue should allow for accurate analysis of the mechanisms regulating the coordinate expression of the subset of keratin genes which demonstrate differential expression under given experimental conditions. The combination of these features makes the keratins one of the most significant model systems for the analysis of developmentally regulated, differential gene expression among members of a large, multigene family.

It is also clear from embryonic tissue recombination studies that the program of epithelial differentiation is not dependent upon the expression of particular keratins, but rather, the expression of keratins is merely the result of the progression of the differentiation program (Sawyer *et al.*, 1984). Therefore, keratins are useful as markers of epithelial differentiation but, in fact, have provided little direct information about the underlying mechanisms which actually regulate epithelial determination and subsequent differentiation. It is in the area of elucidating the mechanisms responsible for this regulation where the least amount of information is available and where detailed developmental analysis offers the greatest potential. In early embryogenesis the various epithelia are capable of becoming determined into a number of more restrictive developmental pathways. It appears to be the direct inductive influence of the mesenchyme resulting from a complex series of reciprocal epithelial/mesenchymal tissue interactions that serves to modulate the ultimate fate of various epithelia (Sawyer and Fallon, 1983; Wessels, 1977). These embryonic interactions provide for the genetic stabilization (determination) of the appropriate program of differentiation which will be maintained and expressed permissively in most adult epithelia. While much remains to be understood about keratin gene regulation, it is obvious that the analysis of keratin production has already provided very useful information for the evaluation and definition of the degree and nature of differentiation in a particular epithelial cell or tissue. Hopefully, in the near future enough will be learned about the properties associated with keratin expression that we may, at last, focus our attention more directly toward understanding the mechanism controlling epithelial differentiation. Ultimately, the primary interest of every developmental biologist lies in understanding the processes responsible for the regulation of both cellular determination and differentiation. Perhaps, armed with the wealth of information available on differential patterns of keratin expression, we can now use the keratins as powerful tools in the analysis of the cellular and molecular mechanisms regulating the more fundamental processes which result in the wonderful diversity of cells and tissues necessary for the very existence of complex metazoan life.

REFERENCES

Baden, H. P., and Kubilus, J. (1984). *J. Invest. Dermatol.* **83,** 327–331.

Banks-Schlegel, S. P. (1982). *J. Cell Biol.***93,** 551–559.

Banks-Schlegel, S. P., and Green, H. (1980). *Transplantation* **29,** 308–313.

Bartnik, E., Osborn, M., and Weber, K. (1985). *J. Cell Biol.* **10,** 427–440.

Cooper, D., and Sun, T.-T. (1986). *J. Biol. Chem.* **261,** 4646–4654.

Cooper, D., Schermer, A., Pruss, R., and Sun, T.-T. (1984). *Differentiation* **28,** 30–35.

Cooper, D., Schermer, A., and Sun, T.-T. (1985). *Lab. Invest.* **52,** 243–256.

Dale, B. A., Stern, I. B., Rubin, M., and Huang, L. Y. (1976). *J. Invest. Dermatol.* **66,** 230–235.

Dale, B. A., Holbrook, K. A., Kimball, J. R., Hoff, M., and Sun, T.-T. (1985). *J. Cell Biol.* **101,** 1257–1269.

Denk, H., Krepler, R., Lackinger, E., Artilieb, U., and Franke, W. W. (1982). *Lab Invest.* **46,** 584–596.

Doran, T. I., Vidrich, A., and Sun, T.-T. (1980). *Cell* **19,** 1033–1042.

Eichner, R., Bonitz, P., and Sun, T.-T. (1984). *J. Cell Biol.* **98,** 1388–1396.

Franke, W. W., Schmid, E., Osborn, M., and Weber, K. (1978). *Proc. Natl. Acad. Sci. U.S.A.* **75,** 5034–5038.

Franke, W. W., Appelhans, B., Schmid, E., Freudenstein, C., Osborn, M., and Weber, K. (1979). *Differentiation* **15,** 7.

Franke, W. W., Denk, H., Kait, R., and Schmid, E. (1981a). *Exp. Cell Res.* **131,** 299–318.

Franke, W. W., Schiller, D. L., Moll, R., Winter, S., Schmid, E., Engelbrecht, I., Denk, H., Krepler, R., and Platzer, E. (1981b). *J. Mol. Biol.* **153,** 933–959.

Friendenwald, J. S. (1944). *Am. J. Physiol.* **141,** 689–694.

Fuchs, E. V., and Green, H. (1980). *Cell* **19,** 1033–1042.

Fuchs, E. V., and Green, H. (1981). *Cell* **25,** 617–625.

Fuchs, E. V., Coppock, S. M., Green, H., and Cleveland, D. W. (1981). *Cell* **27,** 75–84.

Hatzfeld, M., and Franke, W. W. (1985). *J. Cell Biol.* **101,** 1826–1841.

Hronis, T. S., Steinberg, M. L., Defendi, V., and Sun, T.-T. (1984). *Cancer Res.* **44,** 5797–5804.

Jackson, B. W., Grund, C., Schmid, E., Burki, K., Franke, W. W., and Illmensee, K. (1980). *Differentiation* **17,** 161–179.

Lazarides, E. (1982). *Annu. Rev. Biochem.* **51,** 219–250.

Lehtonen, E., Lehto, V. P., Vartio, T., Bradley, R. A., and Virtanen, I. (1983). *Dev. Biol.* **100,** 158–165.

McGuire, J., Osber, M., and Lightfoot, L. (1984). *Br. J. Dermatol.* **III,** 27–37.

Moll, R., Franke, W. W., Schiller, D. L., Geiger, B., and Krepler, R. (1982). *Cell* **31,** 11–24.

Moll, R., Moll, I., and Franke, W. W. (1984). *Arch. Dermatol. Res.* **276,** 349–363.

Nelson, W. G., and Sun, T.-T. (1983). *J. Cell Biol.* **97,** 244–251.

Nelson, W. G., Battifora, H., Santana, H., and Sun, T. T. (1984). *Cancer Res.* **44,** 1600–1603.

O'Guin, W. M., and Sawyer, R. H. (1982). *Dev. Biol.* **89,** 485–492.

O'Guin, W. M., Knapp, L. W., and Sawyer, R. H. (1982). *J. Exp. Zool.* **220,** 371–376.

Osborn, M., and Weber, K. (1983). *Lab Invest.* **48,** 372–394.

Osborn, M., Geisler, N., Shaw, G., Sharp, G., and Weber, K. (1981). *Cold Spring Harbor Symp. Quant. Biol.* **46,** 413–429.

Pruss, R. M., Mivsky, R., Raff, M. C., Thorpe, R., Dowdling, A. J., and Anderton, B. H. (1981). *Cell* **27,** 419–428.

Regauer, S., Franke, W. W., and Virtanen, I. (1985). *J. Cell Biol.* **100,** 997–1009.

Sawyer, R. H., and Fallon, J. F., eds. (1983). "Epithelial-Mesenchymal Interactions in Development." Praeger, New York.

Sawyer, R. H., O'Guin, W. M., and Knapp, L. W. (1984). *Dev. Biol.* **101,** 8–18.

Sawyer, R. H., Knapp, L. W., and O'Guin, W. M. (1985). *In* "Biology of the Integument. II. The Vertebrates," pp. 194–238. Springer-Verlag, Berlin and New York.

Schermer, A., Galvin, S., and Sun, T.-T. (1986). *J. Cell Biol.* **103,** 49–62.

Schiller, D. L., Franke, W. W., and Geiger, B. (1982). *EMBO J.* **I,** 761–769.

Steinert, P. M., Jones, J. C. R., and Goldman, R. D. (1984). *J. Cell Biol.* **99,** 225–275.

Sun, T.-T., and Green, H. (1978a). *Cell* **14,** 468–476.

Sun, T.-T., and Green, H. (1978b). *J. Biol. Chem.* **253,** 2053–2060.

Sun, T.-T., Shih, C., and Green, H. (1979). *Proc. Natl. Acad. Sci. U.S.A.* **76,** 2813–2817.

Sun, T.-T., Eichner, R., Cooper, D., Schermer, A., Nelson, W. G., and Weiss, R. A. (1984). *In* "The Cancer Cell," pp. 169–176. Cold Spring Harbor Laboratories, Cold Spring Harbor, New York.

Sun, T.-T., Tseng, S. C. G., Huang, A. J.-W., Cooper, D., Schermer, A., Lynch, M. H., Weiss, R., and Eichner, R. (1985). *Ann. N.Y. Acad. Sci.* **455,** 307–329.

Tseng, S. C. G., Jarvinen, M. J., Nelson, W. G., Huang, A. J.-W., Woodcock-Mitchell, J., and Sun, T.-T. (1982). *Cell* **30,** 361–372.

Tseng, S. C. G., Hatchell, D., Tierny, N., Huang, A. J.-W., and Sun, T.-T. (1984). *J. Cell Biol.* **99,** 2279.

Van Neste, D., Staguet, M. J., Viac, J., Lachapelle, J. M., and Thivolet, J. (1983). *Br. J. Dermatol.* **108,** 433–439.

Weiss, R. A., Eichner, R., and Sun, T.-T. (1984). *J. Cell Biol.* **98,** 1397–1406.

Wessells, N. K. (1977). "Tissue Interactions and Development." Benjamin/Cummings, Menlo Park, California.

Woodcock-Mitchell, J., Eichner, R., Nelson, W. G., and Sun, T.-T. (1982). *J. Cell Biol.* **95,** 580–588.

CHAPTER 6

DEVELOPMENTAL EXPRESSION OF HUMAN EPIDERMAL KERATINS AND FILAGGRIN

Beverly A. Dale

DEPARTMENTS OF PERIODONTICS, ORAL BIOLOGY,
  AND MEDICINE/DERMATOLOGY
UNIVERSITY OF WASHINGTON
SCHOOLS OF DENTISTRY AND MEDICINE
SEATTLE, WASHINGTON 98195

and

Karen A. Holbrook

DEPARTMENTS OF BIOLOGICAL STRUCTURE AND MEDICINE/DERMATOLOGY
UNIVERSITY OF WASHINGTON
SCHOOL OF MEDICINE
SEATTLE, WASHINGTON 98195

I. Introduction

A. OBJECTIVES

As a part of the overall objective of this volume on the expression of keratins in development we will consider in this chapter the expression and localization of keratins and the keratin-associated protein, filaggrin, during human fetal skin development from approximately 7 weeks estimated gestational age (EGA) until birth at approximately 40 weeks EGA. At the start of this period the epidermis is an embryonic tissue with a germinative layer covered by the periderm, basically a simple epithelium. In contrast, at birth the epidermis is a fully differentiated and keratinized epithelium with the four strata typical of the adult tissue, as well as differentiated pilosebaceous structures, apocrine and eccrine sweat glands and ducts, and nails (Holbrook and Odland, 1975, 1978, 1980; Holbrook and Smith, 1981). Thus, this period of development spans dramatic changes in the structure and function of the epidermis per se as well as the epidermally derived appendages. Our objective in this chapter is to review biochemical and immunological evidence for the time of expression of different members of the family of keratin proteins and filaggrin, and to correlate these changes with morphological changes during development. Wher-

127

ever possible we will try to relate keratin and filaggrin expression with cell and tissue function.

B. SIGNIFICANCE

This review is useful for both basic and applied aspects of epidermal biology. First, the keratins are a large and complex family of proteins that make up the intermediate filaments in all epithelial cells (Franke *et al.*, 1978; Sun and Green, 1978; Sun *et al.*, 1979), but only a limited number of keratins are expressed in any one type of epithelium or in the cells at a particular stage of differentiation of an epithelium (Fuchs and Green, 1980; Franke *et al.*, 1981; Tseng *et al.*, 1982; Woodcock-Mitchell *et al.*, 1982; Wu *et al.*, 1982; Skerrow and Skerrow, 1983; Roop *et al.*, 1983; Schweizer *et al.*, 1984; also see reviews by Moll *et al.*, 1982a; Sun *et al.*, 1983, 1984). The correlation of biochemistry and morphology in developing fetal epidermis may give insights into the role of specific members of the keratin family in cell function.

Second, filaggrin is an unusual protein that aggregates in a stoichiometric manner with keratin filaments (Dale *et al.*, 1978; Steinert *et al.*, 1981; Lynley and Dale, 1983) and is thought to function as the keratin matrix protein in the fully differentiated and cornified cells of epidermis. The interaction of these proteins may account for the so-called keratin pattern of negatively outlined filaments embedded in an electron-dense matrix (Brody, 1959). However, the initial keratinized cells formed during human fetal development do not appear to have a keratin pattern (Holbrook, 1983). Thus fetal development offers a situation in which the proposed role of filaggrin in keratinization can be investigated.

Third, this summary of the time of the expression of the major structural proteins in normal development will serve as a base line by which to evaluate protein abnormalities in fetuses at risk for genetic diseases of the epidermis that are expressed *in utero*. With this in mind, it is significant that the structural proteins considered here are all present by 15 weeks EGA, the time that amniocentesis is generally performed. This suggests that amniocentesis may have potential in the diagnosis of disorders of keratinization in which either keratins or filaggrin are altered, and certainly supports the ability to diagnose disorders of keratinization by fetoscopy and fetal biopsy at 19–21 weeks EGA.

C. RELATED ANIMAL STUDIES

1. Keratins

Expression of keratins during development of rodent epidermis has been investigated by Schweizer and Winter (1982) and Dale *et al.*

(1976) from a time early in the stratification of the epidermis until the postnatal period. Banks-Schlegel (1982) and Sun *et al.* (1985) analyzed keratins in developing rabbit epidermis beginning at the stage when the epidermis is a simple epithelium. In each case, the general pattern is that the higher molecular weight keratins were expressed and increased in quantity as differentiation proceeded and that changes during development occurred in the same order as those in cellular differentiation within the adult epidermis. As succinctly stated by Banks-Schlegel, "Changes observed during embryonic epidermal differentiation appear to be recapitulated during the sequential maturation steps of adult epidermis." An apparent exception is the 40-kDa keratin, expressed in rabbit embryonic epidermis but absent from the normal adult tissue. This keratin is typical of simple epithelium, and as we shall see in the studies of human epidermis has a specific localization within the tissue. Furthermore, even its expression follows a logical rule when viewed in the context of keratins in various epithelia. This is more fully discussed in Chapter 5 (O'Guin *et al.*, this volume).

2. Filaggrin

Filaggrin is frequently cited as a marker of epidermal differentiation (Dale, 1977; Balmain *et al.*, 1977; Ball *et al.*, 1978; Dale and Ling, 1979a; Harding and Scott, 1983; Resing *et al.*, 1984). This protein is synthesized as a large molecular weight precursor (profilaggrin) that is phosphorylated and associated with keratohyalin granules (Lonsdale-Eccles *et al.*, 1980; Ramsden *et al.*, 1983). It is converted to the functional, lower molecular weight filaggrin at the time of conversion of granular cells to those of the cornified layer (Ball *et al.*, 1978; Dale and Ling, 1979a; Lonsdale-Eccles *et al.*, 1984). Because filaggrin and profilaggrin contain relatively more histidine than other epidermal proteins, they can be identified by incorporation of radiolabeled histidine. This technique has been used for autoradiographic studies (Fukuyama and Epstein, 1966), and to aid in the biochemical studies cited above. Antibody to filaggrin reacts with keratohyalin granules and cornified cells (Dale and Ling, 1979b; Murozuka *et al.*, 1979). During the fetal period of development in rodents anti-filaggrin antibody has only a slight reaction with epidermal cells prior to the formation of keratohyalin (Fukuyama *et al.*, 1981). Increased histidine incorporation relative to other amino acids occurs at the time of appearance of keratohyalin granules (Freinkel and Wier, 1975; Balmain *et al.*, 1977, 1979), suggesting little or no expression of filaggrin prior to the morphological appearance of keratohyalin.

These animal studies provide a preview of the results on expression of structural proteins in human epidermal development.

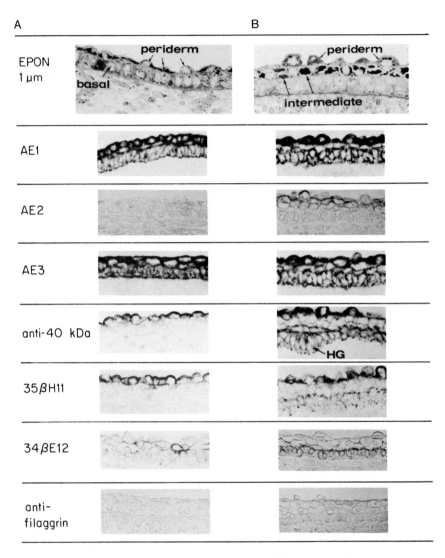

Fig. 1. Morphology and immunohistochemistry of human fetal skin development. Morphology (top) and reaction of Carnoy's-fixed, paraffin-embedded skin using polyclonal and monoclonal antibodies as labeled on the left. The four stages of development are shown: (A) Embryonic stage of simple epithelium, approximately 8 weeks EGA; (B) fetal period of epithelial stratification, 10–13 weeks EGA; (C) fetal period of follicular keratinization, 14–16 weeks EGA; (D) fetal period of interfollicular keratinization, 23 weeks or more EGA.

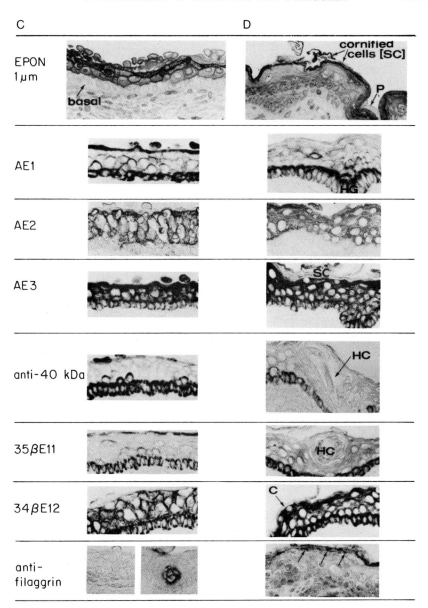

FIG. 1C and D.

II. Definition of Four Stages of Human Epidermal Development

Four periods of human epidermal development are identifiable by histology, ultrastructure, and biochemistry. The first is the embryonic period (approximately 7–9 weeks EGA, Fig. 1A), and the other three are stages within the fetal period identified as epidermal stratification (begins at approximately 9–10 weeks, Fig. 1B); follicular keratinization (begins at approximately 14 weeks, Fig. 1C); and interfollicular keratinization (begins at approximately 24 weeks, Fig. 1D). The embryonic epidermis consists of basal and periderm cell layers. Both are formed from the embryonic ectoderm, but only the basal layer appears to give rise to the epidermis proper. The periderm is a single layer of pavement epithelial cells which covers the developing epidermis until it is fully keratinized. Periderm cells are capable of dividing for a limited period of time and they undergo marked changes in size and structure, but do not seem to differentiate in the same sense as the underlying epidermal cells (Holbrook and Odland, 1975).

Between 9 and 10 weeks a third layer of cells forms between the basal and periderm layers. Cells of the intermediate layer appear randomly at first, but by 10–11 weeks they form a complete middle cell layer. The epidermis shows no evidence of keratinization at this stage as judged by electron microscopy, although the bundles of keratin filaments increase in size and quantity as the period of stratification proceeds and as the number of intermediate cell layers increases. The periderm cells are covered with microvilli and form blebs which may be indicative of transport interactions between the skin and amniotic fluid.

Shortly after the epidermis stratifies into three layers, at approximately 12 weeks, hair follicles begin to form from cells of the basal layer, first as hair germs, then as elongated cords of cells. The follicle has concentric layers of cells which correspond to basal and intermediate layers of the epidermis. At approximately 14 weeks, the follicles begin to keratinize. Granular and cornified cells line the infundibulum of the follicle and the hair canal within the epidermis. This process has been described in careful detail by others (Holbrook and Odland, 1978).

By 24 weeks keratinization has occurred in almost all regions of the body. Basal, spinous, granular, and cornified cell layers are recognized. Large bundles of keratin filaments are present in suprabasal cells. In the granular cells, small keratohyalin granules are associated with filaments. The newly formed stratum corneum shows a loose organization of keratin filaments. The periderm has regressed and is

TABLE I

ANTIBODIES TO EPIDERMAL ANTIGENS

Antibody	Antigen[a]		Reference
	Size (kDa)	Cat. no.[b]	
Anti-keratin	40	19	Woodcock-Mitchell et al. (1982)
AE1	48	16	
	50	14	
	56.5	10	
AE2	56.5	10	Woodcock-Mitchell et al. (1982)
	67	1	
AE3	52/52.5	8	Woodcock-Mitchell et al. (1982)
	58	5	
	67	1	
34βE12	56	6	Gown and Vogel (1982)
	58	5	
35βH11	52/52.5	8	Gown and Vogel (1982)
Anti-40 kDa	40	19	Wu and Rheinwald (1981)
Anti-18	45	18	Moll et al. (1982b)
Anti-filaggrin	37	Filaggrin	Dale et al. (1985)
	300	Profilaggrin	

[a]Based on immunoblot analysis except for 35βH11 antibody, which is based on tissue reactivity. This antibody shows reactivity with most B subfamily keratins on immunoblots.

[b]Catalog number from Moll et al. (1982a).

sloughed from the epidermal surface, although fragments occasionally may remain associated and part of the vernix caseosa.

III. Methods

Samples of normal human embryonic and fetal skin ranging in estimated gestational age (EGA) from 50 days to term, obtained through the Central Laboratory for Human Embryology at the University of Washington, were used for studies of protein changes during development. For biochemical analyses, total epidermal proteins, extracted by homogenization in urea/Tris with reducing agents and protease inhibitors, or cytoskeletal extracts were used for one- and two-dimensional SDS–polyacrylamide gel electrophoresis (Dale et al., 1985; Moll et al., 1982b). Immunoreactivity of specific protein bands on blots of SDS gels (Towbin et al., 1979) and immunohistological localization of the proteins in tissue sections (Hsu et al., 1981) were used to aid in identification of specific keratins.

The antibodies to keratins and filaggrin are listed in Table I. Although incomplete, this table lists some monoclonal and polyclonal antisera whose specificities have been useful in analyses of human epidermal development. AE1 antibody reacts with most members of the A subfamily of keratins (related to type I wool keratins) and AE3 reacts with members of the B subfamily of keratins. AE2 reacts only the 56.5-kDa (no. 10) and 67-kDa (no. 1) keratins. This group of antibodies has been recently reviewed (Sun *et al.*, 1983, 1985) and is described in the chapter by O'Guin *et al.* in this volume. Monoclonal antibodies 34βE12 and 35βH11 react with keratins of the B subfamily in stratified (58 kDa, no. 5) and simple epithelia (52 kDa, no. 8), respectively (Gown and Vogel, 1982, 1984). Keratins of 67kDa (no. 1), 46 kDa (18), and 40 kDa (19) are recognized by individual antibodies (Moll *et al.*, 1982b; Wu and Rheinwald, 1981; Wu *et al.*, 1982). Filaggrin and profilaggrin are both recognized by the anti-human filaggrin polyclonal antiserum (Dale *et al.*, 1985).

IV. Expression of Keratins and Filaggrin

A. POLYACRYLAMIDE GEL ELECTROPHORETIC STUDIES

SDS–polyacrylamide gradient gel electrophoresis of several samples of embryonic, fetal, newborn, and adult epidermis is shown in Figs. 2 and 3. Immunoblots are shown in Figs. 2B–E and 3; these are helpful in identification of specific bands. From these one-dimensional gels and immunoblots it can be seen that the embryonic epidermis (8- to 9-week samples) contains type I keratins of 40 kDa (no. 19) and 50 kDa (no. 14), and type II keratins of 52 kDa (8) and 58 kDa (5). Two-dimensional gel electrophoresis of cytoskeletal preparations of representative specimens has been done by Moll *et al.* (1982b) and is shown in Fig. 4. This allows greater resolution of individual keratins. In Fig. 4a the 58-kDa band can be resolved into component keratins 4 (59 kDa) and 5 (58 kDa). Keratins 13 (54 kDa), 17 (46 kDa), and 18 (45

FIG. 2. One-dimensional SDS–polyacrylamide gradient gel electrophoresis and immunoblot analysis of proteins of embryonic and fetal epidermis. Estimated gestational age (EGA) ranging from 8 to 24 weeks; neonatal foreskin (nb) and adult abdominal epidermal extracts (ad) are also included as indicated. The position of various keratins (40–67 kDa) and filaggrin (37 kDa) is shown on the stained gel (A) and as appropriate on the immunoblots. Note that the keratins of 50 and 58 kDa are present in the entire period shown, while those of 56.5 and 67 kDa are expressed at the time of stratification and increase as it proceeds. Filaggrin is first expressed at the time of follicular keratinization. Keratins of 40, 45, and 52 kDa are present early in development and disappear as keratinization takes place. (A) Coomassie blue-stained gel, (B) AE1 blot, (C) AE3 blot, (D) AE2 blot, (E) anti-filaggrin blot.

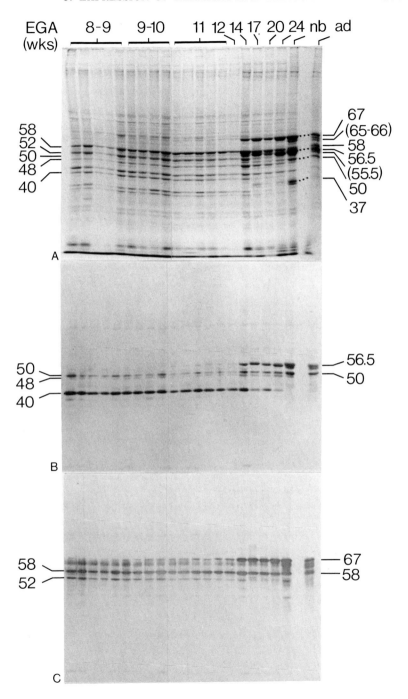

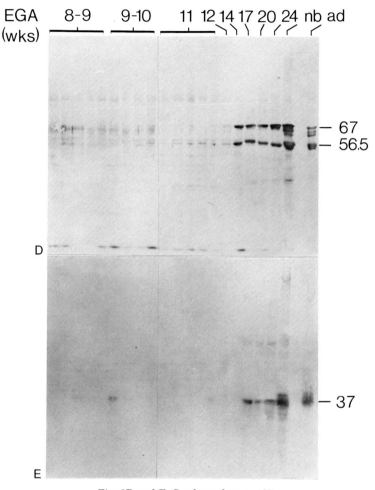

Fig. 2D and E. See legend on p. 135.

kDa) can also be identified in the embryonic period. The 40-kDa (no. 19), 45-kDa (18), and 52-kDa (8) keratins are present from either pre- or postimplantation ages (Jackson *et al.*, 1980, 1981; Lehtonen *et al.*, 1983; Oshima *et al.*, 1983; also see other chapters in this volume) and persist throughout fetal epidermal development. These keratins, as well as the 46-kDa (17), 54-kDa (13), and 59-kDa (4) proteins, gradually decrease in intensity as keratinization proceeds and disappear at birth (Figs. 2B and C, 3, and 4). In contrast, the 50- and 58-kDa keratins are not present in early stages of development but are found throughout the period examined here. These keratins are characteristic of the adult basal cell layer (Woodcock-Mitchell *et al.*, 1982).

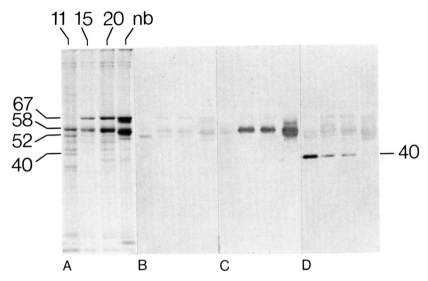

FIG. 3. Four representative ages of 11, 15, and 20 weeks EGA and a neonatal spec-imen (nb) on the stained gel (A) and blots with 35βH11 (B), 34βE12 (C), and the anti-40 kDa antibody (D).

Profiles of the keratins in the stratification period (10–14 weeks) look quite similar to those of the embryonic period except for the faint positive staining of the 56.5 kDa (10) and 67-kDa (1) keratins on the stained gels and as recognized by AE1 and 2, and AE3 and 2 antibodies on immunoblots of the gels, respectively (Figs. 2 and 4b). Both the immunoblots and the two-dimensional gels suggest that the expression of the 67-kDa (1) keratin may slightly precede that of the paired 56.6-kDa (10). These keratins are associated with suprabasal cells in new-born or adult epidermis (Woodcock-Mitchell *et al.*, 1982), and it is noteworthy that they are expressed simultaneously with the mor-phological appearance of the intermediate cell layer.

The period of follicular keratinization between 12 and 14 weeks EGA is distinguished by a marked increase in the coordinated ex-pression of the 67- and 56.5-kDa keratins. By approximately 15 weeks EGA, filaggrin is detectable on both the stained gel and the immu-noblot (Fig. 2A and E). Keratinization of the interfollicular epidermis (23 weeks or greater) is marked by a decrease in several keratins (see above and Section IV,B). The keratin profile in the newborn and adult is somewhat more complex because of the appearance of products of posttranslational modification of the 56.5- and 67-kDa keratins (Figs. 2 and 4e) (Bowden and Cunliffe, 1981).

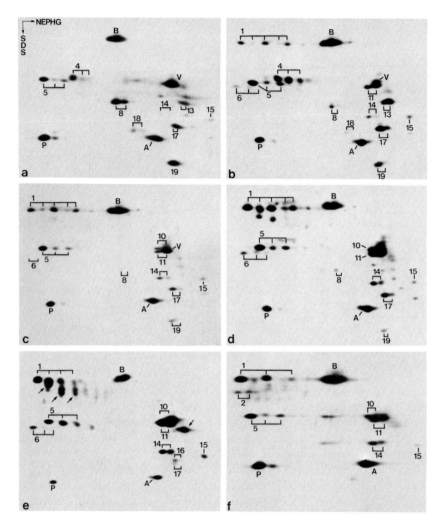

FIG. 4. Two-dimensional gel electrophoresis of cytoskeletal proteins of human fetal epidermis. First dimension (NEPHG): nonequilibrium pH gradient electrophoresis (basic polypeptides on the left, acidic ones on the right); second dimension (SDS), SDS–polyacrylamide gel (top to bottom). larker polypeptides are P, 3-phosphoglycerokinase (43 kDa, pH 7.4); B, bovine serum albumin (68 kDa, pH 6.34); A, rabbit skeletal muscle α-actin (42 kDa, pH 5.4). Keratins are denoted by catalog number (Moll *et al.*, 1982a). Epidermal samples: (a) 10 weeks EGA, (b) 13 weeks EGA, (c) 20 weeks EGA, (d) 24 weeks EGA, (e) 39 weeks EGA (arrows denotes probable degradation products typical of stratum corneum), (f) neonatal epidermis. (Reproduced with permission from Moll *et al.*, 1982b.)

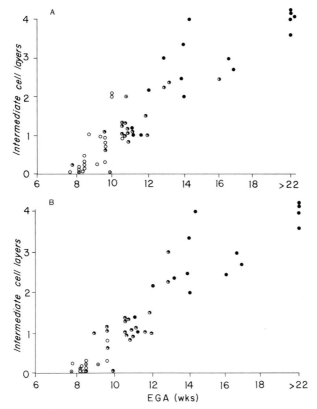

FIG. 5. Expression of (A) 56.5- and (B) 67-kDa keratins as a function of estimated gestational age (EGA) and the number of intermediate cell layers. Expression was coded by reaction with antibodies AE1 and AE3, respectively. ○, Negative; ☉, very faint positive; ◑, + positive; ●, ++ positive.

The SDS gel results emphasize the changes in protein expression with time in a limited number of samples. Although ages of the samples are estimated on the basis of a number of factors, they are subject to error. Figure 5 shows the detection of the 56.5- and 67-kDa keratins by immunoblot analysis as a function of EGA and the number of intermediate cell layers in order to emphasize the morphology and initial age of expression for approximately 50 specimens. Expression of the 56.5- and 67-kDa keratins is highly correlated ($r = 0.848$, $p < 0.001$). Both are negative when there are fewer than one intermediate cell layer, but they become weakly positive at the time of formation of one intermediate cell layer and strongly positive with two or more intermediate cell layers (tested by 3×3 chi square analysis, $p < 0.001$).

B. Immunohistochemical Staining

Antibodies AE1 and AE3 are useful to identify localization of keratin subfamilies, while antibodies with greater specificity allow more subtle interpretation. However, the possibility of masking of antigenic sites cannot be eliminated and results must be interpreted with this in mind. Immunohistochemical staining results are summarized in Table II.

1. Embryonic Epidermis (Fig. 1A)

AE1 and AE3 stain both periderm and basal layers. Periderm cells stained more intensely and evenly than basal cells, which exhibited a patchy distribution of reaction product along basal and upper borders. Keratins of the periderm are stained by the anti-40 kDa keratin antibody and the 34βH11 antibody which recognizes the 52-kDa keratin, as well as by an anti-18 (45-kDa keratin) (Moll et al., 1982b). These antibodies do not stain embryonic basal cells.

2. Fetal Epidermis: Stratification (Fig. 1B)

Antibody localization at this stage indicates a biochemical distinction between the basal layer and the newly formed intermediate cell layer. AE1 stains the basal cells but generally stains the intermediate cells less intensely. In contrast, AE2 and other antibodies to the 67-kDa (no. 1) keratin stain intermediate cells and not the basal cells (Moll et al., 1982b). Basal cells now show more complex keratin expression as the anti-40 kDa, 34βE12, and 35βH11 antibodies react at this stage. The periderm retains the immunohistochemical staining reactions seen in the embryonic stage, suggesting that the keratin expression in this layer is relatively stable.

3. Fetal Epidermis: Follicular Keratinization (Fig. 1C)

This stage marks the initial expression of filaggrin seen in the keratinized cells of the hair canal of the developing hair follicle. Regional variation in immunohistochemical staining of basal cells in the interfollicular areas and developing follicles is also evident with the anti-40kDa keratin antibody, which develops a staining pattern restricted to the bulge and outer layer of cells distal to the bulge, and the 35βH11 antibody, which shows generally weaker staining in the follicle area. AE2 stains the core layers of the developing follicle; however, this staining is far weaker than that of the intermediate cells in adjacent areas (Dale et al., 1985).

TABLE II

Summary of Immunohistochemical Staining in Fetal Epidermis[a]

Antibody	Embryonic (<9 weeks)		Stratified (9–11 weeks)			Follicular keratin (12–22 weeks)			Interfollicular keratin (>23 weeks)			
	Basal	Periderm	Basal	Intermediate	Periderm	Basal	Intermediate	Periderm	Basal	Spinous	Granular	Cornified
A1	+	+++	+	-	+++	+	-	++	++	-	-	-
AE2 and anti-67 kDa[b]	-	-	-	±	-	-	++	-	-	++	+++	++
AE3	++	+++	++	++	++	++	++	++	+++	+++	+++	+
34βE12	-	-	++	+	-	+++	+++	-	+++	+++	+++	-
35βH11	-	+++	(+)	-	+++	+	-	-	±[c]	-	-	-
Anti-40 kDa	-	+++	+	-	+++	++[d]	-	++	++[c]	-	-	-
Anti-18[b]	-	+++	-	-	+++	-	-	+++	-	-	-	-
Anti-filaggrin	-	-	-	-	-	-	-	-	-	-	++	++[e]

[a]From data in this chapter and Dale et al. (1985) unless otherwise noted.

[b]Summarized from Moll et al. (1982b).

[c]Positive staining of interfollicular basal cells disappears between 24 weeks and term.

[d]Interfollicular basal cells only.

[e]Prior to this stage, anti-filaggrin stains keratinized cells in hair canals.

4. Fetal Epidermis: Interfollicular Keratinization (Fig. 1D)

The most dramatic change at this time is the staining of a continuous granular cell layer and the few layers of cornified squames by the anti-filaggrin antibody. The periderm has been shed so that AE1, the anti-40 kDa, and the 35βH11 antibodies stain only the basal cell layer and no longer show the "sandwich" effect seen at earlier stages.

C. Relationship of Antibody Staining to the Distribution of Intermediate Filaments

The immunohistochemical staining with antibodies to the keratins is readily correlated with intermediate filament distribution as shown by electron microscopy (Dale *et al.*, 1985). Within the periderm cells intermediate filaments are organized in small bundles throughout the cytoplasm in early embryonic skin. At later stages they become peripheral and perinuclear in distribution, then lose their bundled organization, and become randomly distributed in regressed periderm cells that lose their organelles and develop a cornified cell envelope (>15 weeks). Staining with antibodies AE1, AE3, 35βH11, and anti-40kDa keratin antibody follows this distribution. In contrast, intermediate filaments in the basal cells are fine, organized into small bundles, are less numerous than in the other cell layers, and stain with less intensity with AE1 and AE3 than those in the periderm.

The immunostaining reaction within the intermediate cells prior to 12 weeks EGA is weak and primarily located at the cell periphery, consistent with the peripheral distribution of intermediate filaments in association with desmosomes as seen by electron microscopy. After about 12 weeks EGA, the quantity of intermediate filament bundles in the upper intermediate cell layers increases. These filaments are organized in larger bundles than in the basal cells; they undergo the most change during development and stain with the greatest intensity relative to other cell layers.

V. Interpretation of Keratins and Filaggrin in Cells of the Epidermal Strata

A. Correlation of Protein Expression and Keratin Hierarchy

The results reviewed here demonstrate the intimate relationship between synthesis of structural proteins and morphological changes during development of the epidermis. The 40-, 45-, 46-, 48-, 50-, 52-, 54-, and 58-kDa keratins, typical of simple and stratified epithelia, are expressed in embryonic epidermis. The 56.5- and 67-kDa keratins, markers of keratinized epithelia, are detectable at the time of formation of the intermediate cell layer, suggesting that the commitment to keratinization has taken place. A very dramatic increase in expression of these proteins occurs between 12 and 14 weeks EGA, the time of hair follicle keratinization. Filaggrin, a marker of the granular and cornified cell layers, appears simultaneously with the morphological occurrence of these cell types at 15 weeks in follicles, and at 21–24 weeks in the interfollicular epidermis. Keratins of 55.5 and 65–66 kDa, produced by posttranslational modification of the 56.5- and 67-kDa bands, respectively, are not present in fetal samples up to 24 weeks EGA. The 40-, 45-, 46-, and 52-kDa keratins generally found in simple epithelia gradually disappear as keratinization proceeds. Although no specimens less than 7 weeks EGA are included in this review, it is reasonable to speculate that younger samples would express only the 40-, 45-, 46-, and 52-kDa keratins, in parallel with the expression of keratins of simple epithelium in rabbits (Banks-Schegel, 1982; Sun et al., 1985).

Thus, the order of expression of individual members of the keratin family is consistent with the known expression of keratins in simple vs stratified vs keratinized epithelia (cf. reviews by Sun et al., 1983, 1985; Eichner et al., 1984). But it should be noted that in the developmental program of the epidermis expression of the keratins typical of stratified epithelia (50 and 58 kDa) precedes stratification, and expression of the keratins typical of keratinized epidermis (56.5 and 67 kDa) precedes keratinization. The order of expression of keratins and filaggrin during fetal development is also consistent with the order of expression during differentiation of an adult epidermal cell, with the exception of several keratins that are not expressed in normal adult epidermis.

B. Localization of Epidermal Proteins in Cell Strata

The distribution of individual keratins within the epidermal strata can be deduced from the specificity of the antibodies, the immunohistochemical reaction, and the biochemical data, and is consistent with the concept of "keratin pairs" (Eichner et al., 1984; Sun et al., 1984).

1. 40-, 45-, and 52-kDa Keratins

Antibodies that are specific for these keratins react with cells of the periderm in the embryo. This reactivity persists until the periderm is lost. These keratins are detected early in development (Jackson et al., 1980, 1981; Lehtonen et al., 1983; Oshima et al., 1983). Thus, judging by the intermediate filament proteins, the periderm is more closely related to ectoderm of the early embryo than it is to the epidermal basal layer. Indeed, it has been suggested to have osmoregulatory and active transport functions in the embryo and fetus, functions typical of simple epithelia in the adult. In the normal adult, expression of these keratins is generally limited to simple and glandular epithelia (cf. Moll *et al.*, 1982a).

With the transition to a stratified epithelium at 9 weeks EGA, the 40- and 52-kDa keratins can be detected in basal cells, or in occasional groups of cells in developing hair follicles (Moll *et al.*, 1982b). A change in the composition of keratin intermediate filament of basal cells may indicate the potential of the basal cells to form the appendages, some of which retain the 40-, 45-, and 52-kDa keratins in the mature structure (apocrine and eccrine sweat glands; Moll *et al.*, 1982c).

Moll and co-workers (1982b) noted that the complexity of keratin expression decreases with development. One reason for the reduction of complexity is the loss of the periderm with the concomitant loss of the 40-, 45-, and 52-kDa keratins.

2. 50- and 58-kDa Keratins

The basal cell layer of the embryonic period reacts with AE1 and AE3, but not with the AE2, 35βH11, or anti-40 kDa antibodies, suggesting the presence of the 50- and 58-kDa keratins. These two keratins are typical of the basal layer in adult epidermis. As in the adult, the 50- and 58-kDa keratins probably persist in the intermediate layer; however, the AE1 antigenic site on the 50-kDa keratin is partially or completely masked in these cells (Sun *et al.*, 1983). At the time of stratification the reaction of 34βE12 becomes positive in the basal and intermediate layers, suggesting that the 56- or 58-kDa keratins may undergo a modification altering their immunoreactivity at this stage of development.

3. 56.5- and 67-kDa Keratins

These keratins are present in the intermediate cell layer as shown by the reaction of AE2 and other antisera specific for the 67-kDa (no. 1) keratin (Moll *et al.*, 1982b). In the adult, these keratins are considered to be specific markers for keratinized epithelium, and are first expressed in spinous cells (Woodcock-Mitchell *et al.*, 1982; Schweizer *et al.*, 1984). The time of expression of these keratins in the fetal epidermis corresponds to the time of stratification. This is a clear demonstration that these keratins are present prior to morphological evidence of keratinization, and may therefore denote commitment of this epithelium to undergo keratinization.

It is striking that at the stratified (three cell layer) stage, each layer has a different set of intermediate filament proteins. Later, when the granular layer develops it has its unique marker, filaggrin. This is a dramatic example of the correlation of the change in expression of structural proteins with differentiation and development.

4. Filaggrin

During follicular and interfollicular keratinization stages, the newly formed granular and cornified layers can be identified by the anti-filaggrin antibody.

The first keratinized cells form at approximately 21 weeks EGA in the absence of a granular layer. These cells are incompletely keratinized with filaments loosely distributed and lack the typical keratin pattern (Holbrook, 1983). Even at this time (19–21 weeks) antibody to filaggrin stains a layer of cells just beneath the remaining periderm. However, the functional and biochemical state of filaggrin in these cells is unknown because the antibody does not distinguish between the phosphorylated profilaggrin, the processing intermediates, and filaggrin (Resing et al., 1984). The keratin filament-aggregating activity of filaggrin is dependent on dephosphorylation (Harding and Scott, 1983; Lonsdale-Eccles et al., 1982) and may be delayed until expression of the necessary processing enzymes.

VI. Potential Application for Fetal Diagnosis of Genetic Disorders

All of the keratins and filaggrin are present by 14–16 weeks EGA, the time at which amniocentesis is performed for diagnosis of sex-linked, chromosomal, and metabolic disorders. It is known that many of the cells present in amniotic fluid express keratins (Ochs et al., 1983). The normal time of expression of specific proteins associated with epidermal keratinization in normal human fetal development is now established. Thus, genetic disorders of keratinization in which the expression of structural proteins is altered may be amenable to early diagnosis via epidermal cells present in amniotic fluid. At the present time, some severe genetic disorders that affect the epidermis are diagnosed by morphological criteria using biopsies obtained by the more difficult and invasive method of fetoscopy, conducted at 19–21 weeks EGA (Anton-Lamprecht, 1981). Biochemical analysis and immunohistochemical staining of amniotic fluid cells may be a valuable adjunct to diagnosis of genetic disorders of keratinization in which the expression of keratins and filaggrin is altered.

A. Epidermolytic Hyperkeratosis

The potential for diagnosis of epidermolytic hyperkeratosis via morphological characteristics of amniotic fluid cells has already been suggested (Eady *et al.*, 1984; Holbrook *et al.*, 1983). The hallmarks of this disorder are bundles of aggregated keratin filament bundles, often in a perinuclear ring, in cells of the spinous layer and cytolysis of spinous and granular cells. The distinctive filament bundles have been noted in amniotic fluid cells from fetuses diagnosed by ultrastructural criteria. Preliminary studies show increased levels of filaggrin in children and adults with this disorder (Holbrook *et al.*, 1983). Immunostaining of amniotic fluid cell smears with antibodies to the high molecular weight keratins and filaggrin could be diagnostic in this disorder, and certainly should be attempted. If successful, this method for diagnosis would have the advantages of being rapid, performed approximately 1 month earlier than fetoscopy is performed, and could be done in many more clinical centers. Ideally, one would like to develop a DNA probe which could be used to detect the disorder in chorionic villi, thus facilitating diagnosis at approximately 8–10 weeks EGA.

B. Constrictive Dermopathy

This newly described autosomal recessive disorder is characterized by a tight skin with both dermal and epidermal abnormalities and hypoplastic development of pilosebaceous structures and eccrine sweat glands (Fig. 6). Affected infants die within a few days of birth (Witt *et al.*, 1985). Skin biopsies from three newborn infants of two unrelated families have been examined by electron microscopy; biochemistry and immunohistochemistry have been done on an affected newborn of each family. Both show a decrease in the relative proportion of the 67-kDa keratin, and an increase in keratins of 48 and 56 kDa that are absent from the normal newborn (Fig. 7, top). These abnormalities are readily detected by antibodies AE1 (reaction with the 48-kDa keratin) and AE3 (reacting with the 56-kDa keratin). Immunohistochemical staining (Fig. 7, bottom) also clearly differed from normal newborn. AE2 gave very weak staining, consistent with the lower than normal amount of the 67-kDa keratin (Fig. 7). AE1 also showed very weak staining in epidermis from one affected infant, but strong suprabasal staining in the other case (shown in Fig. 7). The abnormal AE1 staining was correlated with the amount of intermediate filaments; the former case had few filaments, while the latter had large filament networks. AE1 staining of suprabasal layer has been previously reported in several hyperproliferative disorders (Weiss *et al.*, 1983) of

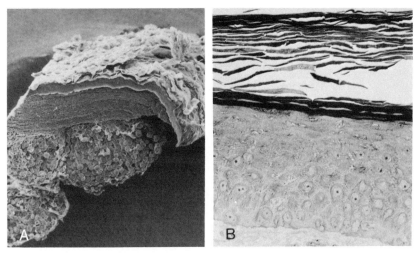

FIG. 6. Constrictive dermopathy. Scanning electron micrograph showing dense layers of collagen beneath the epidermis (A), light micrograph showing epidermal hyperplasia (B).

postnatal onset. It is correlated with increased expression of the 48- and 56-kDa keratins, and frequently associated with reduced amounts of the 56.5- and 67-kDa keratins (Weiss *et al.*, 1984). This pattern of keratin synthesis seems to represent an altered program of differentiation that is also found in the lethal disorder, constrictive dermopathy. The molecular basis of this disorder is not understood, but it seems evident that immunohistochemistry using antibodies to the keratins could, at the very least, be a useful supplement to morphology in either pre- or postnatal diagnosis of the disorder.

VII. Concluding Remarks

A comparison of the time of expression of keratins and filaggrin in fetal development with that of adult epidermal cell differentiation suggests that the epidermal cell layer (excluding periderm) of the embryonic period is similar to the basal cell layer of the adult, the stratified period parallels formation of the spinous layer, and the interfollicular keratinization period parallels formation of the granular and cornified layers. Thus, the program of development of the keratinized epidermal cell takes approximately 16 weeks (the period from 8 to 24 weeks EGA) in contrast to the time of differentiation of an adult basal cell to a terminally differentiated keratinocyte, which takes 14 days.

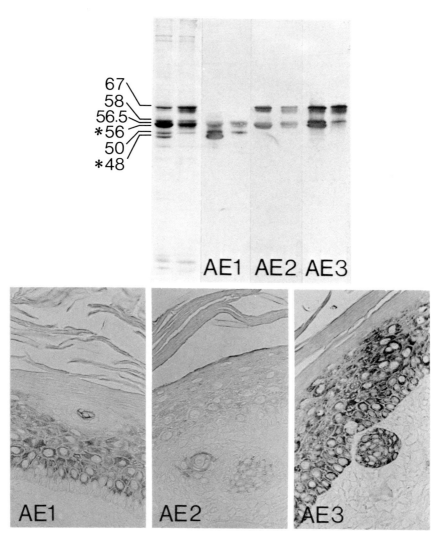

FIG. 7. Constrictive dermopathy. SDS–polyacrylamide gradient gel electrophoresis and immunoblots (top) of an epidermal extract from autopsy of an affected 1-week-old infant (left) compared with a normal neonatal sample (right). The keratins are labeled (in kilodaltons) on the left, and the two abnormal keratins are indicated by an asterisk (*). Immunohistochemistry of Carnoy's-fixed, paraffin-embedded skin from the affected infant is shown below. Note the suprabasal reaction using AE1 which normally stains only the basal cell layer, and the very weak reaction of AE2 which normally stains suprabasal layers strongly.

These studies demonstrate the intimate relationship between expression of structural proteins and morphological changes during development of the epidermis. By 14–15 weeks of development the keratins and filaggrin are all present and their distribution is similar to that of the adult. The developmental expression of these proteins follows a logical progression. As the morphology changes from simple to stratified to keratinized cells, so the main keratins associated with each type of differentiation are expressed at a time suggestive of commitment to that type of differentiation. Note that while expression of the 56.5- and 67-kDa keratins seems to denote commitment to keratinization, the expression of filaggrin denotes the morphological occurrence of cornification. Both keratins and filaggrin may be useful markers for abnormal development and diagnosis of genetic disorders of keratinization.

These results show a strong relationship between the biochemical expression and cell/tissue morphology, and once again raise the question of how this precise regulation of protein expression is controlled.

ACKNOWLEDGMENTS

Portions of this study were supported by USPHS Grant Nos. AM21557, HD17664, and DE04660. We gratefully acknowledge assistance from Mrs. Janet Kimball, Julie Scofield, Mary Hoff, and Bob Underwood for technical assistance. We also acknowledge the generous gifts of antibodies AE1,2,3 from Dr. T.-T. Sun, Dept. of Dermatology, New York University; 34βE12 and 35βH11 from Drs. Arthur Vogel and Allen Gown, Dept. of Pathology, University of Washington; and the anti-40K keratin from Dr. James Rheinwald, Dana Farber Cancer Research Institute, Boston, MA.

REFERENCES

Anton-Lamprecht, I. (1981). *Hum. Genet.* **59**, 392–405.
Ball, R. C., Walker, G. K., and Bernstein, I. A. (1978). *J. Biol. Chem.* **253**, 5861–5868.
Balmain, A., Loehren, D., Fischer, J., and Alonso, A. (1977). *Dev. Biol.* **60**, 442–452.
Balmain, A., Loehren, D., Alonso, A., and Goerttler, K. (1979). *Dev. Biol.* **73**, 338–344.
Banks-Schlegel, S. P. (1982). *J. Cell Biol.* **93**, 551–559.
Bowden, P. E., and Cunliffe, W. J. (1981). *Biochem. J.* **199**, 145–154.
Brody, I. (1959). *J. Ultrastruct. Res.* **3**, 84–104.
Dale, B. A. (1977). *Biochim. Biophys. Acta* **491**, 193–204.
Dale, B. A., and Ling, S. Y. (1979a). *Biochemistry* **18**, 3539–3546.
Dale, B. A., and Ling, S. Y. (1979b). *J. Invest. Dermatol.* **72**, 257–261.
Dale, B. A., Stern, I. B., Rabin, M., and Huang, L.-Y. (1976). *J. Invest. Dermatol.* **66**, 230–235.
Dale, B. A., Holbrook, K. A., and Steinert, P. M. (1978). *Nature (London)* **276**, 729–731.
Dale, B. A., Holbrook, K. A., Kimball, J. R., Hoff, M., and Sun, T.-T. (1985). *J. Cell Biol.* **101**, 1257–1269.
Eady, R. A. J., Gunner, D. B., and Leigh, I. M. (1984). *J. Cut. Pathol.* **11**, 212.
Eichner, R., Bonitz, P., and Sun, T.-T. (1984). *J. Cell Biol.* **98**, 1388–1396.
Franke, W. W., Weber, K., Osborn, M., Schmid, E., and Freudenstein, C. (1978). *Exp. Cell Res.* **116**, 429–445.

Franke, W. W., Schiller, D. L., Moll, R., Winter, S., Schmid, I., Engelbrecht, I., Denk, H., Krepler, R., and Platzer, E. (1981). *J. Mol. Biol.* **153**, 933–959.

Freinkel, R. K., and Wier, K. A. (1975). *J. Invest. Dermatol.* **65**, 482–487.

Fuchs, E., and Green, H. (1980). *Cell* **19**, 1033–1042.

Fukuyama, K.,and Epstein, W. L. (1966). *J. Invest. Dermatol.* **47**, 551–560.

Fukuyama, K., Marshburn, I., and Epstein, W. L. (1981). *Dev. Biol.* **81**, 201–207.

Gown, A. M., and Vogel, A. M. (1982). *J. Cell Biol.* **95**, 414–424.

Gown, A. M., and Vogel, A. M. (1984). *Am. J. Pathol.* **114**, 309–321.

Harding, C. R., and Scott, I. R. (1983). *J. Mol. Biol.* **170**, 651–673.

Holbrook, K. A. (1983). *In* "Biochemistry and Physiology of the Skin" (L. A. Goldsmith, ed.), pp. 64–101. Oxford Univ. Press, New York.

Holbrook, K. A., and Odland, G. F. (1975). *J. Invest. Dermatol.* **65**, 16–38.

Holbrook, K. A., and Odland, G. F. (1978). *J. Invest. Dermatol.* **71**, 385–390.

Holbrook, K. A., and Odland, G. F. (1980). *J. Invest. Dermatol.* **80**, 161–168.

Holbrook, K. A., and Smith, L. T. (1981). *In Birth Defects Orig. Art. Ser.* **17**, 9–38.

Holbrook, K. A., Dale, B. A., Sybert, V. P., and Sagebiel, R. W. (1983). *J. Invest. Dermatol.* **80**, 222–227.

Hsu, S. M., Raine, L., and Fanger, H. (1981). *J. Histochem. Cytochem.* **29**, 577–580.

Jackson, B. W., Grund, C., Schmid, E., Burk, K., Franke, W. W., and Illmensee, K. (1980). *Differentiation* **17**, 161–179.

Jackson, B. W., Grund, C., Winter, S., Franke, W. W., and Illmensee, K. (1981). *Differentiation* **20**, 203–216.

Lehtonen, E., Lehto, V. P., Vartio, T., Badley, R. A., and Virtanen, I. (1983). *Dev. Biol.* **100**, 158–165.

Lonsdale-Eccles, J. D., Haugen, J. A., and Dale, B. A. (1980). *J. Biol. Chem.* **255**, 2235–2238.

Lonsdale-Eccles, J. D., Teller, D. C., and Dale, B. A. (1982). *Biochemistry* **21**, 5940–5948.

Lonsdale-Eccles, J. D., Resing, K. A., Meek, R. L., and Dale, B. A. (1984). *Biochemistry* **23**, 1239–1245.

Lynley, A. M., and Dale, B. A. (1983). *Biochim. Biophys. Acta* **744**, 28–35.

Moll, R., Franke, W. W., Schiller, D. L., Gieger, B., and Krepler, R. (1982a). *Cell* **31**, 11–24.

Moll, R., Moll, I., and Wiest, W. (1982b). *Differentiation* **23**, 170–178.

Moll, R., Franke, W. W., Volc-Platzer, B., and Krepler, R. (1982c). *J. Cell Biol.* **95**, 285–295.

Murozuka, T., Fukuyama, K., and Epstein, W. L. (1979). *Biochim. Biophys. Acta* **579**, 334–345.

Ochs, B. A., Franke, W. W., Moll, R., Grund, C., Cremer, M., and Cremer, T. (1983). *Differentiation* **24**, 153–173.

Oshima, R. G., Howe, W. E., Klier, F. G., Adamson, E. D., and Shevinsky, L. H. (1983). *Dev. Biol.* **99**, 447–455.

Ramsden, M., Loehren, D., and Balmain, A. (1983). *Differentiation* **23**, 243–249.

Resing, K. A., Walsh, K. A., and Dale, B. A. (1984). *J. Cell Biol.* **99**, 1372–1378.

Roop, D. R., Hawley-Nelson, P., Cheng, C. K., and Yuspa, S. H. (1983). *Proc. Natl. Acad. Sci. U.S.A.* **80**, 716–720.

Schweizer, J., and Winter, H. (1982). *Differentiation* **22**, 19–24.

Schweizer, J., Kinjo, M., Furstenberger, G., and Winter, H. (1984). *Cell* **37**, 159–170.

Skerrow, D., and Skerrow, C. J. (1983). *Exp. Cell Res.* **143**, 27–35.

Steinert, P. M., Cantieri, J. S., Teller, D. C., Lonsdale-Eccles, J. D., and Dale, B. A. (1981). *Proc. Natl. Acad. Sci. U.S.A.* **78**, 4097–4101.

Sun, T.-T., and Green, H. (1978). *Cell* **14,** 469–476.

Sun, T.-T., Shih, S., and Green, H. (1979). *Proc. Natl. Acad. Sci. U.S.A.* **76,** 2813–2817.

Sun, T.-T., Eichner, R., Nelson, W. G., Tseng, S. C. G., Weiss, R. A., Jarvinen, M., and Woodcock-Mitchell, J. (1983). *J. Invest. Dermatol.* **81,** 109s–115s.

Sun, T.-T., Eichner, R., Schermer, A., Cooper, D., Nelson, W. G., and Weiss, R. A. (1984). *In* "Cancer Cell" (A. Levine, W. Topp, G. VandeWoude, and J. D. Watson, eds.), pp. 169–176. Cold Spring Harbor Laboratory, Cold Spring Harbor, New York.

Sun, T.-T., Tseng, S. C. G., Huang, A. J. W., Cooper, D., Schermer, A., Lynch, M. H., Weiss, R., and Eichner, R. (1985). *Ann. N.Y. Acad. Sci.* **455,** 307–329.

Towbin, H., Staehelin, T., and Gordon, J. (1979). *Proc. Natl. Acad. Sci. U.S.A.* **76,** 4350–4354.

Tseng, S. C. G., Jarvinen, M., Nelson, W. G., Huang, H. W., Woodcock-Mitchell, J., and Sun, T.-T. (1982). *Cell* **30,** 361–372.

Weiss, R. A., Guillet, G. Y. A., Freedberg, I. M., Farmer, E. R., Small, E. A., Weiss, M. M., and Sun, T.-T. (1983). *J. Invest. Dermatol.* **81,** 224–230.

Weiss, R. A., Eichner, R., and Sun, T.-T. (1984). *J. Cell Biol.* **98,** 1397–1406.

Witt, D. A., Holbrook, K. A., and Dale, B. A. (1986). *Am. J. Hum. Genet.* **24,** 631–648.

Woodcock-Mitchell, J., Eichner, R., Nelson, W. G., and Sun, T.-T. (1982). *J. Cell Biol.* **95,** 580–588.

Wu, Y., and Rheinwald, J. G. (1981). *Cell* **25,** 627–635.

Wu, Y., Parker, L., Binder, N., Beckett, M., Sinard, J., Griffiths, C., and Rheinwald, J. (1982). *Cell* **31,** 693–703.

CHAPTER 7

CYTOKERATINS IN OOCYTES AND PREIMPLANTATION EMBRYOS OF THE MOUSE

Eero Lehtonen

DEPARTMENT OF PATHOLOGY
UNIVERSITY OF HELSINKI
SF-00290 HELSINKI, FINLAND

I. Introduction

It is believed that formation of different types of intermediate filaments (IFs) is associated with cell differentiation, and that once the expression of specific IF proteins has started, it is a stable feature of a differentiated cell. Therefore, IF proteins, including specific combinations of keratin polypeptides, are now used increasingly as cell-type-specific markers in studies on various differentiating systems (e.g., Lehtonen *et al.*, 1985). Analysis of IF proteins might yield information on cell lineages, and special interest should obviously be addressed to the composition of the IF cytoskeleton of germ cells and early embryonic cells. In this review I will summarize the current—partially controversial—knowledge of the IF cytoskeleton of mouse oocytes and preimplantation embryos. The expression of IF proteins in germ cells of other species and in germ cell-derived tumor cells, viz. teratocarcinoma stem cells, will also be reviewed.

II. Preimplantation Development of the Mouse

A. CONTROL OF DIFFERENTIATION

The mouse embryo implants about 4.5 days after fertilization. The preimplantation development begins with cleavage divisions; during early cleavage, the cells of the embryo are still spherical and alike (Fig. 1). Toward the end of the 8-cell stage, the blastomeres undergo the process of "compaction" in which they flatten on each other, thus maximizing their intercellular contacts (Lewis and Wright, 1935; Lehtonen, 1980). By about 3.5 days after fertilization, the embryo reaches the blastocyst stage. Two cell populations can be distinguished in the blastocyst, viz. the trophectoderm and the inner cell mass (ICM). These cells differ from each other in several respects, including mor-

CURRENT TOPICS IN
DEVELOPMENTAL BIOLOGY, VOL. 22

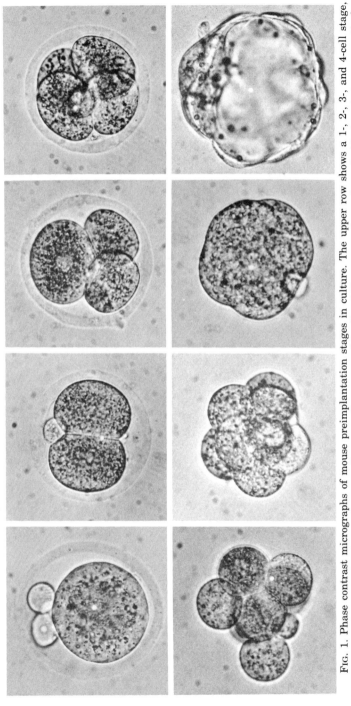

FIG. 1. Phase contrast micrographs of mouse preimplantation stages in culture. The upper row shows a 1-, 2-, 3-, and 4-cell stage, respectively; the lower row shows a loose 8-cell, a partially compacted 8-cell, a fully compacted morula, and a blastocyst stage, respectively. The inner cell mass is clearly visible in the uppermost part of the blastocyst. The embryos in the lower row have been denuded from their zona pellucida.

phology, physiology, surface antigens, synthetic profiles, and developmental fate: the trophectoderm cells form placenta and extraembryonic membranes, whereas the ICM cells form other extraembryonic structures and the embryo proper. By the time of implantation, a third cell type appears in the embryo, the primitive endoderm. It is derived from the ICM and forms as a flattening layer of cells on the side of the ICM that faces the blastocoel cavity.

Cleavage-stage embryos can adapt to rough experimental manipulations. Thus, half the cells of the embryo can be removed, and several embryos or cells isolated from embryos can be aggregated to form a chimeric individual, and yet the development occurs in an apparently normal fashion (cf. Lehtonen et al., 1984; Lehtonen and Saxén, 1986). These experiments suggest that all the cells of the embryo have retained fhe full developmental potential. This has been confirmed by disaggregation–reaggregation experiments: all the blastomeres of the 4-cell embryo, and possibly all blastomeres of the 8-cell embryo, are totipotent (Hillman et al., 1972; Kelly, 1977). At the late morula and early blastocyst stages, the segregation of the cells to the trophectoderm or ICM lineage is not yet irreversibly determined (for review, see Gardner, 1983; Lehtonen and Saxén, 1986).

The remarkable developmental flexibility of the embryonic cells suggests that the differentiation of the blastocyst does not depend on differences between the individual cleavage-stage cells but rather on extracellular factors. This view was expressed in the "inside–outside" hypothesis of Tarkowski and Wroblewska (1967), which proposes that the development of blastomeres depends on their microenvironment: all the blastomeres of an 8-cell embryo have the capacity to differentiate into trophectoderm cells, and in order to differentiate into ICM cells, the blastomeres must occupy an inside position in the embryo. The movement of cells to different positions depends on cell interactions (Graham and Lehtonen, 1979; Lehtonen, 1980), and the developmental fate of a blastomere is clearly correlated with its relative position in the embryo (Wilson et al., 1972; Graham and Deussen, 1978; Hillman et al., 1972; Kelly, 1977). It has been assumed that cells in the interior of the embryo respond to their microenvironment by differential gene expression. An alternative "polarization" hypothesis (Johnson, 1981) emphasizes the polarization of blastomeres and intercellular communication via gap junctions, both established during the 8-cell stage. Accordingly, distinct inside and outside cells develop gradually as a result of polarization, and simultaneously the morphogenetic processes occur which lead to the formation of the blastocyst.

Present knowledge does not allow distinction between the "inside–outside" and "polarization" hypotheses, and it should be concluded that the cytodifferentiation of ICM versus trophectoderm may be controlled by microenvironmental factors and/or gradual formation of distinct cells as a result of radial polarization of the blastomeres. Both hypotheses clearly imply radical changes in the organization of the cytoskeleton of the embryo cells, like polarization of cells or creation of an internal microenvironment that depends on the formation of specialized junctions between the cells of the embryo.

B. CYTOSKELETON AND INTERCELLULAR CONNECTIONS

Morphogenetic movements occur in the embryo before implantation, including drastic changes in cell shape at compaction of the 8-cell embryo and actual segregation of cells to the ICM and the trophectoderm of the blastocyst. The exact role of the cytoskeletal structures in the preimplantation development is not known, but they are probably responsible for shaping the embryo and involved in the regulation of blastocyst differentiation (Sołtyńska, 1982; Lehtonen and Badley, 1980; Kimber and Surani, 1982; Lehtonen et al., 1984). The organization of different cytoskeletal components, including actin (Lehtonen and Badley, 1980; Johnson and Maro, 1984), α-actinin (Lehtonen and Badley, 1980), vinculin (Lehtonen and Reima, 1986), myosin (Sobel, 1984), tubulin (Lehtonen and Badley, 1980; Maro and Pickering, 1984), and spectrin (Sobel and Alliegro, 1985; Reima and Lehtonen, 1985; Damjanov et al., 1986), during preimplantation development have been described. Several of these components form a cortical layer, which may be important in the regulation of the shape and contacts of the embryo cells.

During the first cleavage divisions, the blastomeres remain spherical. The cells are adherent to each other, and toward the end of the second and third cell cycles, there is some increase in the extent of the intercellular contacts (Lehtonen, 1980). In electron microscopy, no specialized membrane junctions have been observed between the blastomeres before the 8-cell stage (see, however, Shivers and McLachlin, 1984), although Lo and Gilula (1979) and Goodall and Johnson (1984) have demonstrated transfer of dye and ionic coupling between twin-cell pairs already at the 2- and 4-cell stages. These phenomena may, however, have occurred via remnants of the intercellular contact at the cleavage furrow. Starting from the compact morula stage, adherent, tight, and gap junctions as well as desmosomes with attached tonofilaments appear between blastomeres (Calarco and Brown, 1969; Ducibella et al., 1975; Magnuson et al., 1978; Jackson et al., 1980;

Lehtonen *et al.*, 1984). Simultaneously, the peripheral cells of the embryo assume a flattened morphology, and at the blastocyst stage, the trophectoderm cells are flat, epithelial-like cells with peripheral circular (zonular) tight junctions and well-developed desmosomes.

III. Cytokeratins in Oocytes and Cleavage-Stage Embryos

A. DISTRIBUTION OF 10-nm FILAMENTS AND CYTOKERATIN-ASSOCIATED ANTIGENS

The outer wall of the blastocyst-stage embryo consists of morphologically and functionally epithelial-like trophectoderm cells which are connected by desmosomes. Although these cells contain desmosome-attached cytokeratin filaments, there is no obvious reason for believing that the nondifferentiated spherical cells of the cleavage-stage embryo would possess IF proteins. However, the exact function of IFs is not known, and suggestions for functions such as nuclear anchorage (Lehto *et al.*, 1978), spatial organization of the cellular space (Lazarides, 1980), or general skeletal role apply to early embryonic cells as well as to any other cell type.

Electron microscopy has revealed abundant microtubules and microfilaments in mouse oocytes and cleavage-stage embryos (Calarco and Brown, 1969; Opas and Soltyńska, 1978; Ducibella *et al.*, 1977; Lehtonen *et al.*, 1984), but unequivocal 10-nm filaments have not been discerned in routinely fixed cells of the early developmental stages. However, even in normal cultured cells, 10-nm filaments are not easily visualized without first extracting the cells with detergent. When embryos are subjected to this kind of treatment, most of the cytoplasmic organelles are removed from the cells (Figs. 2–5). In the extracted embryos, scattered 10-nm-thick filaments can be visualized already at the earliest cleavage stages. The filaments are often connected with the nuclear residue or with the paracrystalline arrays present in mouse oocytes and early embryos (Figs. 4 and 5). The composition of these structures, easily discernible in intact embryos as well, has remained unknown (cf. Pikó and Clegg, 1982).

Filaments 10 nm thick have now been detected in unfertilized oocytes and in blastomeres of all cleavage stages (Lehtonen *et al.*, 1983c; Lehtonen and Virtanen, 1985; Lehtonen, 1985; van Blerkom, 1983). Such filaments are easily visualized in high-voltage electron microscopy and especially in paracrystalline array preparations of detergent-extracted oocytes. In these preparations also, the filaments often appear closely associated with the paracrystalline arrays (van Blerkom, 1983). Apart from the association with the nuclear residue

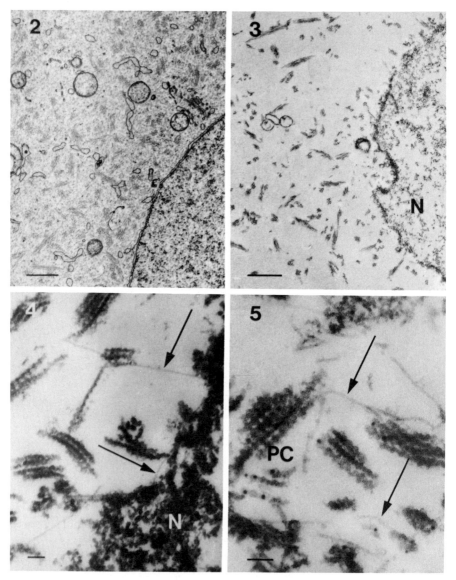

FIGS. 2–5. Electron micrographs of early cleavage-stage embryos. (2) An intact 8-cell stage. (3–5) A 3-cell stage extracted with Triton X-100. The paracrystalline arrays (PC) are the major cytoplasmic component resisting the detergent treatment. Note the 10- to 11-nm-thick filaments (arrows). N, Nuclear residue. 2, Bar, 1 μm; 3, bar, 1 μm; 4, bar, 100 nm; 5, bar, 100 nm. (Lehtonen *et al.*, 1983c; Lehtonen and Virtanen, 1985.)

TABLE I

INTERMEDIATE FILAMENT ANTIBODIES REACTING WITH MOUSE OOCYTES
AND/OR PREIMPLANTATION EMBRYOS

Immunization material; animal	Reference
IFs from T.D.M.I. trophoblastoma cells; rat (monoclonal)	Brûlet et al. (1980) (TROMA 1 antibodies)
Total reconstituted bovine hoof prekeratin; guinea pig	Jackson et al. (1980); Paulin et al. (1980)
Desmosome attached tonofilaments of bovine muzzle epidermis; guinea pig	Jackson et al. (1980)
Human epidermal cytokeratin polypeptides; rabbit	Lehtonen et al. (1983c)
Endo B protein (50 kDa) from PFHR9 parietal endodermal cells; rabbit	Oshima et al. (1983)
Endo A protein (55 kDa) from PFHR9 parietal endodermal cells; rabbit	Oshima et al. (1983)
Mouse oocyte cytoskeleton preparation; mouse (monoclonal)	Lehtonen (1985) (OCS-1 antibodies)

and the paracrystalline arrays, no other specific organization pattern of the 10-nm-thick filaments has been observed in these cells.

In addition to electron microscopy, immunohistochemical methods have been employed to study the presence and distribution of IF proteins in early embryonic cells. At the moment, views vary on the appearance of IF proteins during early development, perhaps due to differences in the specificities of the antibodies (Table I). Lehtonen et al. (1983c) obtained a positive immunofluorescence staining in the oocytes and all cleavage stages with rabbit antibodies to cytokeratin polypeptides. The stainings were usually quite diffuse with some perinuclear concentration of the label; fibrillar staining was never seen at the early stages (Fig. 6). Jackson et al. (1980), using guinea pig antibodies to cytokeratin, observed filamentous staining in blastocysts and late morulae, but no significant fibrillar organization in the precompaction embryos. Unfortunately, no comment was provided on the possible nonfibrillar staining of the early blastomeres. Interestingly, Franz et al. (1983) observed a fibrillar staining in Xenopus laevis oocytes and fertilized eggs with antibodies similar to those in the above study. Oshima et al. (1983) reported synthesis of cytokeratin-related proteins Endo A and Endo B in 4- to 8-cell-stage embryos. They also found cytokeratin-type staining in trophectoderm cells with antibodies to

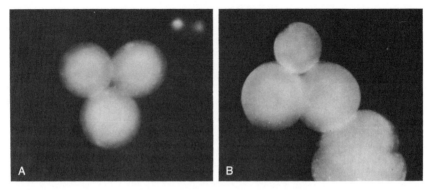

FIG. 6. Fluorescence micrographs of cleavage-stage cells stained with polyclonal antibodies to cytokeratin polypeptides. (A) Three blastomeres of a 4-cell embryo. (B) An aggregate containing one blastomere (the uppermost cell) of an 8-cell embryo, a 2-cell embryo, and an 8-cell embryo (partially in the field). The aggregate was treated with demecolcine before fixation. The staining pattern in all blastomeres is the same and shows some perinuclear concentration of fluorescence. (From Lehtonen et al., 1983c.)

Endo B, but apparently did not study embryos before the blastocyst stage. Johnson et al. (1986), using TROMA 1 antibodies (Brûlet et al., 1980), reported assembled cytokeratin filaments in 8-cell-stage blastomeres and 55-kDa cytokeratin protein in immunoblots of 4-cell-stage embryos. Finally, the OC5-1 antibodies (Lehtonen, 1985) reveal some fibrillar organization in 8-cell-stage blastomeres (E. Lehtonen, unpublished).

Although scattered 10-nm-thick filaments can be demonstrated in early cleavage-stage cells with electron microscopy, fibrillar staining with antibodies to IFs has not been reported in these cells before the 8-cell stage. The oocytes and blastomeres are large spherical cells, and it might be very difficult to visualize single fluorescent filaments in this kind of cells. On the other hand, bearing in mind the relative scarcity of 10-nm-thick filaments in the blastomeres, the immunoblotting and immunofluorescence stainings obtained by Lehtonen et al. (1983c) are quite intense (Fig. 6; see also Section III,C). There may also be a nonfilamentous pool of cytokeratin in the early embryonic cells.

B. POLYPEPTIDE COMPOSITION

Four different reports deal with the polypeptide composition of intermediate filaments in preimplantation embryos (Table II). Jackson et al. (1980) detected three nonionic detergent-resistant, high salt-resistant protein spots in two-dimensional gel electrophoresis of meta-

TABLE II

CYTOKERATIN-RELATED POLYPEPTIDES REPORTED IN MOUSE
OOCYTES AND/OR PREIMPLANTATION EMBRYOS

Molecular mass (kDa)	Stage	Reference
46, 54, 61	Late morula, blastocyst. Relative increase of 61-kDa polypeptide at blastocyst stage	Jackson et al. (1980)
50, 54, 57	Oocyte, 2-cell, 4- to 8-cell, blastocyst	Lehtonen et al. (1983c)
50, 55	4- to 8-cell, morula, blastocyst	Oshima et al. (1983)
55	4-cell	Johnson et al. (1986)

bolically labeled morulae and blastocysts. The molecular mass of these "X," "Y," and "Z" spots, tentatively identified as prekeratin-like proteins, was 46, 54, and 61 kDa, respectively. The synthesis of the 61-kDa component increased during morula-to-blastocyst transition. Lehtonen et al. (1983c), using immunoblotting with rabbit antibodies to cytokeratin polypeptides, observed three polypeptides of 50, 54, and 57 kDa in mouse oocytes, cleavage-stage embryos, and blastocysts. Immunoprecipitations with antibodies to Endo B (50 kDa) and Endo A (55kDa) protein, respectively, revealed both of these components in 4- to 8-cell-stage embryos, morulae, and blastocysts, but not in 2- to 4-cell-stage embryos (Oshima et al., 1983). TROMA 1 antibodies revealed the 55-kDa cytokeratin polypeptide in immunoblots of 4-cell-stage embryos (Johnson et al., 1986).

Comparing the two-dimensional gel electrophoresis data, Oshima et al. (1983) concluded that Endo B (50 kDa) and Endo A (55 kDa) are the "X" (46 kDa) and "Y" (54 kDa) proteins, respectively. These conceivably correspond to the 50-kDa and 54-kDa components identified by Lehtonen et al. (1983c), and to the 55-kDa polypeptide recognized by the TROMA 1 antibodies (Johnson et al., 1986). Only the report by Oshima et al. (1983) included data on the synthesis of intermediate filament protein at premorula stages: synthesis of Endo A and Endo B proteins was detected in 4- to 8-cell embryos but not in 2- to 4-cell embryos. However, in accordance with earlier studies (e.g., Mintz, 1964), the rate of incorporation of [^{35}S]methionine into 2- to 4-cell-stage embryos was found to be extremely low. Thus it is possible that low levels of synthesis may have remained undetected. On the other hand, in the immunoblotting experiments of Lehtonen *et al.* (1983c), the oocytes, early cleavage stages, and blastocysts showed a clear 54- and 57-kDa doublet of polypeptides; with the same antibodies, the 50-kDa component was barely detectable before the blastocyst stage.

The above results suggest that even though appreciable quantities of IF proteins are present already in the oocytes, the synthesis of these polypeptides begins, or reaches a detectable level, first at the 4- to 8-cell stage. In this context, it should be borne in mind that oocytes and early embryos may contain components of maternal origin which are not actively synthesized by the embryos. Such components may be detectable with, e.g., immunological methods.

C. Monoclonal Antibodies to Oocyte Cytoskeleton

Several poly- and monoclonal antibodies to IF proteins have been tested for their affinity to preimplantation mouse embryos (Table I). A fibrillar cytokeratin organization has been found consistently at stages after the late morula or early blastocyst, and recently also in 8-cell-stage blastomeres (Johnson *et al.*, 1986; E. Lehtonen, unpublished). Only Brûlet *et al.* (1980) and Lehtonen *et al.* (1983c) mentioned immunofluorescence experiments in which embryos before the 8-cell stage were studied for the presence of IF proteins. In the latter study, cytokeratin was found in mouse oocytes and cleavage-stage embryos. Based on this, monoclonal antibodies were raised to detergent-extracted cytoskeletons of mouse oocytes (Lehtonen, 1985). The major cytoplasmic components resisting the detergent treatment are the paracrystalline arrays with the closely associated 10-nm-thick filaments (Lehtonen *et al.*, 1983c; Lehtonen and Virtanen, 1985; Figs. 2–5). One of the monoclonal antibodies obtained, OCS-1 (oocyte cytoskeleton-1), stains a vinblastine-resistant fibrillar network in epithelial cells, but not in other cell types. It stains exclusively epithelial cells in tissue sections (Fig. 7). Both stratified and simple epithelia, including glandular epithelia, react with this antibody (Lehtonen, 1985). In immunoblots of human Tera-2 EC cells the antibody reacts with a 55- to 57-kDa polypeptide band (E. Lehtonen, unpublished).

In mouse oocytes and cleavage-stage embryos, the OCS-1 antibody gives a staining pattern including distinct spot structures (Fig. 8); starting from the 8-cell stage, the antibody also reveals some fibrillar organization in the blastomeres (E. Lehtonen, unpublished). It would be tempting to suggest that the paracrystalline arrays, occupying about 25% of the cytoplasmic matrix in oocytes (García *et al.*, 1979) and diminishing gradually in number during development, are recognized

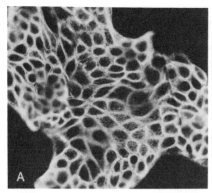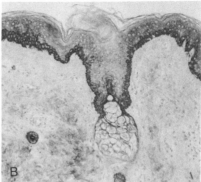

FIG. 7. Immunostainings with OCS-1 antibodies raised against detergent-extracted mouse oocyte cytoskeletons. (A) Cultured dog kidney epithelial cells (MDCK), treated with vinblastine. Note the keratin-type fibrillar fluorescence. (B) Paraffin section of human skin, immunoperoxidase staining. In addition to the epidermis, the sweat gland ducts and sebaceous glands are recognized by the antibodies.

by the OCS-1 antibody. The paracrystalline arrays might contain cytokeratin-related protein(s). This would agree with the close association of these structures with the 10-nm-thick filaments, observable in electron microscopy (Figs. 4–5; Lehtonen *et al.*, 1983c; Lehtonen and Virtanen, 1985; Van Blerkom, 1983). The paracrystalline arrays have been suggested to represent a storage form of various components, but the exact composition of these structures has remained unknown (Pikó and Clegg, 1982).

In mouse blastocyst-stage embryos, the OCS-1 antibody decorates a distinct fibrillar network in the trophectoderm cells (Fig. 9). The antibody reveals a cytokeratin-type organization in bovine, ovine, porcine, and rabbit blastocysts as well (Fléchon and Lehtonen, 1986). In immunoelectron microscopy, OCS-1 binds exclusively to 10-nm filaments, often identifiable as desmosome-attached tonofilaments (Fig. 10; Lehtonen, 1985).

The antigen(s) recognized by the OCS-1 antibody is apparently present in, or closely associated with, cytokeratin filaments. This cytokeratin-related antigen is shared by mouse oocytes and early embryos and by a wide variety of different epithelial-type cells in several species. The antigenic determinant defined by this antibody thus seems to be present in many members of the cytokeratin family. However, in contrast with the monoclonal antibody of Pruss *et al.* (1981), which reacts with all types of IFs, the OCS-1 antibody recognizes only cytokeratin-type IFs.

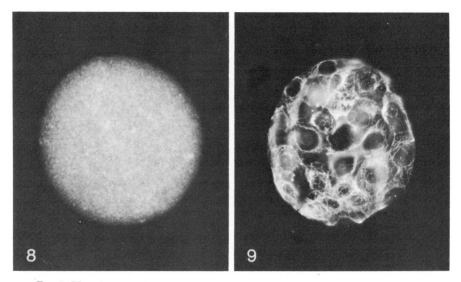

Fig. 8. Mouse oocyte, immunofluorescence staining with the OCS-1 antibody. Note the distinct cytoplasmic spot structures.

Fig. 9. Mouse blastocyst, immunofluorescence staining. The OCS-1 antibody decorates a distinct fibrillar organization in the trophectoderm cells.

IV. Cytokeratins in Blastocyst-Stage Embryos

At the blastocyst stage, the mouse embryo is composed of two distinct tissues, the trophectoderm and the ICM. These structures differ in morphology, function, and developmental fate: the trophectoderm cells are typically epithelial cells and form extraembryonic structures, whereas the ICM represents a nondifferentiated, proliferating cell population with the capacity to form all the tissues of the adult organism (see Sections I and II,B).

A. Distribution of 10-nm Filaments and Cytokeratin-Associated Antigens

Electron microscopy studies (Calarco and Brown, 1969; Ducibella and Anderson, 1975; Jackson *et al.,* 1980) have made it clear that the trophectoderm cells of the blastocyst are connected by desmosomes with attached tonofilaments. Correspondingly, the trophectoderm cells contain 10-nm filaments which are recognized by cytokeratin antibodies (See Table I, Figs. 9–11). The filamentous organization of cytokeratin is even more obvious in blastocyst outgrowths in which the trophectoderm cells flatten on the substratum (Fig. 11).

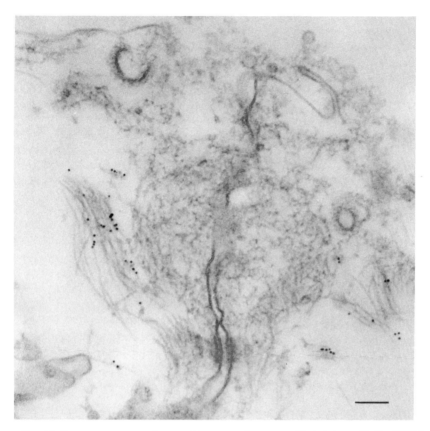

FIG. 10. Detergent-extracted mouse blastocyst, immunogold staining with the OCS-1 antibody. The label is exclusively found in close association with 10-nm-thick filaments. Bar, 100 nm.

The available immunofluorescence data on the presence of IFs in the ICM cells are controversial, probably due to differences in the specificities of the antibodies used (see Table I). Jackson *et al.* (1980) and Paulin *et al.* (1980), apparently using the same polyclonal cytokeratin antibodies, scored the weak fluorescence as negative they observed in the ICM cells. Stainings with antibodies to Endo A and Endo B, respectively, resulted in a weak fluorescence "difficult to ascribe to specific reactions"; the fluorescence obtained with vimentin serum was "negative" (Oshima *et al.*, 1983). Brûlet *et al.* (1980) also scored as negative the weak fluorescence they obtained with monoclonal TROMA 1 antibodies. On the other hand, the polyclonal cytokeratin

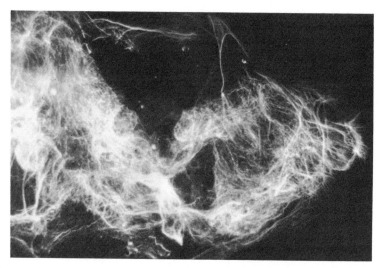

FIG. 11. Blastocyst outgrowth, cytokeratin filaments demonstrated with the OCS-1 antibody.

antibodies used by Lehtonen *et al.* (1983c) gave a relatively bright staining in the ICM cells. The organization of fluorescence in the ICM cells was comparable with that in the cleavage-stage cells: a non-fibrillar, diffuse staining. This is not an unexpected observation in rapidly proliferating spherical cells.

B. POLYPEPTIDE COMPOSITION

The transformation from morula to blastocyst involves profound morphological and functional changes in the embryo. It is obvious that the organization of the cytoskeleton in the ICM cells differs from that in the trophectoderm, and both of these probably differ from that in the cleavage-stage cells.

Unfortunately, all investigations on the polypeptide composition of the IF cytoskeleton of the blastocyst have been performed on whole embryos comprising both the ICM and the trophectoderm. The reports now available (Jackson *et al.*, 1980; Lehtonen *et al.*, 1983c; Oshima *et al.*, 1983; summarized in Table II) agree that the blastocyst-stage embryos synthesize two cytokeratin polypeptides, one of 46 or 50 kDa, and the other of 54 or 55 kDa. In addition, Jackson *et al.* (1980) found a detergent-resistant and high-salt-resistant protein of 61 kDa, which greatly increased in quantity between the morula and blastocyst stages. This polypeptide, designated similar to the cytokeratin class, was not recognized by the antibodies used by Lehtonen *et al.* (1983c) or by Oshima *et al.* (1983).

The blastocyst-stage embryos contain cytokeratin-related proteins, but there are some differences in the observations on the exact polypeptide composition of these structures. These inconsistencies are probably due to differences in the methods used.

V. Intermediate Filament Proteins in Germ Cells

A. Oocytes and Spermatozoa

It has been believed until quite recently that germ cells, such as oocytes, eggs, spermatids, and spermatozoa, do not contain IFs (Franke *et al.*, 1982; Osborn and Weber, 1983). In addition to electron microscopy studies, this view has been based on immunofluorescence stainings and on failure to detect known IF proteins in gel electrophoresis after metabolic labeling of the cells. However, a negative conclusion based on these methods might not be warranted: the germ cells might contain IF proteins not recognized by the antibodies used, or they might possess a maternally contributed supply of IF proteins which cannot be visualized in assays based on metabolic labeling. Consequently, it is not surprising that several recent studies have suggested the presence of IF proteins in certain germ cells.

Picheral *et al.* (1982) and Gall *et al.* (1983), using polyclonal antibodies to bovine hoof prekeratin, showed a distinct fibrillar organization of cytokeratin in *X. laevis* oocytes and fertilized eggs. The presence of cytokeratin in *Xenopus* oocytes has been confirmed (Franz *et al.*, 1983; Godsave *et al.*, 1984b; see also Wylie *et al.*, 1986). Two of the three cytokeratin polypeptides synthesized in *Xenopus* oocytes, eggs, and early embryos (M_r 56,000, IEP 5.4; and M_r 46,000, IEP 5.28) are closely related to the corresponding components at mouse early stages (Franz *et al.*, 1983; see also Table II, Section II,B). Interestingly, a recent immunofluorescence and immunoblotting study with several independent vimentin antibodies showed that, in addition to cytokeratin, *Xenopus* oocytes also contain vimentin-type IFs (Godsave *et al.*, 1984a; see also Wylie *et al.*, 1986).

Only a few investigations are available concerning the expression of IF proteins in spermatozoa. In their early immunofluorescence study with polyclonal antibodies to vimentin and keratin, respectively, Franke *et al.* (1979) failed to detect any IFs in the spermatozoa in frozen sections of adult rat testis. Similarly, spermatozoa in frozen

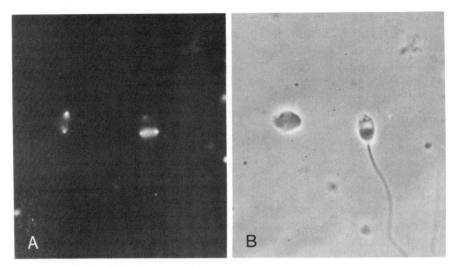

Fig. 12. (A and B) Human spermatozoa, stained with antibodies to vimentin. A
distinct band of vimentin encircles the sperm head. (Courtesy of Dr. I. Virtanen; Virtanen *et al.*, 1984.)

sections of fetal and neonatal pig testis were found negative in immunofluorescence stainings with polyclonal antibodies to keratin, vimentin, and desmin, respectively (van Vorstenbosch *et al.*, 1984). In contrast with these reports, Virtanen *et al.* (1984) recently showed
expression of vimentin in human spermatozoa isolated from ejacu-
lates. They used both polyclonal and monoclonal antibodies to different types of IFs and found a narrow band of vimentin encircling the
sperm head (Fig. 12). Immunoblotting experiments confirmed the presence of vimentin in human spermatozoa. Differences in materials and
methods can explain the varying results of the above investigations. It
should also be noted that Virtanen *et al.* (1984) studied fully differentiated spermatozoa, whereas the other two study groups focused on less
mature stages.

B. TERATOCARCINOMA STEM CELLS

The malignant stem cells in teratocarcinoma tumors, the embryonal carcinoma (EC) cells, resemble early embryonic cells in many respects. These two cell types are apparently closely related, and most
human teratocarcinomas and embryonal carcinomas are thought to
arise from parthenogenetically activated germ cells. Experimentally,
teratocarcinomas have been formed by transplanting early embryos
into extrauterine sites (Stevens, 1970; Solter *et al.*, 1981), and pluripo-

tential cell lines similar to EC cells have also been derived by culturing early embryos *in vitro* (Martin, 1981; Evans and Kaufman, 1981). Human and mouse teratocarcinomas differ, for instance, in that the human tumors often synthesize chorionic gonadotropin which has not been observed in the mouse tumors (Damjanov and Andrews, 1983). Thus, it has been postulated that the stem cells of human teratocarcinomas correspond to embryonic cells still capable of differentiating to trophectodermal derivatives, i.e., to morula or early ICM cells (see Section II,B), whereas mouse EC cells correspond to a later developmental stage, i.e., to late ICM or primitive ectoderm cells. During early embryogenesis, the first cell type to arise from the ICM is the primitive endoderm, which later on gives rise to both the visceral and the parietal endoderm (Gardner, 1983; Lehtonen *et al.*, 1983b). This sequence of differentiation can be mimicked by many EC cell lines *in vitro:* depending on the experimental conditions, the cells differentiate to cell types resembling either the primitive, visceral, or parietal endoderm of the mouse embryo (Hogan *et al.*, 1983; Strickland, 1981).

In vitro, different EC cell lines vary in their capacity to express IF proteins. Thus, undifferentiated mouse EC cells generally express only vimentin type of IFs, but after having been induced to differentiate they may start to express other types of IF proteins, including cytokeratins (Fig. 13; Paulin *et al.*, 1982; Lehtonen *et al.*, 1983a; Ramaekers *et al.*, 1984). The exact polypeptide composition of the cytokeratins synthesized by differentiated EC cells remains to be studied, but Ramaekers *et al.* (1984) have shown that when treated with retinoic acid and cAMP, up to 55% of F9 EC cells start to synthesize the cytokeratin polypeptide 18 (Moll *et al.*, 1982). In contrast with the murine EC cells, undifferentiated human EC cells can express cytokeratins (Fig. 14): in a recent immunoblotting study, Damjanov *et al.* (1984) found three keratin polypeptides (40, 45, and 52 kDa) in several human EC cell lines. The cell lines also contained a small population of vimentin-positive cells, and the number of vimentin-positive cells increased upon retinoic acid treatment.

In vivo, the stem cells in human teratocarcinomas and embryonal carcinomas generally express cytokeratin (Battifora *et al.*, 1984; Miettinen *et al.*, 1986), and only patchy expression of vimentin has been reported in these tumor cells (Miettinen *et al.*, 1986). Antibodies to epidermal and simple epithelial keratins react with human embryonal carcinomas. The results vary concerning IF expression in seminomas, the other group of human germ cell tumors. Battifora *et al.* (1984) failed to detect cytokeratin-specific staining in seminoma cells with polyclonal antibodies to epidermal keratin and with monoclonal anti-

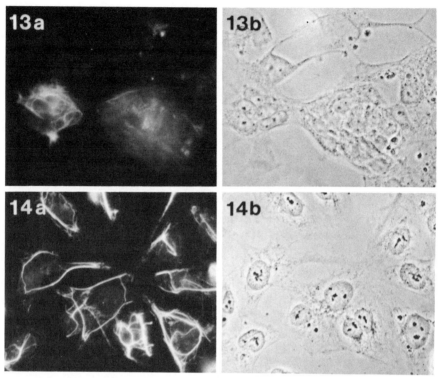

FIG. 13. (a and b) Retinoic acid-treated murine F9 EC cells. The differentiated cells start to express cytokeratin, demonstrated here with the OCS-1 antibody.

FIG. 14. (a and b) Cultured human Tera-2 EC cells express cytokeratin. Staining with OCS-1 antibodies.

bodies reacting with keratin classes 40, 50, and 56.6 kDa. In contrast with this, Miettinen *et al.* (1986), using monoclonal antibodies to the cytokeratin polypeptide 18 (Moll *et al.*, 1982), found single cells or groups of cells positive for cytokeratin in 17 of 40 classical seminomas, and in 1 of 7 spermatocytic seminomas. In the latter study, areas with vimentin-positive cells were seen in all seminomas.

VI. Concluding Remarks

In contrast with earlier views, IF proteins have now been identified in germ cells. Thus, human spermatozoa contain vimentin, *Xenopus* oocytes and early embryos show vimentin and cytokeratin filaments, and mouse oocytes and early embryos seem to contain cytokeratin. A highly organized distribution of IF proteins is found in human sperm cells and in *Xenopus* oocytes. Although mouse oocytes and early embryos also show 10-nm filaments, their IF proteins may largely be in a nonfibrillar form. They may be, e.g., stored in the paracrystalline arrays which are abundant at the early stages and gradually diminish in number during development. Mouse oocytes and preimplantation embryos may thus contain a maternally contributed supply of cytokeratin, which is not actively synthesized by the embryo cells.

Nonfibrillar cytokeratin would presumably serve as a storage of IF protein, whereas the function of 10-nm filaments in mouse oocytes and cleavage-stage cells is not known. The filaments might be important in maintaining the cytoarchitecture of the early embryos, and they might have a role in the compaction and the polarization of the blastomeres. The differentiation of the cleavage-stage cells to trophectoderm cells involves formation of desmosomes with attached tonofilaments. Filamentous organization of cytokeratin is thus essential for the development of the blastocyst. Adhesion to a substratum triggers reorganization of cytoskeletal elements in trophectoderm cells. Comparable changes in cytoskeletal organization may be important in the interactions of trophectoderm cells with the uterine epithelium during implantation.

ACKNOWLEDGMENTS

The author is grateful to Ilkka Reima, Lauri Saxén, and Ismo Virtanen for comments, and to Ms. Ulla Kiiski and Ms. Ulla Waris for technical assistance. This work was supported by the Medical Research Council of the Academy of Finland, the Cancer Society of Finland, and the Sigrid Jusélius Foundation, Finland.

REFERENCES

Battifora, H., Sheibani, K., Tubbs, R. R., Kopinski, M. I., and Sun, T.-T. (1984). *Cancer* **54,** 843–848.

Brûlet, P., Babinet, C., Kemler, R., and Jacob, F. (1980). *Proc. Natl. Acad. Sci. U.S.A.* **77,** 4113–4117.

Calarco, P. G., and Brown, E. H. (1969). *J. Exp. Zool.* **171,** 253–284.

Damjanov, I., and Andrews, P. W. (1983). *Cancer Res.* **43,** 2190–2198.

Damjanov, I., Clark, R. K., and Andrews, P. W. (1984). *Cell Differ.* **15,** 133–139.

Damjanov, I., Damjanov, A., Lento, V.-P., and Virtanen, I. (1986). *Dev. Biol.* **114,** 132–140.

Ducibella, T., and Anderson, E. (1975). *Dev. Biol.* **47,** 45–58.

Ducibella, T., Albertini, D. F., Anderson, E., and Biggers, J. D. (1975). *Dev. Biol.* **45,** 231–250.

Ducibella, T., Ukena, T., Karnovsky, M., and Anderson, E. (1977). *J. Cell Biol.* **74,** 153–167.

Evans, M. J., and Kaufman, M. H. (1981). *Nature (London)* **292,** 154–156.

Fléchon, J.-E., and Lehtonen, E. (1986). *Arch. Anat. Microsc.* (in press).

Franke, W. W., Grund, C., and Schmid, E. (1979). *Eur. J. Cell Biol.* **19,** 269–275.

Franke, W. W., Schmid, E., Schiller, D. L., Winter, S., Jarasch, E.-D., Moll, R., Denk, H., Jackson, B. W., and Illmensee, K. (1982). *Cold Spring Harbor Symp. Quant. Biol.* **46**, 431–453.

Franz, K., Gall, L., Williams, M. A., Picheral, B., and Franke, W. W. (1983). *Proc. Natl. Acad. Sci. U.S.A.* **80**, 6254–6258.

Gall, L., Picheral, B., and Gounon, P. (1983). *Biol. Cell* **47**, 331–342.

García, R. B., Pereyra-Alfonso, S., and Sotelo, J. R. (1979). *Differentiation* **14**, 101–106.

Gardner, R. L. (1983). *Int. Rev. Exp. Pathol.* **24**, 63–133.

Godsave, S. F., Anderton, B. H., Heasman, J., and Wylie, C. C. (1984a). *J. Embryol. Exp. Morphol.* **83**, 169–187.

Godsave, S. F., Wylie, C. C., Lane, E. B., and Anderton, B. H. (1984b). *J. Embryol. Exp. Morphol.* **83**, 157–167.

Goodall, H., and Johnson, M. H. (1984). *J. Embryol. Exp. Morphol.* **79**, 53–76.

Graham, C. F., and Deussen, Z. A. (1978). *J. Embryol. Exp. Morphol.* **48**, 53–72.

Graham, C. F., and Lehtonen, E. (1979). *J. Embryol. Exp. Morphol.* **49**, 277–294.

Hillman, N., Sherman, M. I., and Graham, C. (1972). *J. Embryol. Exp. Morphol.* **28**, 263–278.

Hogan, B. L. M., Barlow, D. P., and Tilly, R. (1983). *Cancer Surv.* **2**, 115–140.

Jackson, B. W., Grund, C., Schmid, E., Bürki, K., Franke, W. W., and Illmensee, K. (1980). *Differentiation* **17**, 161–179.

Johnson, M. H. (1981). *Int. Rev. Cytol. Suppl.* **12**, 1–37.

Johnson, M. H., and Maro, B. (1984). *J. Embryol. Exp. Morphol.* **82**, 97–117.

Johnson, M. H., Chisholm, J. C., Fleming, T. P., and Houliston, E. (1986). *J. Embryol. Exp. Morphol.* **97** (Suppl.), 97–121.

Kelly, S. J. (1977). *J. Exp. Zool.* **200**, 365–376.

Kimber, S. J., and Surani, M. A. H. (1982). *J. Cell Sci.* **56**, 191–206.

Lazarides, E. (1980). *Nature (London)* **283**, 249–256.

Lehto, V.-P., Virtanen, I., and Kurki, P. (1978). *Nature (London)* **272**, 175–177.

Lehtonen, E. (1980). *J. Embryol. Exp. Morphol.* **58**, 231–249.

Lehtonen, E. (1985). *J. Embryol. Exp. Morphol.* **90**, 197–209.

Lehtonen, E., and Badley, R. A. (1980). *J. Embryol. Exp. Morphol.* **55**, 211–225.

Lehtonen, E., and Reima, I. (1986). *Differentiation* **32**, 125–134.

Lehtonen, E., and Saxén, L. (1986). *In* "Human Growth: A Comprehensive Treatise" (F. Falkner and J. M. Tanner, eds.), pp. 27–51. Plenum, New York.

Lehtonen, E., and Virtanen, I. (1985). *Ann. N.Y. Acad. Sci.* **455**, 744–747.

Lehtonen, E., Lehto, V.-P., Badley, R. A., and Virtanen, I. (1983a). *Exp. Cell Res.* **144**, 191–197.

Lehtonen, E., Lehto, V.-P., Paasivuo, R., and Virtanen, I. (1983b). *EMBO J.* **2**, 1023–1028.

Lehtonen, E., Lehto, V.-P., Vartio, T., Badley, R. A., and Virtanen, I. (1983c). *Dev. Biol.* **100**, 158–165.

Lehtonen, E., Wartiovaara, J., and Reima, I. (1984). *J. Embryol. Exp. Morphol.* **81**, 17–35.

Lehtonen, E., Virtanen, I., and Saxén, L. (1985). *Dev. Biol.* **108**, 481–490.

Lewis, W. H., and Wright, E. S. (1935). *Contrib. Embryol. Carnegie Inst.* **148**, 115–143.

Lo, C. W., and Gilula, N. B. (1979). *Cell* **18**, 399–409.

Magnuson, T., Jacobsen, J. B., and Stackpole, C. W. (1978). *Dev. Biol.* **67**, 214–224.

Maro, B., and Pickering, S. J. (1984). *J. Embryol. Exp. Morphol.* **84**, 217–232.

Martin, G. R. (1981). *Proc. Natl. Acad. Sci. U.S.A.* **78**, 7634–7638.

Miettinen, M., Virtanen, I., and Talerman, A. (1986). *In* "Pathology of the Testis and its

Adnexa" (A. Talerman and L. M. Roth, eds.), pp. 181–191. Churchill Livingstone, London.

Mintz, B. (1964). *J. Exp. Zool.* **157**, 85–100.

Moll, R., Franke, W. W., Schiller, D. L., Geiger, B., and Krepler, R. (1982). *Cell* **31**, 11–24.

Opas, J., and Soltyńska, M. S. (1978). *Exp. Cell Res.* **113**, 208–211.

Osborn, M., and Weber, K. (1983). *Lab. Invest.* **48**, 372–394.

Oshima, R. G., Howe, W. E., Klier, F. G., Adamson, E. D., and Shevinsky, L. H. (1983). *Dev. Biol.* **99**, 447–455.

Paulin, D., Babinet, C., Weber, K., and Osborn, M. (1980). *Exp. Cell Res.* **130**, 297–304.

Paulin, D., Jakob, H., Jacob, F., Weber, K., and Osborn, M. (1982). *Differentiation* **22**, 90–99.

Picheral, P., Gall, L., and Gounon, P. (1982). *Biol. Cell* **45**, 208.

Picó, L., and Clegg, K. B. (1982). *Dev. Biol.* **89**, 362–378.

Pruss, R. M., Mirsky, R., Raff, M. C., Thorpe, R., Downing, A. J., and Anderton, B. H. (1981). *Cell* **27**, 419–428.

Ramaekers, F., Schaap, H., Mulder, M., Huysmans, A., and Vooijs, P. (1984). *Cell Biol. Int. Rep.* **8**, 721–730.

Reima, I., and Lehtonen, E. (1985). *Differentiation* **30**, 68–75.

Shivers, R. R., and McLachlin, J. R. (1984). *J. Submicrosc. Cytol.* **16**, 423–430.

Sobel, J. S. (1984). *J. Cell Biol.* **99**, 1145–1150.

Sobel, J. S., and Alliegro, M. A. (1985). *J. Cell Biol.* **100**, 333–336.

Solter, D., Dominis, M., and Damjanov, I. (1981). *Int. J. Cancer* **28**, 479–483.

Soltyńska, M. S. (1982). *J. Embryol. Exp. Morphol.* **68**, 137–147.

Stevens, L. (1970). *Dev. Biol.* **21**, 364–382.

Strickland, S. (1981). *Cell* **24**, 277–278.

Tarkowski, A. K., and Wróblewska, J. (1967). *J. Embryol. Exp. Morphol.* **18**, 155–180.

Van Blerkom, J. (1983). Table Ronde Roussel Uclaf No. 47, Cellular Diversification in the Early Mouse Embryo, 6–7 October 1983, Paris.

van Vorstenbosch, C. J. A. H. V., Colenbrander, B., Wensing, C. J. G., Ramaekers, F. C. S., and Vooijs, G. P. (1984). *Eur. J. Cell Biol.* **34**, 292–299.

Virtanen, I., Badley, R. A., Paasivuo, R., and Lehto, V.-P. (1984). *J. Cell Biol.* **99**, 1083–1091, 1984.

Wilson, J. B., Bolton, E., and Cutler, R. H. (1972). *J. Embryol. Exp. Morphol.* **27**, 467–479.

Wylie, C. C., Heasman, J., Parke, J. M., Anderton, B., and Tang, P. (1986). *J. Cell Sci.* Suppl. 5, 329–341.

CHAPTER 8

ROLE OF EPIDERMAL GROWTH FACTOR IN EMBRYONIC DEVELOPMENT

Robert M. Pratt

LABORATORY OF REPRODUCTIVE AND DEVELOPMENTAL TOXICOLOGY
NATIONAL INSTITUTE OF ENVIRONMENTAL HEALTH SCIENCES
NATIONAL INSTITUTES OF HEALTH
RESEARCH TRIANGLE PARK, NORTH CAROLINA 27709

I. Introduction

The central theme of this volume is the keratinization process whether it be adult or embryonic. At first thought, most investigators would presume that the keratinization process in the embryonic and fetal epidermis to be the main tissue of interest for this volume. However, the embryonic development of the secondary palate (roof of the mouth) provides an excellent model system in which to understand the cellular and molecular biology of the keratinization process.

There are three cell types which initially constitute the palatal epithelium, and it is the oral cell type that is of greatest interest to readers of this chapter. The oral epithelial cells are somehow programmed differently during embryogenesis from the nasal and medial palatal epithelial cells, and they become the squamous keratinizing cells that line the roof of the mouth. Without this essential programming during development, the palate will not form normally, and a cleft palate results.

The developing secondary palate constitutes an ideal morphogenetic system since its development occurs towards the end of embryogenesis in the rodent, and the palate is easily accessible and large enough for a number of experimental manipulations including cell and organ culture. The growth and differentiation of the oral epithelium are especially dependent upon epidermal growth factor (EGF); most of this chapter will deal with details of studies which have convinced us that EGF or a related growth factor found in the embryo (transforming growth factor-α) is a very important regulatory molecule in the palate.

175

II. Influence of EGF in Various Developing Tissues

While work was in progress to purify nerve growth factor (NGF) from mouse submaxillary glands (Cohen, 1965), it was observed that when injected into newborn mice, purified extracts of the glands produced biological effects quite distinct from NGF, e.g., precocious opening of the neonatal eyelids and premature eruption of the incisors. The molecule responsible for this activity was called epidermal growth factor (EGF). Following the discovery of these *in vivo* effects, EGF (molecular mass, 6045 Das) was shown to be a potent mitogen for a variety of cultured cells of ectodermal and mesodermal origin (Carpenter and Cohen, 1979). These include ectodermal keratinocytes derived from skin, conjunctival, and pharyngeal tissue, mesodermal granulosa and corneal endothelial cells, vascular smooth muscle, chondrocytes, and fibroblasts (Gospodarowicz *et al.*, 1978).

EGF has been fully sequenced and shows no significant homology with the insulin/relaxin/nerve growth factor polypeptide family (Scott *et al.*, 1983). EGF does show a considerable degree of amino acid sequence conservation (70% between mouse and man) and a wide phylogenetic distribution, suggesting a fundamental physiological role (Hollenberg, 1979). It is stored in the duct cells of the convoluted tubules of the submaxillary gland in mouse and man as a high molecular weight complex with arginine esterase. EGF has been shown to be mitogenic for a variety of epithelial and other tissues, eliciting the classic pleiotropic response consisting of increased ion and precursor uptake, enhanced glycolysis, RNA and protein synthesis, and finally enhanced DNA synthesis (Carpenter and Cohen, 1979).

The action of EGF can be enhanced in some tissues by cortisol, high concentrations of insulin, glucagon, thrombin, and certain cofactors. The primary mechanism of action of EGF is unclear; however, it is known that low levels of EGF receptor occupancy induce receptor clustering followed by internalization into membrane vesicles and ultimate degradation (Fig. 1). Immediately after binding of EGF to the receptor, there is a rapid stimulation in the phosphorylation of tyrosine residues of general membrane-associated proteins including the receptor itself (Schlesinger *et al.*, 1983; Zendegui and Carpenter, 1984). The exact relationship of these events to the mechanism of action of EGF is unknown.

The ability of EGF to trigger cell proliferation in neonatal and adult animals raised the possibility that EGF could be an embryonic/fetal growth hormone responsible for specific epithelial territories in the embryo (Gospodarowicz, 1981). This possibility has been tested

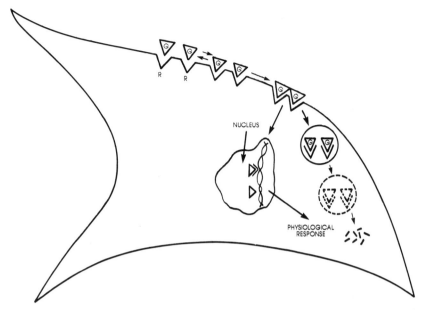

FIG. 1. Mechanism of EGF action. EGF (G) is schematically depicted interacting with a responsive fibroblast cell. In the initial phase, EGF binds to specific cell surface receptors (R) (180-kDa glycoproteins). These EGF–receptor complexes then undergo an aggregation or patching at the cell surface. At some point in this initial stage, EGF binding to its receptor results in an autophosphorylation of the EGF receptor which may somehow be involved in triggering the action of EGF. The receptor–hormone complexes are next internalized into lysosomal structures called receptosomes which are then degraded. Alternatively, it is possible that some intact EGF–receptor complexes reach the nucleus and directly affect transcription.

in different developing tissues and organs such as the lung and palate. Sundell *et al.* (1975) showed that constant infusion of EGF into fetal lambs for 3–5 days stimulated epithelial growth in many sites, including upper and lower airways. In addition, EGF appeared to afford protection against the development of hyaline membrane disease when given *in utero* at 123–130 days of gestation. Injection of EGF into 24-day-old rabbit fetuses also induced accelerated maturation of the lung (Catterton *et al.*, 1979). It therefore seems that EGF is capable of promoting not only epithelial cell growth in the fetal lung, but cell differentiation as well. EGF may therefore be an important influence in the maturation of the human lung and be capable of protecting the prematurely delivered fetus against the development of hyaline membrane disease.

Various other developing tissues have been shown to be responsive and even dependent upon EGF for their growth and differentiation *in vivo* as well as *in vitro*. EGF administered intraperitoneally on gestation days 15–17 in the mouse results in an accelerated appearance of various enzymes assayed in the mouse intestinal mucosa (Calvert *et al.*, 1982). EGF is specifically required for morphological development of the fetal mouse mammary lobuloalveoli *in vitro* (Tonelli and Sorof, 1980). In the chick embryo, EGF was detected over a substantial period of development, with a peak value occurring on days 10–12 (Mesiano *et al.*, 1985); EGF has also been reported to stimulate the induction *in vitro* of supernumerary tracheal buds and to stimulate DNA synthesis in the day 5 chick embryo lung rudiments (Goldin and Opperman, 1980).

Green *et al.* (1983, 1984) have provided evidence for a possible role for the EGF receptor and associated EGF or EGF-like ligands in specific areas of epithelial tissue morphogenesis during embryonic rat skin maturation, hair follicle development, and hair cycling. In organ culture, EGF has been reported to stimulate the growth of embryonic mouse tooth epithelium but was inhibitory in the adjacent mesenchyme (Partanen *et al.*, 1985). This resulted in an inhibition of the morphogenesis of the epithelial cells that give rise to enamel.

The developing system that has been studied the most extensively, with respect to EGF, is the formation of the mammalian secondary palate or roof of the mouth. The remainder of this chapter is devoted to describing these studies with special emphasis placed on the effects of EGF on the keratinizing epithelial cells of the palate.

III. Development of the Mammalian Secondary Palate

In the mouse the secondary palate first becomes morphologically distinct on day 11 of gestation, at which time it exists as two bilateral processes extending from the paired maxillary processes (Greene and Pratt, 1976). Between days 13 and 14 the palatal processes become reoriented from a vertical position alongside the tongue to one above it and fuse with each other along their medial surfaces. This fusion brings about the separation of the oral and nasal cavities (Fig. 2). The medial epithelial lamina formed between the opposing palatal processes is disrupted during palatal fusion, and the mesenchymal tissues of the two processes become confluent. By day 17 of gestation the dorsal epithelium of the palate, which constitutes the floor of the nasal cavity, has differentiated into a pseudostratified ciliated columnar epithelium, and the ventral epithelium, which constitutes the roof of the

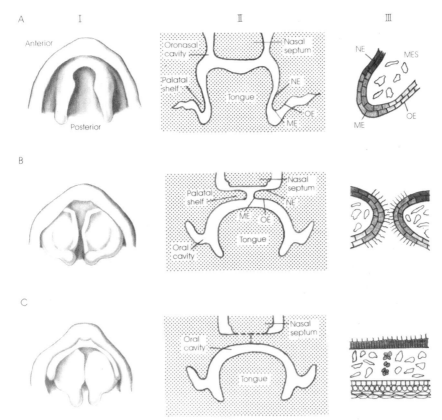

FIG. 2. Secondary palate development. Schematic view (I) of the developing embryonic roof of the mouth at the following gestational ages: (A) day 12 mouse, stage II human palate; (B) day 13 mouse, stage III human palate; (C) day 14 mouse, stage IV human palate. Schematic frontal sections (II) through the anterior embryonic head are shown at ages corresponding to I. Schematics of the palatal shelves (III) show that the epithelial cells of the medial edge (ME) cease DNA synthesis (A), undergo glycoconjugate-mediated (shown by wavy projections) adhesion (B), and finally cell death (C). This sequence of events does not occur in the ciliated nasal epithelium (NE) nor the keratinizing oral epithelium (OE).

oral cavity, has differentiated into a stratified squamous keratinizing epithelium.

Both *in vivo* and *in vitro* studies have suggested that tissue interactions are important in the differentiation of the secondary palate. The occurrence of cell death within the medial epithelial lamina between the fusing palatal processes has been well documented (Greene and

Pratt, 1976). Cell death as a mechanism of morphogenesis has been shown to be one way of eliminating various tissues and organs during development. In the case of the palate, it appears that programmed cell death assists in the removal of the medial palatal epithelium. Organ culture studies have demonstrated that cell death within the medial palatal epithelium does not depend upon the presence of the palatal mesenchyme, at least not during the 3 days (days 11–13 in the mouse) that precede the fusion events (Tyler and Koch, 1977). Cell death occurs within the medial region of cultured palatal epithelia that have been isolated from their mesenchyme and occurs in accordance with the *in vivo* schedule.

IV. Effect of EGF on Palatal Epithelial Development in Organ Culture

EGF can inhibit the degeneration of the medial palatal epithelium and promote hypertrophy and keratinization of these cells (Hassell, 1975). It has also been shown that cessation of DNA synthesis and cell death in the medial palatal epithelium (ME) can be inhibited in organ culture by addition of EGF (Pratt, 1980) (Fig. 3). If EGF is present in culture with day 13 mouse palatal shelves after ME cells have lost their ability to make DNA, although it no longer stimulates ME cells to divide, it can nevertheless promote survival and prevent cell death in this region. In contrast, if present in the culture medium before ME cells have lost their ability to synthesize DNA (day 11 or 12), EGF will both induce ME hyperplasia and prevent cell death. If EGF is added to isolated palatal epithelia in their final stage of differentiation (day 14 of gestation in mice), it can still affect the morphology of the isolated ME epithelium, but it will not stimulate DNA synthesis or prevent cell death (Tyler and Pratt, 1980).

Therefore, depending on the temporal sequence of epithelial cell differentiation in the palate, some aspects of palatal shelf growth and differentiation will respond to EGF. Evidence to suggest that EGF is necessary for palatal development was provided by the demonstration that palatal shelves can be successfully cultured in serum-free medium containing EGF as well as other growth factors and hormones (Pratt et al., 1980). Selective removal of EGF from the medium resulted in drastically reduced overall growth and in death of the palatal medial epithelial cells. Therefore, physiological levels of EGF or similar growth factors may be important for the normal growth and differentiation of epithelial and mesenchymal cells of the palate. However, under certain conditions, the presence of EGF in culture will interfere with the normal programmed epithelial cell death that oc-

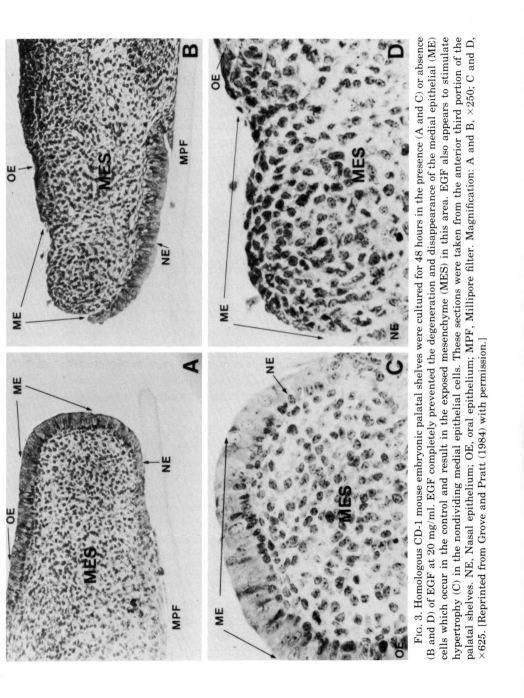

Fig. 3. Homologous CD-1 mouse embryonic palatal shelves were cultured for 48 hours in the presence (A and C) or absence (B and D) of EGF at 20 mg/ml. EGF completely prevented the degeneration and disappearance of the medial epithelial (ME) cells which occur in the control and result in the exposed mesenchyme (MES) in this area. EGF also appears to stimulate hypertrophy (C) in the nondividing medial epithelial cells. These sections were taken from the anterior third portion of the palatal shelves. NE, Nasal epithelium; OE, oral epithelium; MPF, Millipore filter. Magnification: A and B, ×250; C and D, ×625. [Reprinted from Grove and Pratt (1984) with permission.]

curs in the anterior regions of the medial palatal epithelium. Our results suggest that an EGF-like growth factor, which has been detected in rodent embryos (Nexo *et al.*, 1980; Proper *et al.*, 1982; Twardzik *et al.*, 1982), may play a role in normal palatal development (also see Section VIII). EGF or some EGF-like molecule along with hormones such as the glucocorticoids (Pratt and Salomon, 1981) may regulate proliferation and differentiation of palatal epithelial cells *in vivo* as well as *in vitro*.

V. Influence of EGF on Palatal Extracellular Matrix Synthesis in Organ Culture

The effects of EGF on the synthesis of collagen, fibronectin, and hyaluronic acid in the developing palate in organ culture has recently been reported (Silver *et al.*, 1984; Turley *et al.*, 1985). Palatal shelves (day 13 CD-1 mouse) grown in the presence of EGF were substantially larger with increases occurring in DNA content as well as in protein synthesis; EGF also prevented the normal programmed cell death of the anterior region medial epithelial cells (Silver *et al.*, 1984).

Fibronectin is an important extracellular matrix glycoprotein which appears to be produced by cells of mesenchymal and epithelial origin. Fibronectin appears to serve as an organizer for other matrix components such as collagen, heparin, and hyaluronate since it contains multiple binding domains (Yamada, 1983). The presence of EGF during 48 hours of organ culture results in a dramatic enhancement in the immunofluorescent localization of fibronectin which appears mainly in the mesenchymal extracellular matrix (Silver *et al.*, 1981, 1984). In addition, fibronectin appears to be enhanced in the basal lamina between the mesenchyme and all three regions of palatal epithelium. This fibronectin in the basal lamina may in part be contributed from the palatal epithelium, since preliminary studies using isolated palatal epithelia in culture (also see Section VI) indicate that the epithelial cells, especially the oral keratinizing cells, can produce fibronectin (unpublished observations). This is not surprising since other work (O'Keefe *et al.*, 1984; Clark *et al.*, 1985) demonstrates that human neonatal foreskin keratinocytes produce fibronectin in culture; apparently this fibronectin production is related to the morphogenesis of keratinocytes as they migrate into a wounded region of the epidermis. Therefore, it appears that embryonic keratinizing epithelial cells, such as occur in the palate, and adult keratinocytes, which have dedifferentiated into an embryonic type of cell, utilize fibronectin for a critical role in their growth and differentiation.

Net collagen synthesis in palatal organ culture, as measured by the determination of the ratios of labeled hydroxyproline to proline, appears to be stimulated by EGF to approximately the same extent as does net protein synthesis; the percentage of protein synthesis devoted to collagen synthesis is approximately 10% in both groups (Silver *et al.*, 1984). However, under these conditions, EGF preferentially stimulates the synthesis of type V collagen, and this is the first report of such an effect of EGF. Which cells in the palate are responsible for synthesis of type V collagen and its role is unknown; the distribution of type V collagen in the embryo, fetus, and adult is rather widespread, including epithelial cells (Burgeson, 1982).

The presence of large amounts of extracellular hyaluronic acid (HA), which is a large molecular weight glycosaminoglycan, has been correlated with embryonic morphogenesis (Toole *et al.*, 1980) and palatal development, especially movement of palatal shelves from the vertical to horizontal orientation (Pratt *et al.*, 1973; Brinkley, 1980). Turley *et al.* (1985) demonstrated in palatal organ culture that EGF stimulates (two- to eightfold) the incorporation of labeled glucosamine into hyaluronic acid. The maximal effect was obtained at gestational ages corresponding to palatal elevation and fusion, whereas after fusion had occurred stimulation was not observed. In the presence of EGF, there was a marked alteration in the histochemical distribution of hyaluronidase-sensitive, alcian blue-staining material in the mesenchyme of the cultured palates. The HA-rich areas normally lining the support filter (adjacent to the nasal epithelium) and medial edges were not present. Rather, the HA staining was evenly distributed throughout the mesenchyme and along the outer edge of the junction between the oral and medial epithelium (Turley *et al.*, 1985).

VI. EGF Influence on Cultured Palatal Epithelial Cells

The epithelium covering the developing palatal shelves plays a key role in normal palatogenesis. Prior to palatal shelf fusion, three distinct cell regions are evident in the epithelium which covers the shelf. These include the dorsal nasal, the ventral oral, and the medial epithelial cells. After contact, the medial cells undergo programmed cell death, and the nasal cells develop functional cilia and secrete mucus, while the oral cells become squamous and keratinize (Greene and Pratt, 1976; Meller, 1980). In addition, alterations in the growth and differentiation of the palatal epithelium have been reported to be involved in abnormal palatogenesis induced by certain teratogens (Greene and Pratt, 1976; Pratt, 1983). To facilitate a clearer understanding of epithelial development in both normal and abnormal palatogenesis, we have developed conditions which allow for growth and differentiation of intact palatal epithelia *in vitro* in the absence of any palatal mesenchyme (Grove and Pratt, 1983, 1984). It is clear that differentiation occurs *in vitro* since cilia appear on nasal cells, and oral cells flatten into a squamous keratinizing phenotype after 3–4 days in culture (Fig. 4).

Palatal epithelial cell culture represents an important advance in the study of palatal epithelial development. Previous methods for studying the epithelium *in vitro* include whole shelf organ culture (Pourtois, 1972) and culture of isolated and then recombined epithelium and mesenchyme (Tyler and Koch, 1977). Using this latter transfilter culture technique, EGF had been shown to stimulate DNA synthesis in the dissociated palatal epithelium (Tyler and Pratt, 1980). Our results demonstrate that day 13 palatal epithelial cells synthesize DNA and proliferate optimally in the absence of the palatal mesenchyme when cultured on an endothelial cell-derived extracellular matrix (ECM) in DME/F-12 medium supplemented with EGF (Grove and Pratt, 1983, 1984).

Recent findings (unpublished) demonstrate that fibronectin can also serve as a substrate for the palatal epithelium in culture. Apparently fibronectin and the ECM substrates can, for the most part, replace the requirement for mesenchyme. It was surprising to find that laminin and/or type IV collagen were not suitable substrates for the epithelia unless cyclic AMP and EGF were present in the culture media together. We interpret these results to indicate that EGF by itself stimulates the reappearance of fibronectin receptors in the epithelia following enzymatic separation from the mesenchyme, which allows them to attach to substrates rich in fibronectin, such as the ECM. However, in the presence of both cyclic AMP and EGF, receptors for laminin and type IV collagen are synthesized, allowing the epithelia to attach to matrices rich in these components (Gospodarowicz *et al.*, 1984). The most prominent cell type in these cultures with EGF appears to be the oral keratinizing cells, and this palatal cell type is clearly the most responsive to EGF.

The recent development of serum-free conditions that allow mouse embryonic palatal epithelial cells to synthesize DNA, undergo cell division, and differentiate in culture (Grove and Pratt, 1983, 1984) has made it possible to investigate programmed cell death in medial epithelial cells under more controlled and defined conditions. Degeneration in the epithelium between the nasal and oral cells areas within 24 hours of culture corresponds both temporally and spatially to medial epithelial cell autolysis in whole palatal shelves in organ culture as well as *in vivo,* and thus constitutes a morphological indicator for

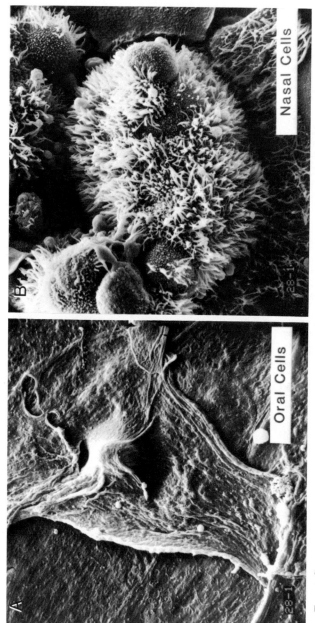

Fig. 4. Scanning electron micrographs of cultured palatal epithelial cells. The cells were grown on an ECM substrate for 4 days in medium containing 10% fetal calf serum and EGF (20 ng/ml). The squamous keratinizing oral cells are shown in A (×3500) and the ciliated nasal epithelial cells in B (×1900).

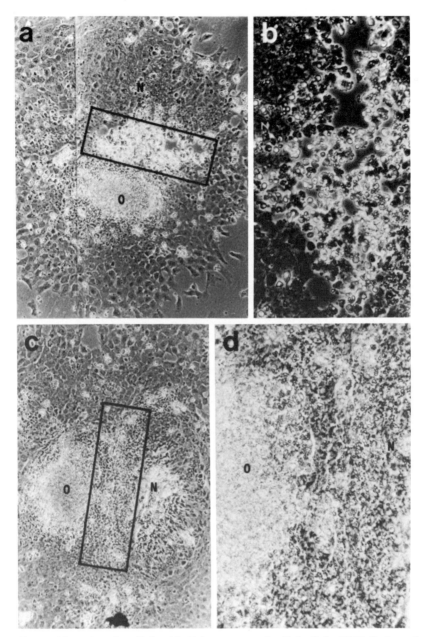

Fig. 5. Alteration of medial epithelial programmed cell death by EGF. Embryonic mouse palatal epithelia were cultured in serum-free medium in the presence or absence of EGF (20 ng/ml). The enclosed rectangular areas in a and c are the medial epithelia and are shown at higher magnification in b and d. Pictures were taken after 20 hours in culture. − EGF (a) ×100, (b) ×1000; + EGF (c) ×100, (d) ×1000. N, Nasal epithelium; O, oral epithelium. [Reprinted from Grove and Pratt (1984) with permission.]

programmed medial epithelial cell death (Fig. 5). The ability of EGF to prevent medial epithelial cell death in culture is also consistent with findings in palatal shelf organ culture studies (Hassell and Pratt, 1977) and reinforces the validity of this indicator. In addition, it provides evidence that the presence of the palatal mesenchyme is not required in order for EGF to prevent epithelial cell death under these conditions, and suggests that EGF directly affects the medial epithelium. Development of a serum-free culture system in which differentiation of the epithelial cells takes place in the absence of the palatal mesenchyme provides an ideal system in which to investigate the influence of and mechanism by which various growth factors, hormones, and cleft palate teratogens exert their effects on the epithelial cells.

VII. Cyclic AMP Levels Alter EGF Effects on the Palate

Since the initial isolation of adenosine 3′,5′-monophosphate by Sutherland and Rall (1958), it has become clear that cyclic AMP plays an important role in a variety of cellular activities including growth and differentiation (Pastan and Willingham, 1981). Pratt and Martin (1975) demonstrated an increase in cyclic AMP in the rat secondary palate during the time of elevation and fusion, and they proposed that the programmed cell death of the medial palatal epithelium was related to this increased cyclic AMP. Hassell and Pratt (1977) demonstrated that inhibition of palatal medial epithelial death by EGF in organ culture was partially prevented by addition of cyclic AMP, suggesting that some of the EGF effects may be associated with lowered levels of cyclic AMP. Greene et al. (1980), using immunohistochemical localization techniques, demonstrated that the increase in palatal cyclic AMP was transient, was correlated with increased adenylate cyclase activity in medial epithelial cells, and occurred predominantly in these epithelial cells.

The transient change in level of cyclic AMP (but not cyclic GMP) observed in the palate is presumably under hormonal control. Waterman et al. (1976, 1977) examined hamster palates in vivo and in vitro to define the hormonal basis for these changes in cyclic AMP. Norepinephrine and epinephrine were the catecholamines most capable of inducing increased activation of adenylate cyclase during palatal growth and development. The remaining catecholamines, isoproterenol and dopamine, displayed a lesser ability to activate adenyl cyclase. Other hormones, histamine, serotonin, thyrotropin, growth hormone, thyroxine, and glucagon, were not stimulatory. Using tissue homogenate, Palmer et al. (1980) found that the most potent agents capable of activating adenylate cyclase were parathyroid hormone and calcitonin; this activity is most likely in the preosteoblastic region, which is found in the palatal mesenchyme beneath the nasal epithelium. Palmer *et al.* (1980) also observed that prostaglandins (PG) E_1, E_2, and $F_{2\alpha}$ stimulated adenylate cyclase activity in the intact hamster palate. Chepenik and Greene (1981) reported the presence of prostaglandin-like compounds in primary cultures of mouse palatal mesenchyme.

The response of medial epithelial cells to EGF can be partially inhibited by the presence of cyclic AMP and theophylline in organ cultures of rodent palatal shelves (Hassell and Pratt, 1977). Grove and Pratt (1984) were unable to inhibit the effect of EGF on medial epithelial cell death in cell culture using several agents which increase intracellular cyclic AMP levels, including cholera toxin and 8-bromo-cyclic AMP. These findings suggest that the mesenchyme is required in order for cyclic AMP to alter the effect of EGF on the medial epithelial cells.

By day 4 of culture, EGF and cyclic AMP synergistically stimulated the appearance of a long-lived, proliferating epithelial cell type (Grove and Pratt, 1984). These cells most likely originate from the oral epithelium and are distinguished from differentiating oral cells by their smaller size. They may arise from a cyclic AMP-sensitive, EGF-sensitive population of epithelial stem cells. These findings are similar to those of Muller-Glauser and Preisig (1983), who reported that adult and neonatal human oral epithelial cells are stimulated to proliferate in culture by cholera toxin and EGF.

VIII. Role of the EGF Receptor and Transforming Growth Factor-α in Palatal Development

Yoneda and Pratt (1981) showed that human embryonic palatal mesenchymal cells contain a high level of EGF receptors and were quite responsive to the growth-promoting properties of EGF. EGF receptor binding sites can be detected in mouse embryos as early as day 11–12 of gestation, and autoradiographic studies have demonstrated their presence in the palatal epithelium by day 13 of gestation (Nexo *et al.*, 1980). Adamson and Warshaw (1982) and Adamson and Meek (1984) found that a variety of other embryonic mouse tissues contained EGF receptors and displayed downregulation (decrease) of these receptors when EGF was injected into the amniotic sac. Functional EGF receptors appear around gestational days 10 and 11 in the rat embryo, and various organs express functional EGF receptor kinase at different times (Hortsch *et al.*, 1983).

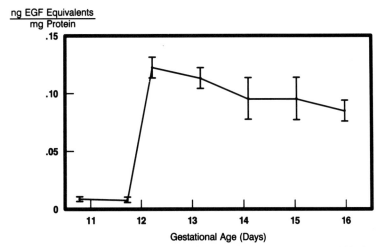

FIG. 6. Level of EGF-like growth factor during mouse embryogenesis. Whole mouse embryos (NIH-Swiss Webster) were taken at various times and processed according to Nexo *et al.* (1980). The extracts were examined for EGF-like activity by RIA and RRA. No RIA competing activity was observed until day 15 (not shown), and the levels here represent RRA assayable material, presumable TGF-α.

The appearance of an EGF-like substance as a function of the age of the embryo was analyzed by radioimmunoassay (RIA) and radio-receptor assay (RRA) (Nexo *et al.*, 1980). In the embryonic extracts, EGF proved to be labile, requiring the presence of soybean trypsin inhibitor and sodium azide to stabilize the recovery of added EGF in test samples. Even with added stabilizing agents, immunoreactive EGF was barely detectable before day $14\frac{1}{2}$ (less than 20 fmol per embryo), whereas a substantial increase was observed from day $15\frac{1}{2}$ to $17\frac{1}{2}$ (from 70 to 200 fmol per embryo). In contrast, the radioreceptor assay detected appreciable amounts of an EGF-like substance at $11\frac{1}{2}$ days (50 fmol per embryo) (Fig. 6); the values estimated by radioreceptor assay (about 10-fold higher than by radioimmunoassay) also increase markedly between days $15\frac{1}{2}$ and $17\frac{1}{2}$ (an average increase from 500 to 3000 fmol per embryo). This increase in an EGF-like substance closely paralleled the increase in specific binding of labeled EGF to membranes of palatal homogenates, which increase 10-fold from days 12 to 14 (Nexo *et al.*, 1980). The source and composition of the EGF present in the embryo are uncertain. The maternal level of EGF could not contribute to the fetal levels since transplacental transport does not occur (unpublished). The embryonic growth factor does not cross-react to the same extent as maternal EGF with anti-EGF antibodies, although

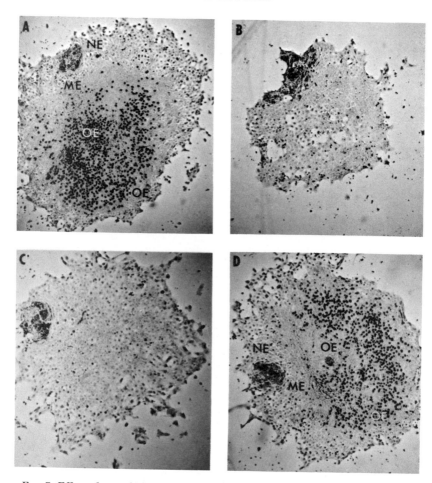

FIG. 7. Effect of growth factors on proliferation of palatal epithelial cells. Primary cultures of day 13 CD-1 mouse palatal epithelia were cultured for 4 days as previously described (Grove and Pratt, 1984). The cultures were exposed to [^{3}H]thymidine at 2.5 μCi/ml during the last 16 hours of incubation and processed for autoradiography. (A) EGF, 10 ng/ml; (B) no growth factors; (C) somatomedin C, 10 ng/ml; (D) TGF-α, 10 ng/ml. NE, Nasal epithelium; OE, oral epithelium; ME, medial epithelium.

both can cross-react to the same extent with the EGF receptor. This suggests that the embryonic growth factor is distinct from adult EGF immunologically.

I suggest that the embryonic growth factor may be identical to one of the recently discovered transforming growth factors (Twardzik *et al.*, 1982; Proper *et al.*, 1982). Transforming growth factor-α (TGF-α) is

● MESENCHYME-DERIVED GROWTH FACTOR
○ EPITHELIAL-DERIVED GROWTH FACTOR

FIG. 8. Role of TGF-α in secondary palatal development. Schematic frontal sections of the day 12, 13, and 14 mouse secondary palatal shelves. Medial epithelial (ME), nasal epithelial (NE), and oral epithelial (OE) cells on day 13 presumably synthesize TGF-α (○) which acts in an autocrine manner to stimulate epithelial proliferation; the mesenchymal cells also produce TGF-α (●). By day 13, the ME cells cease production of TGF-α and then undergo a series of events termed "programmed cell death."

structurally and functionally similar to EGF. Structurally, EGF and TGF-α are approximately the same size, EGF being 53 amino acids in length and TGF-α being 50. More importantly, these two growth factors share considerable homology which is mostly centered about the three disulfide bonds thought to be important in maintenance of tertiary structure and receptor binding. Furthermore, EGF and TGF-α appear to have approximately the same affinity for the EGF receptor (Todaro *et al.*, 1985). TGF-α is the most likely candidate for an embryonic growth factor and human TGF-α (provided by R. Derynck, Genentech, Inc.) proved to be able to support the proliferation and differentiation of palatal epithelial cells in culture in a manner and concentration similar to that of mouse EGF (unpublished, Fig. 7).

I have proposed a testable model (Fig. 8) in which to account for the role of TGF-α in palatal development. On day 12 of mouse development, the oral and medial epithelial cells as well as the mesenchymal cells produce TGF-α which acts in an autocrine fashion to support the rapid growth of these cells during early palatal development. By day 13 of gestation, the medial epithelial cells cease to produce TGF-α, although these cells still appear to retain their EGF/TGF-α receptors. This cessation in TGF-α synthesis is presumably due to a prior programming of the medial epithelium early in its embryonic life. Since these cells no longer have TGF-α, they cease to synthesize DNA and begin a series of morphological and biochemical events leading to cell death. In contrast, the oral cells retain their ability to produce TGF-α which is important for the differentiation of these cells into keratinocytes, which populate the epidermis of the roof of the mouth into adult life. Studies that are in progress using recombinant DNA techniques will critically test this hypothesis in the near future by examining the levels and distribution of TGF-α and its mRNA during embryonic development. We also plan to examine the synthesis and distribution of specific keratin proteins in the palatal epithelial cells as markers for EGF/TGF-α modulation of growth and differentiation.

REFERENCES

Adamson, E. D., and Meek, J. (1984). *Dev. Biol.* **103**, 62–70.

Adamson, E. D., and Warshaw, J. B. (1982). *Dev. Biol.* **90**, 430–434.

Brinkley, L. L. (1980). *In* "Current Research Trends in Prenatal Craniofacial Development" (R. M. Pratt and R. L. Christiansen, eds.), pp. 203–220. Elsevier, New York.

Burgeson, R. E. (1982). *J. Invest. Dermatol.* **79**, 255–305.

Calvert, R., Beaulieu, J.-F., and Menard, D. (1982). *Experientia* **38**, 1096–1097.

Carpenter, G., and Cohen, S. (1979). *Annu. Rev. Biochem.* **48**, 193–216.

Catterton, W. Z., Escobeds, M. B., Sexson, W. R., Gray, M. E., Sundell, H. W., and Stahlman, M. T. (1979). *Pediatr. Res.* **13**, 104–108.

Chepenik, K. P., and Greene, R. M. (1981). *Biochem. Biophys. Res. Commun.* **100**, 951–958.

Clark, R. A. F., Nielsen, L. D., Howell, S. E., and Folkvord, J. M. (1985). *J. Cell. Biochem.* **28**, 127–141.

Cohen, S. (1965). *Dev. Biol.* **12**, 394–407.

Goldin, G. V., and Opperman, L. A. (1980). *J. Embryol. Exp. Morphol.* **60**, 235–243.

Gospodarowicz, D. (1981). *Annu. Rev. Physiol.* **43**, 251–263.

Gospodarowicz, D., Greenburg, G., Bialecki, H., and Zetter, B. R. (1978). *In Vitro* **14**, 85–118.

Gospodarowicz, D., Lepine, J., Massoglia, S., and Wood, I. (1984). *J. Cell Biol.* **99**, 947–961.

Green, M. R., Basketter, D. A., Couchman, J. R., and Rees, D. A. (1983). *Dev. Biol.* **100**, 506–512.

Green, M. R., Phil, D., and Couchman, J. R. (1984). *J. Invest. Dermatol.* **83**, 118–123.

Greene, R. M., and Pratt, R. M. (1976). *J. Embryol. Exp. Morphol.* **36**, 225–245.

Greene, R. M., Shanfeld, J. L., Davidovitch, Z., and Pratt, R. M. (1980). *J. Embryol. Exp. Morphol.* **60**, 271–281.

Grove, R. I., and Pratt, R. M. (1983). *Exp. Cell Res.* **148**, 195–205.

Grove, R. I., and Pratt, R. M. (1984). *Dev. Biol.* **106**, 427–437.

Hassell, J. R. (1975). *Dev. Biol.* **45**, 90–103.

Hassell, J. R., and Pratt, R. M. (1977). *Exp. Cell Res.* **106**, 55–62.

Hollenberg, M. D. (1979). *Vit. Horm.* **37**, 69–110.

Hortsch, M., Schlesinger, J., Gootwine, E., and Webb, C. G. (1983). *EMBO J.* **2**, 1937–1941.

Meller, S. M. (1980). *In* "Current Research Trends in Prenatal Craniofacial Development" (R. M. Pratt and R. L. Christiansen, eds.), pp. 221–235. Elsevier, Amsterdam.

Mesiano, S., Browne, C. A., and Thorburn, G. D. (1985). *Dev. Biol.* **110**, 23–28.

Müller-Glauser, W., and Preisig, E. (1983). *Arch. Oral Biol.* **28**, 765–771.

Nexo, E., Hollenberg, M. D., Figueroa, A., and Pratt, R. M. (1980). *Proc. Natl. Acad. Sci. U.S.A.* **77**, 2782–2785.

O'Keefe, E. J., Woodley, D., Castillo, G., Russell, N., and Payne, R. E. (1984). *J. Invest. Dermatol.* **82**, 150–155.

Palmer, G. C., Palmer, S. J., Waterman, R. E., and Palmer, S. M. (1980). *Pediatr. Pharm.* **1**, 45–54.

Partanen, A.-M., Ekblom, P., and Thesleff, I. (1985). *Dev. Biol.* **111**, 84–94.

Pastan, I. H., and Willingham, M. C. (1981). *Science* **214**, 504–509.

Pourtois, M. (1972). *In* "Developmental Aspects of Oral Biology" (H. C. Slavkin and L. A. Bavetta, eds.), pp. 81–108. Academic Press, New York.

Pratt, R. M. (1980). *In* "Developmental of Mammals" (M. H. Johnson, ed.), Vol. 4, pp. 203–231. Elsevier, Amsterdam.

Pratt, R. M. (1983). *Trends Pharm. Sci.* **4**, 160–162.

Pratt, R. M., and Martin, G. R. (1975). *Proc. Natl. Acad. Sci. U.S.A.* **72**, 874.

Pratt, R. M., and Salomon, D. S. (1981). *In* "Biochemical Basis of Chemical Teratogenesis" (M. R. Juchau, ed.), pp. 179–193. Elsevier, Amsterdam.

Pratt, R. M., Goggins, J. R., Wilk, A. L., and King, C. T. G. (1973). *Dev. Biol.* **32**, 230–237.

Pratt, R. M., Yoneda, T., Silver, M. H., and Salomon, D. S. (1980). *In* "Research Trends in Prenatal Craniofacial Development" (R. M. Pratt and R. L. Christiansen, eds.), pp. 367–386. Elsevier, Amsterdam.

Proper, J. A., Bjornson, C. L., and Moses, H. L. (1982). *J. Cell. Physiol.* **110**, 169–174.

Schlesinger, J., Schrieber, A. B., Levi, A., Lax, I., Liberman, T., and Yarden, Y. (1983). *Crit. Rev. Biochem.* **14**, 93–111.

Scott, J., Urdea, M., Quiroga, M., Sanchez-Pescadov, R., Fong, N., Selby, M., Rutter, W. J., and Bell, G. I. (1983). *Science* **221**, 236–241.

Silver, N. H., Foidart, J. M., and Pratt, R. M. (1981). *Differentiation* **18**, 141–149.

Silver, M. H., Murray, C., and Pratt, R. M. (1984). *Differentiation* **27**, 205–208.

Sundell, H., Serenius, F. G., Barthe, P., Friedman, Z., Kanarek, K. S., Esobedo, M. B., Orth, D. N., and Stahlman, M. T. (1975). *Pediatr. Res.* **9**, 371–376.

Sutherland, E. W., and Rall, T. W. (1958). *J. Biol. Chem.* **232**, 1077–1086.

Todaro, G. J., Lee, D. C., Webb, N. R., Rose, T. M., and Brown, J. P. (1985). *In* "Cancer Cells 3/Growth Factors and Transformation" (J. Feramisco, B. Ozanne, and C. Stiles, eds.), pp. 51–58. Cold Spring Harbor Laboratory, Cold Spring Harbor, New York.

Tonelli, Q. J., and Sorof, S. (1980). *Nature (London)* **285**, 250–252.

Toole, B. P., Underhill, C. B., Mikuni-Takagaki, Y., and Orkin, R. W. (1980). *In* "Current Research Trends in Prenatal Craniofacial Development" (R. M. Pratt and R. L. Christiansen, eds.), pp. 263–276. Elsevier, New York.

Turley, E. A., Hollenberg, M. D., and Pratt, R. M. (1985). *Differentiation* **28**, 279–285.

Tyler, M. S., and Koch, W. E. (1977). *J. Embryol. Exp. Morphol.* **38**, 19–34.

Tyler, M. S., and Pratt, R. M. (1980). *J. Embryol. Exp. Morphol.* **58**, 93–106.

Twardzik, D. R., Ranchalis, J. E., and Todaro, G. J. (1982). *Cancer Res.* **42**, 590–593.

Waterman, R. E., Palmer, G. C., Palmer, S. J., and Palmer, S. M. (1976). *Anat. Rec.* **185**, 125–138.

Waterman, R. E., Palmer, G. C., Palmer, S. J., and Palmer, S. M. (1977). *Anat. Rec.* **188**, 431–444.

Yamada, K. M. (1983). *Annu. Rev. Biochem.* **52**, 761–799.

Yoneda, T., and Pratt, R. M. (1981). *Science* **213**, 563–565.

Zendegui, J. G., and Carpenter, G. (1984). *Cell Biol. Int. Rep.* **8**, 619–633.

CHAPTER 9

REGULATION OF KERATIN GENE EXPRESSION DURING DIFFERENTIATION OF EPIDERMAL AND VAGINAL EPITHELIAL CELLS

Dennis R. Roop

LABORATORY OF CELLULAR CARCINOGENESIS AND TUMOR PROMOTION
NATIONAL CANCER INSTITUTE
NATIONAL INSTITUTES OF HEALTH
BETHESDA, MARYLAND 20892

I. Introduction

Keratins constitute a family of approximately 20 related α-helix-rich structural proteins of 40–70 kDa (kilodaltons) and make up the subunits of the intermediate filaments present in all epithelial cells (Lazarides, 1980; Steinert, 1982). This multigene family has been divided into two distinct types on the basis of sequences that are predicted to form coiled coils (Fuchs and Hanukoglu, 1983; Steinert *et al.*, 1984a): the acidic keratins form type I and the neutral-basic keratins form type II. Epithelial cells, in general, always express at least one member of each type and various factors influence which specific members are expressed, such as cell type (Moll *et al.*, 1982), period of embryonic development (Banks-Schlegel, 1982), state of differentiation (Dale and Stern, 1975; Baden and Lee, 1978; Skerrow and Hunter, 1978; Fuchs and Green, 1980; Roop *et al.*, 1984b), and growth environment of the cell (Steinert and Yuspa, 1978; Sun and Green, 1978; Doran *et al.*, 1980; Fuchs and Green, 1981; Roop *et al.*, 1983; Eichner *et al.*, 1984). However, the mechanisms regulating the expression of this family of genes is not known. To define the mechanism regulating keratin genes, it was necessary to have specific probes to monitor their expression at the molecular level. Therefore, cDNA clones corresponding to the major keratins synthesized in mouse epidermis were isolated and characterized (Roop *et al.*, 1983, 1985). Several lines of evidence are presented which suggest that the expression of subsets of keratin genes is coordinately regulated and dependent on the state of differentiation. In addition, on the basis of amino acid sequence information deduced from the nucleotide sequence of these cloned cDNAs (Steinert

195

et al., 1983, 1984b, 1985a,b), it is postulated that the sequence differences observed for keratins expressed at different states of differentiation will change the properties and function of the filaments that they form.

To study the mechanism by which differentiation and consequently the expression of specific keratin genes is regulated, it is desirable to have a system in which induction of the differentiation process is easily controlled. The epidermis is not well suited for this type of study since it is difficult to manipulate the differentiation process in a controlled manner *in vivo*. Vaginal epithelium is an attractive alternative to the epidermis since the state of differentiation of this tissue is hormone dependent and can be easily changed in ovariectomized animals by administering exogenous hormone (Long and Evans, 1922). In addition, the differentiation state of this epithelium has also been shown to be very sensitive to retinoids (Kahn and Bern, 1950). Evidence is presented correlating the expression of keratin genes with changes in the differentiation program induced in vaginal epithelium by estrogen and vitamin A.

II. Evidence Correlating Keratin Gene Expression with Differentiation State

A. Slot-Blot Analysis of Steady-State RNA

In order to isolate cDNA clones for all the major keratins synthesized by epidermal cells, we prepared cDNA libraries from poly(A) RNA isolated from newborn mouse epidermis and primary cultures of mouse epidermal cells. This approach was chosen because the concentrations of mRNAs coding for different keratins, as judged by cell-free translation, were different in RNA preparations from the two sources. The major keratins synthesized by newborn mouse epidermis are 67 and 59 kDa and to a lesser extent, keratins of 60, 55, and 50 kDa (Roop *et al.*, 1983). Placing newborn mouse epidermal cells in culture in medium containing low Ca^{2+} results in growth as a monolayer without stratification. These cells proliferate rapidly and display many characteristics associated with basal cells found in intact epidermis (Yuspa *et al.*, 1980). The major keratins synthesized by these cells are 60, 59.5, 55, and 50 kDa. We were able to identify and characterize cDNA clones corresponding to the 67- and 59-kDa keratins synthesized *in vivo* (Roop *et al.*, 1983) and the 60-, 55-, and 50-kDa keratins synthesized *in vitro* (Roop *et al.*, 1985).

Although mRNAs coding for these keratin proteins share some sequence homology due to common structural features (summarized

50 55 60 59 67

Newborn

Cell Culture

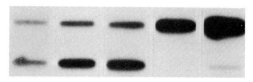

FIG. 1. Quantitation of keratin mRNAs synthesized by mouse epidermal cells *in vivo* and *in vitro*. A constant amount of mRNA isolated from newborn mouse epidermis or primary cultures of mouse epidermal cells was analyzed by slot-blot analysis. The keratin cDNA probes used for this analysis are indicated.

below), it is possible to prepare very specific probes for each keratin mRNA by subcloning regions of the cDNAs corresponding to the 3′ noncoding regions of each mRNA, which are approximately 350–450 nucleotides in length. Since these regions do not code for amino acids, they have not been evolutionarily conserved and are therefore useful as specific hybridizations probes. The specificity of these 3′ noncoding probes was demonstrated by Northern (RNA) blot hybridization (Roop *et al.*, 1983, 1985).

Slot-blot analysis of steady-state RNA isolated from newborn mouse epidermis and primary cultures of mouse epidermal cells revealed that the 59- and 67-kDa keratin genes are not expressed at all or only at very low levels in primary epidermal cell cultures compared to newborn epidermis (Fig. 1). Transcripts complementary to the cDNA clones isolated from the *in vitro* library, the 50-, 55-, and 60-kDa keratins, are present in RNA isolated from intact epidermis but at reduced concentrations compared to those found in cell culture. These results presumably reflect the relative contribution of RNA in basal cells (which consists of a single cell layer) to that of total epidermis (which consists of many cell layers at different stages of differentiation) and indicate that the 50-, 55-, and 60-kDa keratin genes are predominantly expressed in proliferating basal cells and that the 59- and 67-kDa keratins are predominantly expressed in differentiated cells. The low level of transcripts for the 50-, 55-, and 60-kDa keratin genes in intact epidermis also suggests that the stability of keratin mRNAs synthesized in basal cells decreases as cells differentiate and migrate into the suprabasal layers. Additional experiments will be required to establish this.

```
67 kDa  T  V  K  F  V  S  T  S  Y  S  R  G  T  K -COOH
59 kDa  T  S  G  G  G  D  Q  S  S  K  G  P  R  Y -COOH
60 kDa  K  Y  T  T  T  S  S  S  K  K  S  Y  R  Q -COOH
55 kDa  K  V  V  S  T  H  E  Q  V  L  R  T  K  N -COOH
```

Fig. 2. Comparison of amino acid sequences at the carboxy terminus of mouse keratins. Amino acid sequences were deduced from the nucleotide sequence of cDNA clones. Peptides were synthesized for the regions underlined.

B. Subunit Localization with Monospecific Antisera

All keratin subunits contain a central domain of about 300 residues which form a coiled coil α-helical structure (summarized below). The production of antisera that are monospecific for individual keratin subunits has been difficult due to the presence of common antigenic determinants within this conserved region. A comparison of available sequences for mouse keratin subunits revealed that the carboxy-terminal sequences were unique, with the exception of the 55- and 50-kDa subunits which have identical C-terminal residues (Fig. 2). This finding, coupled with a previous observation that these C-terminal sequences have a peripheral location within filaments (Steinert et al., 1983), encouraged us to try to elicit specific antibodies for keratin subunits with synthetic peptides corresponding to the C-terminal sequences.

Our initial attempt used synthetic peptides for the residues underlined for the 59- and 67-kDa subunits (Fig. 2). The antisera produced against these synthetic peptides were highly specific for the appropriate keratin subunits as judged by immunoblot analysis (Roop et al., 1984a). This same approach was then used to produce antisera that were monospecific for the 55- and 60-kDa subunits (Roop et al., 1985). These antisera were used to localize these keratin subunits within newborn mouse skin by indirect immunofluorescence (Fig. 3). The 59- and 67-kDa subunits were only present within the differentiated cells of the epidermis (the suprabasal layers) and not in the proliferating cells (the basal layer); in contrast, the 55- and 60-kDa subunits are detected within the basal and suprabasal layers. These results are consistent with the expression data obtained by RNA analysis as discussed above. The reduced staining of the stratum corneum by antisera specific for the 67-, 60-, and 55-kDa keratins suggest that these antigenic determinants are masked or missing in this layer of the epidermis. The proteolytic processing of some keratin subunits within the stratum corneum has been reported (Fuchs and Green, 1980; Schweizer and Winter, 1982; Bowden et al., 1984) and these results suggest that residues are removed from the carboxy termini.

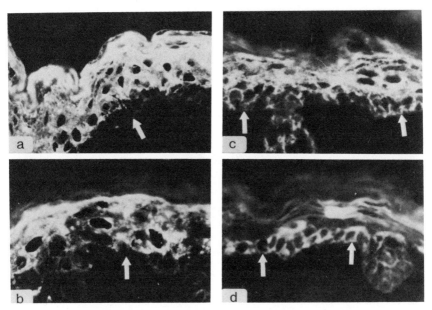

FIG. 3. Detection of keratin subunits by immunofluorescence microscopy with mono-specific antisera. Frozen sections of newborn mouse skin were stained with the following antisera: (a) the anti-59 kDa keratin peptide, (b) the anti-67 kDa keratin peptide, (c) the anti-55 kDa keratin peptide, (d) the anti-60 kDa keratin peptide. Arrows indicate the dermal–epidermal junction.

C. Localization of Keratin mRNAs by *in Situ* Hybridization

We have recently been able to detect mRNA coding for different keratin subunits within cells in different layers of the epidermis by *in situ* hybridization to histological sections of newborn mouse skin. We have subcloned the keratin cDNAs into newly developed vectors (SP64 and SP65, Promega Biotec, Madison, WI) that permit the synthesis of RNA transcripts that can be labeled with ^{35}S using [^{35}S]uridine 5′-(α-thio)triphosphate. Insertion of the cDNAs into the vector in the correct orientation and subsequent transcription with bacteriophage SP6 RNA polymerase result in the synthesis of transcripts that are complementary to mRNA. The use of these RNA probes has two advantages. First, their high specific activities permit short exposure times for autoradiography (typically 2 days) and the sensitivity to detect low levels of transcripts. Second, low backgrounds result from removal of nonspecifically bound probe by treatment with RNase after hybridization is complete. In our preliminary experiments, we have been able to localize the majority of the mRNA coding for the 55-kDa keratin to the

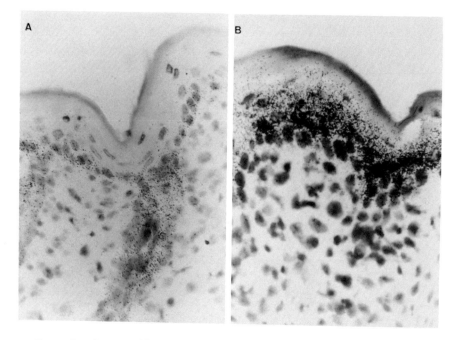

FIG. 4. Localization of keratin mRNAs by *in situ* hybridization. Frozen sections of newborn mouse skin were fixed in paraformaldehyde and hybridized with ^{35}S-labeled RNA probes corresponding to the 55-kDa keratin (A) and 67-kDa keratin (B) as described by Harper *et al.* (1986). After treatment with ribonucleases A and T_1, preparations were autoradiographed, exposed for 2 days, developed, and stained with Wright stain.

basal layer of the epidermis and hair follicles (Fig. 4). Very little of this mRNA is found in the differentiated cell layers, suggesting that expression of this keratin gene is "turned off" as cells differentiate and migrate into the suprabasal layer. Furthermore, the stability of this mRNA probably decreases in the suprabasal layers. Just the opposite was observed for the mRNA coding for the 67-kDa keratin; i.e., this mRNA was predominantly localized within the differentiated suprabasal layers and not the basal layer.

Some grains were observed in the basal layer with the 67-kDa probe. This may indicate that expression of the 67-kDa keratin gene is induced soon after cells are committed to differentiate and before they have migrated completely out of the basal layer. However, new fixation procedures that preserve morphology better will be required to confirm this. Note that the higher density of grains observed with the

67-kDa keratin probe as compared to the 55-kDa keratin probe is consistent with the steady-state level of these mRNAs detected by slot-blot analysis (Fig. 1).

On the basis of the combined data presented in Section II,A–C, we believe that the expression of specific subsets of keratin genes is correlated with the state of differentiation, and we consider expression of the 50-, 55-, and 60-kDa keratin genes to be associated with proliferation and expression of the 59- and 67-kDa keratin genes to be associated with epidermal cell maturation.

III. Modulation of Differentiation State and Keratin Gene Expression in Vaginal Epithelium

During the normal estrous cycle, vaginal epithelium changes from a thin mucus-secreting epithelium to a highly stratified squamous epithelium (Long and Evans, 1922). It is possible to induce this change in the differentiation program by administering estradiol to rats that have been ovariectomized (Peckham and Kiekhofer, 1962). Unstimulated epithelium from control ovariectomized animals consists of two to three layers of unspecialized cells that are cuboidal in shape and possess prominent nuclei (Fig. 5A). Within 12 hours after exposure to a single injection of estradiol benzoate (10 μg) in sesame oil, cells in the basal layer increased slightly in height and cells in the suprabasal layers appeared to reorganize (data not shown). There was no increase in cell number at this point. However, by 24 hours (Fig. 5B) the basal layer contained several mitotic figures and the epithelium had increased to six to eight cell layers. A fully differentiated stratified squamous epithelium, characterized by 10–12 layers of progressively flattened cells covered by a layer of loosely associated mature squames, was evident 48 hours after exposure to estradiol (Fig. 5C). Histologically, terminal differentiation induced in vaginal epithelium 72 hours after exposure to estrogen (Fig. 5D) resembles that of the epidermis.

Since the differentiation program induced by estrogen in rat vaginal epithelium was similar to that of the epidermis histologically, it was of interest to determine if the same keratin genes that have been studied extensively in the epidermis were also expressed in vaginal epithelium. Initially, the cytoskeletal proteins were isolated from vaginal epithelium of ovariectomized rats 48 hours after exposure to estradiol. A comparative immunoblot analysis, employing a multivalent antiserum produced against mouse keratins, indicated that the keratins produced in both tissues were similar (F. Huang and D. Roop, unpublished data). Therefore, we performed a more stringent assay for

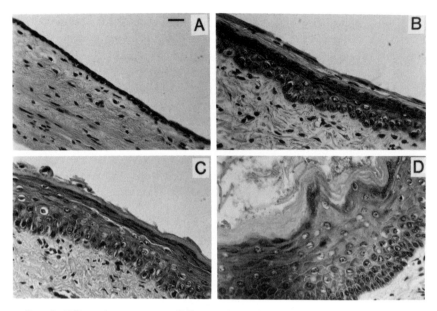

FIG. 5. Effect of estrogen on differentiation of rat vaginal epithelium. Ovariectomized animals received a single injection of estradiol benzoate (10 μg) in sesame oil.
Excised vaginas were fixed in buffered formalin and embedded in paraffin. Sections
were stained with hematoxylin–eosin. (A) control, (B) 24 hours, (C) 48 hours (D) 72
hours.

identity, molecular hybridization of ^{32}P-labeled mouse cDNA probes to
estrogenized rat vaginal RNA that had been separated under denaturing conditions on an agarose gel and transferred by blotting onto nitrocellulose paper. Using identical hybridization conditions, we showed
that rat vaginal epithelium contained transcripts for the 50-, 55-, 60-,
59-, and 67-kDa keratin genes that were identical in size to those
detected in mouse epidermis (D. Roop, unpublished data). These results indicate that the same keratin genes expressed in mouse epidermis are also expressed in rat vaginal epithelium when an estrogen-
induced change in the differentiation program occurs.

The conservation in sequence homology of the keratin genes between the two species allowed us to use the mouse keratin cDNA
probes to monitor the hormone-induced expression of keratin genes in
rat vaginal epithelium. This was most conveniently done by RNA slot-
blot analysis (Roop et al., 1984b). Total RNA was isolated from vaginal
epithelium obtained from ovariectomized animals at 0, 24, and 48
hours after exposure to a single injection of estradiol and analyzed as

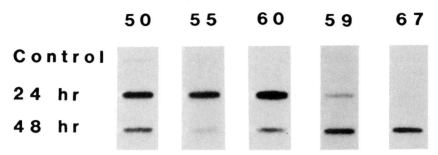

FIG. 6. Quantitation of keratin mRNAs synthesized by rat vaginal epithelium after estrogen-induced differentiation. Total RNA was isolated from vaginal epithelium of ovariectomized animals at 0, 24, and 48 hours after exposure to estradiol. Equivalent amounts of total RNA were analyzed by slot-blot analysis. The keratin cDNA probes used for this analysis are indicated.

described in Fig. 6. The very low level of expression of both the proliferation-associated (50, 55, and 60 kDa) and the differentiation-associated (59 and 67 kDa) keratin genes in control vaginal epithelium from ovariectomized rats is consistent with the lack of specialization detected histologically (Fig. 5A). There is a dramatic induction of the proliferation-associated keratin genes within 24 hours after exposure to estradiol (Figure 6), and this correlates with the onset of proliferation as seen in Fig. 5B. The decrease in the level of transcripts of these genes observed at 48 hours suggests that the synthesis of these RNAs ceases in differentiated cells and a dilution effect occurs due to the concentration of differentiated cells present at this time. A decrease in the stability of these mRNAs, analogous to that thought to occur in differentiated epidermal cells (see Section II), may also occur in vaginal epithelial cells and implies additional regulation at a posttranscriptional level.

Induction of expression of the differentiation-associated genes is also observed 24 hours after exposure to estradiol; however, transcripts of these genes continue to accumulate at 48 hours. The continued synthesis of the differentiation-associated genes at 48 hours is consistent with the pronounced stratification and differentiation observed histologically (Fig. 5C). The induction of these genes also appears to occur sequentially in that induction of the 59-kDa keratin gene appears to occur first, followed by the 67-kDa keratin gene. These results establish firmly that the induction of expression of these keratin genes occurs at the level of transcription, since only very low levels of transcripts were found in the uninduced epithelium. As was observed in the epidermis (see Section II), the expression of different subsets of keratin genes in vaginal epithelium is also correlated with the state of differentiation.

Vaginal cornification (i.e., the appearance of cornified epithelial cells in vaginal smears) has been used experimentally as an indication of vitamin A deficiency for many years (Baumann and Steenbock, 1932). It was of interest to determine if the differentiation program induced by vitamin A deficiency was similar to that induced by estrogen. Both differentiation programs appear to be similar as judged by histological examination and by the pattern of keratin expression (i.e., a high level of expression of the differentiation-associated keratins was observed in both cases). Intravaginal application of retinoic acid reversed the morphological appearance of this epithelium to that of a simple unstratified epithelium similar to that observed in control ovariectomized animals, and this was accompanied by a decrease in the concentration of the differentiation-associated keratins (F. Huang and D. Roop, unpublished data). These results suggest that the effects of vitamin A on the differentiation program of vaginal epithelium are opposite to those observed by estrogen.

IV. Correlation of Keratin Subunit Structure with Differential Expression

The availability of amino acid sequence data, deduced from the nucleotide sequence of the mouse cDNA clones described in Section II,A (Steinert et al., 1983, 1984b, 1985a,b) and two human cDNA clones (Hanukoglu and Fuchs, 1982, 1983), permitted the formulation of a model for the organization of keratin subunits into different subdomains, depicted in Fig. 7 (Steinert et al., 1985b). All epidermal keratin subunits sequenced to date contain a central α-helical domain of highly conserved size and secondary structure, containing four distinct tracts that can form α-helical coiled coils interrupted by three regions that do not form coiled coils. Comparisons of the α-helical sequences show, however, that they are of two distinct sequence types: acidic keratin subunits are type I, and neutral-basic keratin subunits are type II. The presence of several more basic charges in the coiled coil tract 2B of type II keratins probably accounts for the overall charge of type II keratins.

On either side of the central α-helical domain are end domains. The end domains display bilateral symmetry with respect to the central domain and can be divided into subdomains. Type II keratins, but not type I, contain short globular sequences, termed H1 and H2, immediately adjacent to the central domain. These have been conserved in size and sequence. The absence of the H1 and H2 subdomains from type I

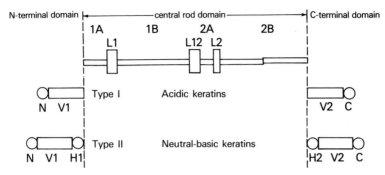

FIG. 7. Schematic diagram of predicted secondary structure of keratin subunits. Keratin subunits contain three distinct domains: a central α-helical domain and non-α-helical domains on each end. Each domain can be further subdivided into subdomains. The central α-helical domain consists of four coiled coil tracts, termed 1A, 1B, 2A, and 2B, drawn as rods, interspersed by three non-coiled-coil linkers, drawn as vertical rectangles. The discontinuity on tract 2B marks the position of the heptad polarity reversal. The end domains each consist of three subdomains: H1 and H2 globular domains on the left and right sides of the central α-helical domain; longer subdomains V1 and V2; and smaller globular subdomains at C and N. Type I keratins are acidic and type II keratins are basic.

keratins is the primary reason for the difference in mass of about 6–9 kDa between type I and type II keratins of a coexpressed pair (e.g., the 59- and 67-kDa keratins coexpressed in differentiated epidermal cells).

The H1 and H2 subdomains are flanked by subdomains V1 and V2 that are highly variable in both length and amino acid sequence. The variability in mass among keratins of a given type (e.g., the 60- and 67-kDa keratins are both type II) appears to reside in the size of their V1 and V2 subdomains. V1 and V2 subdomains often contain peptide repeats that are conspicuously rich in glycines and/or serines. Even though these subdomains tend to vary in sequence, type I and type II keratins that are coexpressed generally have similar V1 and V2 sequences (e.g., the type I and type II keratins expressed in basal cells contain peptide repeats enriched in serines and the type I and type II keratins expressed in differentiated cells contain peptide repeats enriched in glycines). Variations in these end domain sequences in keratins that are expressed at different states of differentiation implicate their involvement in changes in keratin filament properties and function during differentiation and provide an explanation for the differential expression of keratin subunits. It is postulated that the V1 and V2 sequences of the 59- and 67-kDa keratins interact with filaggrin, thought to function as an interfilamentous matrix protein, to form the densely packed tonofilaments observed in terminally differentiating epidermal cells (Steinert *et al.*, 1985b).

At the termini are strongly basic subdomains (N and C, respectively) that are variable in sequence. The unique sequence of the C-terminal residues and their accessible location on the periphery of keratin filaments were exploited to produce antisera that are monospecific for individual keratin subunits (Roop *et al.*, 1984a, 1985).

V. Conclusions

The use of cDNA clones, corresponding to the major keratins synthesized in mouse epidermal cells, to monitor keratin gene expression has established that the expression of specific subsets of keratin genes is highly correlated with the state of differentiation. The nucleotide sequence of these cDNA clones also permitted the deduction of the amino acid sequences for these keratin subunits, which was previously not feasible due to the insolubility of keratin proteins. This sequence information allowed the formulation of a general model for keratin subunit structure and suggested that sequences present within the V1 and V2 subdomains of subunits that are coexpressed during terminal differentiation (i.e., the 59- and 67-kDa keratins) may play important roles in changing the properties and function of filaments that they form. The coordinate induction of expression of these keratin genes at an early stage during terminal differentiation indicates a vital role for keratin filaments in this process. An understanding of the mechanism regulating the expression of keratin genes should ultimately provide insight into the mechanism regulating the normal differentiation process. Toward this end, genomic clones for the 59- and 67-kDa keratins have been isolated and sequenced (Krieg *et al.*, 1985; Johnson *et al.*, 1985). These sequences are currently being analyzed to determine if they contain common regulatory sequences. The ability to modulate the expression of keratin genes in vaginal epithelium by both estrogen and vitamin A should facilitate the identification of factors which regulate their expression.

ACKNOWLEDGMENTS

I would like to thank my colleagues for their contributions to the work presented: Peter Steinert, Stuart Yuspa, Rune Toftgard, Thomas Krieg, John Stanley, Jim Clark, Mark Kronenberg, and Freesia Huang. I would also like to thank Christina Cheng for excellent technical assistance.

REFERENCES

Baden, H. P., and Lee, L. D. (1978). *J. Invest. Dermatol.* **71**, 148–151.
Banks-Schlegel, S. P. (1982). *J. Cell Biol.* **91**, 551–559.

Baumann, C. A., and Steenbock, H. (1932). *Science* **76**, 417–420.

Bowden, P. E., Quinlan, R. A., Breitkreutz, D., and Fusenig, N. E. (1984). *Eur. J. Biochem.* **142**, 29–36.

Dale, B. A., and Stern, E. B. (1975). *J. Invest. Dermatol.* **65**, 223–227.

Doran, T. I., Vidrich, A., and Sun, T.-T. (1980). *Cell* **22**, 17–25.

Eichner, R., Bonitz, P., and Sun, T.-T. (1984). *J. Cell Biol.* **98**, 1388–1396.

Fuchs, E., and Green, H. (1980). *Cell* **19**, 1033–1042.

Fuchs, E., and Green, H. (1981). *Cell* **25**, 617–625.

Fuchs, E., and Hanukoglu, I. (1983). *Cell* **34**, 332–334.

Hanukoglu, I., and Fuchs, E. (1982). *Cell* **31**, 243–252.

Hanukoglu, I., and Fuchs, E. (1983). *Cell* **33**, 915–924.

Harper, M. E., Marselle, L. M., Gallo, R. C., and Wong-Staal, F. (1986). *Proc. Natl. Acad. Sci. U.S.A.* **83**, 772–776.

Johnson, L. D., Idler, W. W., Zhou, X.-M. Roop, D. R., and Steinert, P. M. (1985). *Proc. Natl. Acad. Sci. U.S.A.* **82**, 1896–1900.

Kahn, R. H., and Bern, H. A. (1950). *Science* **111**, 516–517.

Krieg, T. M., Schafer, M. P., Cheng, C. K., Fipula, D., Flaherty, P., Steinert, P. M., and Roop, D. R. (1985). *J. Biol. Chem.* **260**, 5867–5870.

Lazarides, E. (1980). *Nature (London)* **283**, 249–256.

Long, J. A., and Evans, H. M. (1922). *Mem. Univ. Calif.* **6**, 1–148.

Moll, R., Franke, W. W., Schiller, D. L., Geiger, B., and Krepler, R. (1982). *Cell* **31**, 11–24.

Peckham, B., and Kiekhofer (1962). *Am. J. Obstet. Gynecol.* **83**, 1021–1027.

Roop, D. R., Hawley-Nelson, P., Cheng, C. K., and Yuspa, S. H. (1983). *Proc. Natl. Acad. Sci. U.S.A.* **80**, 716–720.

Roop, D. R., Cheng, C. K., Titterington, L., Meyers, C. A., Stanley, J. R., Steinert, P. M., and Yuspa, S. H. (1984a). *J. Biol. Chem.* **259**, 8037–8040.

Roop, D. R., Toftgard, R., Yuspa, S. H., Kronenberg, M. S., and Clark, J. H. (1984b). *In* "Molecular Biology of the Cytoskeleton" (G. G. Borisy, D. W. Cleveland, and D. B. Murphy, eds.), pp. 409–414. Cold Spring Harbor Laboratory, Cold Spring Harbor, New York.

Roop, D. R., Cheng, C. K., Toftgand, R., Stanley, J. R., Steinert, P. M., and Yuspa, S. H. (1985). *Ann. N.Y. Acad. Sci.* **455**, 426–435.

Schweizer, J., and Winter, H. (1982). *Biochim. Biophys. Acta* **537**, 474–484.

Skerrow, D., and Hauter, I. (1978). *Biochim. Biophys. Aeta* **537**, 474–484.

Steinert, P. M. (1982). *In* "Electron Microscopy of Proteins" (J. R. Harris, ed.), Vol. 1, pp. 125–166. Academic Press, London.

Steinert, P. M., and Yuspa, S. H. (1978). *Science* **200**, 1491–1493.

Steinert, P. M., Rice, R. H., Roop, D. R., Trus, B. L., and Steven, A. C. (1983). *Nature (London)* **302**, 794–800.

Steinert, P. M., Jones, J. C. A., and Goldman, R. D. (1984a). *J. Cell Biol.* **99**, 22s–27s.

Steinert, P. M., Parry, D. A. D., Racoosin, E. L., Idler, W. W., Steven, A. C., Trus, B. L., and Roop, D. R. (1984b). *Proc. Natl. Acad. Sci. U.S.A.* **81**, 5709–5713.

Steinert, P. M., Idler, W. W., Zhou, X.-M., Johnson, L. D., Parry, D. A. D., Steven, A. C., and Roop, D. R. (1985a). *Ann. N. Y. Acad. Sci.* **455**, 451–461.

Steinert, P. M., Parry, D. A. D., Idler, W. W., Johnson, L. D., Steven, A. C., and Roop, D. R. (1985b). *J. Biol. Chem.* **260**, 7142–7149.

Sun, T.-T., and Green, H. (1978). *J. Biol. Chem.* **253**, 2053–2060.

Yuspa, S. H., Hawley-Nelson, P., Stanley, J. R., and Hennings, H. (1980). *Transplant. Proc.* **12** (Suppl. 1), 114–122.

CHAPTER 10

ABNORMAL DEVELOPMENT IN THE SKIN OF THE PUPOID FETUS (pf/pf) MUTANT MOUSE: ABNORMAL KERATINIZATION, RECOVERY OF A NORMAL PHENOTYPE, AND RELATIONSHIP TO THE REPEATED EPILATION (Er/Er) MUTANT MOUSE

Chris Fisher

DEPARTMENT OF BIOLOGICAL STRUCTURE
UNIVERSITY OF WASHINGTON
SCHOOL OF MEDICINE
SEATTLE, WASHINGTON 98195

I. Introduction

The skin has proved to be an excellent organ in which to study various aspects of embryonic development. It is easy to obtain in large quantities, even at early stages of development. The two tissues of skin, the epidermis and the dermis, are easily separated, manipulated, cultured, and grafted. In addition, the epidermis, the epithelial component of skin, undergoes an orderly sequence of proliferation, stratification, and terminal differentiation. The complex process of terminal differentiation involves the coordinated synthesis, in the proper epidermal strata, of a battery of proteins including, among others, the keratins (Fuchs and Green, 1980), the proteins of keratohyalin (Matoltsy and Matoltsy, 1970; Fukuyama and Epstein, 1973, 1975), and involucrin (Rice and Green, 1977). This chapter will discuss an important aspect of epidermal differentiation, keratinization, as it relates to the abnormal development of the pupoid fetus (*pf/pf*) mutant mouse.

A. NORMAL EPIDERMAL DEVELOPMENT AND KERATINIZATION IN MICE

Between 12 and 13 days of development (DuBrul, 1972), the normal epidermis of the mouse stratifies from a single, cuboidal cell layer into a multilayered epithelium. At 13–14 days of development the normal murine epidermis is three to four cell layers thick and has a well-defined dermal–epidermal junction (DEJ) (Fig. 1). These properties,

209

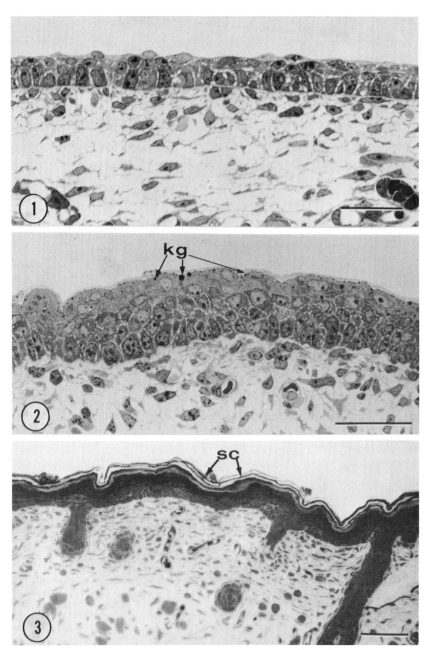

FIG. 1. The epidermis of 14 days gestation normal mice is even in thickness, with three to four cell layers and a well-defined DEJ. Bar, 50 μm.

FIG. 2. The 16 day normal epidermis is five to six cell layers thick. The DEJ is well defined and keratohyalin granules (kg) are just beginning to appear. Bar, 50 μm.

FIG. 3. The newborn epidermis has well-developed hair follicles and well-formed granular and cornified (sc) layers. Bar, 50 μm. (From Fisher and Kollar, 1985; reproduced with permission of The Company of Biologists Limited.)

even thickness and well-defined DEJ, are maintained throughout the course of development. Formation of the granular layer occurs at 16 days gestation (Fig. 2; Fisher *et al.*, 1984), and formation of the stratum corneum at 18 days gestation, so that at birth (Fig. 3) the normal epidermis is well keratinized and ~50 μm thick. The regulation of this complex and orderly process is poorly understood. It is clear, however, that the developing epidermis, in order to form a continuous, functional adult epithelium that is capable of withstanding environmental stress, must resist innervation and vascularization. Epidermal development must also ensure that proper tissue polarity is established so that a proliferating basal cell layer will form and give rise to differentiating cells that stratify outward from the DEJ.

The process of keratinization involves the coordinated synthesis of proteins that compose the keratin intermediate filaments and keratohyalin granules, and the assembly of these components into a complex that forms the bulk of the stratum corneum. In the lower layers of the stratum corneum this complex has the typical ultrastructural "keratin pattern" (Brody, 1959; Matoltsy and Parakkal, 1967) of keratin filaments embedded in a dense matrix derived from keratohyalin protein. The keratin filaments are formed from a family of proteins (Franke *et al.*, 1981; Green *et al.*, 1981), while the major matrix protein is filaggrin (Dale, 1977; Steinert *et al.*, 1981).

The dorsal epidermis of the newborn mouse contains seven to eight major keratin polypeptides (Schweizer and Winter, 1982a; Schweizer *et al.*, 1984; Breitkrutz *et al.*, 1984). The synthesis of these proteins is regulated such that as cells move from the basal layer through the suprabasal compartment, different members of the keratin family are synthesized (Fuchs and Green, 1980; Schweizer *et al.*, 1984). In addition, it has been demonstrated (Breitkrutz *et al.*, 1984; Bowden *et al.*, 1984) that the major murine epidermal keratins can be further divided into the keratins of the living layers (67, 60, 58, and 53 kDa) and the disulfide cross-linked keratins of the dead, horny layers (64, 62, 58.5, and 57.5 kDa). Since these proteins arise from processing during the granular cell–cornified cell transition (Schweizer and Winter, 1982a; Breitkrutz *et al.*, 1984; Bowden *et al.*, 1984), they serve as excellent markers of keratinization.

Keratin expression is also regulated developmentally (Schweizer and Winter, 1982b). The most notable change in keratin expression affects the 64- and 62-kDa keratins. These keratins are not expressed before 17 days of development. However, between 17 and 18 days, concomitant with the appearance of the stratum corneum, these keratins appear. By 19 days of development the epidermal keratin polypeptide pattern resembles the neonatal pattern.

Filaggrin is the best characterized intermediate filament-associated protein. In the mouse it is a 27-kDa, histidine-rich protein (Steinert *et al.*, 1981) that is synthesized in a series of proteolytic steps from higher molecular weight precursors (profilaggrin) (Ball *et al.*, 1978; Resing *et al.*, 1984). Profilaggrin is found in keratohyalin granules in a highly phosphorylated condition and it is thought that the conversion of profilaggrin to filaggrin depends on a dephosphorylation step (Lonsdale-Eccles *et al.*, 1982). Filaggrin is first detected biochemically (Balmain *et al.*, 1977) and immunofluorescently (Fisher, unpublished observation) in mouse skin at 16 days of development, the period of keratohyalin granule formation (Fig. 2).

Filaggrin and the stratum corneum keratins are excellent markers for two crucial stages of epidermal maturation, granular layer formation and stratum corneum formation. Indeed, normal keratinization is certainly not possible in the absence of either set of proteins, and the synthesis of both families of proteins must be coordinately regulated, both during development and in adulthood. While much information regarding the molecular aspects of keratinization has recently appeared, still little is known of the developmental processes regulating keratinization. For instance, it is well established that the dermis directs the fate of the epidermis during development in birds (for reviews see Sengel, 1976; Shames and Sawyer, this volume) and mammals (Kollar, 1966, 1970). It is equally well known that the dermis, with its extracellular matrix, plays an important role in the developmental regulation of such diverse epidermal cell processes as proliferation (McGloughlin, 1961a,b; Briggaman and Wheeler, 1968), stratification (Saywer, 1975; Lillie *et al.*, 1982), and basal lamina deposition (Briggaman *et al.*, 1971; Hirone and Taniguchi, 1980), which in turn may have profound effects on epidermal cell metabolism and keratinization. These observations, however, remain phenomenological, as the nature of the influence has yet to be determined. How communication between cells and tissues regulates development and differentiation remains one of the most confounding and important problem facing the developmental biologist.

B. Keratinization as Studied with Genetic Variants of Mice

One approach to elucidating factors important in the regulation of epidermal differentiation is to identify genetic variants in which differentiation is abnormal. The ultimate goal, of course, is to identify the abnormal gene products responsible for the developmental abnormality. The events between abnormal gene expression and the development of the morphologically identifiable defect can then be established. Insights into the regulation of normal development and differentiation can be extrapolated from such findings.

There are many mutations of the mouse that affect epidermal differentiation. The great majority of these mutations affect hair development and in all but one (hairless, as referenced by Billingham and Silvers, 1973) expression of the mutant gene has been localized to the epidermis (for review see Briggaman, 1981). Mutations resulting in a failure of keratinization are much rarer, perhaps due to the disastrous consequences of affecting such a fundamental process. Recently, however, an autosomal recessive mutation of the mouse resulting in a complete failure of terminal differentiation of the epidermis was described (Fisher *et al.*, 1984).

This chapter will decribe various aspects of the abnormal development and keratinization of the pupoid fetus (*pf/pf*) mutant skin. Both morphological and biochemical abnormalities of the *pf/pf* epidermis will be described, efforts to localize the site of mutant gene expression will be discussed, and our attempts to understand the shortcomings of embryonic regulation that cause the abnormalities will be reported. In addition, the similarities between the *pf* mutation and the related repeated epilation (*Er*) mutation of the mouse will be explored. All studies were conducted with back skin unless otherwise indicated.

II. Abnormal Development and Keratinization of the Epidermis of Pupoid Fetus (*pf/pf*) Mutant Mice

A. INVASION OF THE MUTANT EPIDERMIS BY CELLS FROM THE DERMIS

1. Identification of Members of the Invading Cell Population

The pupoid fetus (*pf/pf*) mutation results in a markedly thickened, unkeratinized epidermis and affects other epithelia of ectodermal origin as well (e.g., oral epithelia; see Kollar, 1983). Abnormalities in the *pf/pf* epidermis are first noted during the period of transition from a simple to a multilayered epithelium. In the *pf/pf* mutant this transition occurs abnormally so that at 13–14 days of development the *pf/pf* epidermis may have between 1 and 10 cell layers (Fisher *et al.*, 1984; Fisher and Kollar, 1985). Subsequent to this abnormal epidermal behavior, as early as 14 days of development, striking abnormalities are noted in the dermis (Fig. 4). Cells crowd beneath the epidermis, obscuring the DEJ. These cells are polarized and are aligned perpendicular to the plane of the epidermis in a manner that suggests they are oriented by, and moving toward, the epidermis. The ultrastructure of the DEJ

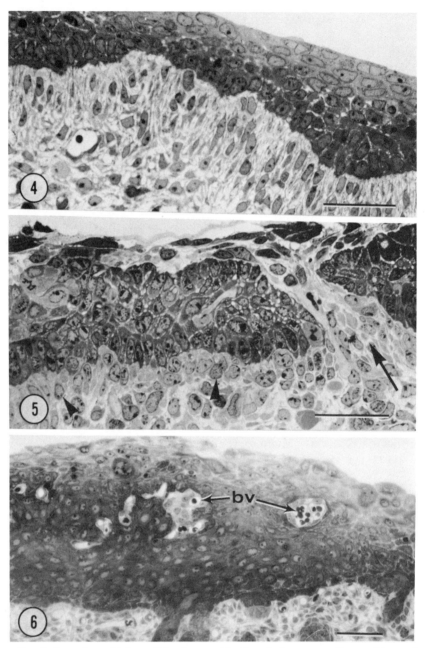

Fig. 4. As early as 14 days of development in the *pf/pf* mutant, cells crowd beneath the DEJ in a manner that suggests they are oriented by the epidermis. The epidermis is already variable in thickness and hyperplastic. Bar, 50 μm.

Fig. 5. By 16 days cells from the dermis may be found extending through the *pf/pf* mutant epidermis (arrow) and lying upon its surface. Dermal cells (arrowheads) are found crowding beneath the epidermis obscuring the DEJ. Keratohyalin granules have

shows that processes of these cells approach and sometimes contact the basal lamina, but penetration of individual cells into the epidermis has not been noted (Fisher and Kollar, 1985).

By 15 days of development, dermal cells extend into and through the mutant epidermis and spread out on its surface (Fig. 5; Fisher *et al.*, 1984; Fisher and Kollar, 1985). This invading cell population becomes established throughout the mutant epidermis, so that by the time of birth, the mutant epidermis is tremendously thickened and permeated throughout by a network of cells that is continuous with the dermis. In addition, the mutant epidermis fails to keratinize.

Blood vessels extend throughout the newborn mutant epidermis (Fig. 6). It is surmised that endothelial cells are among the invading cells at 15–16 days of development, although it is possible that they migrate in later. Ultrastructural and immunofluorescence observations (Fisher *et al.*, 1984; Fisher and Kollar, 1985) have helped identify several other members of the invading cell population. Collagen fibers and fibronectin are observed along with the ectopic cells at 15–16 days of development, indicating that fibroblasts are also among these cells. Finally, ultrastructural observations demonstrate that nerve fibers and Schwann cells are among the first cells entering the mutant epidermis. Watson and Ede (1977) suggested that nerve fibers and/or Schwann cells are the primary target of the *pf* gene; however our observations and experiments have been unable to demonstrate a vanguard cell type leading the invasion of the *pf/pf* epidermis. Nerve fibers and associated cells are certainly identified among the invading cell population, but other cells, fibroblasts and probably migrating endothelial cells, are also present in this population.

During normal development the integrity of the epidermis is faithfully maintained. A basal lamina separates the epidermis from the underlying dermis and only a select few immigrant cell types (Langerhans cells, Merkel cells, and melanocytes) transverse this structure to enter the epidermis. Endothelial cells, nerve fibers, and fibroblasts, in spite of their prevalence in the dermis, are excluded. The *pf/pf* mutant epidermis appears to have lost the ability to exclude these dermal cells. The nature of the defect that results in the loss of the ability to selectively exclude cell entry into the mutant epidermis is unknown. A lack of epidermal cell adhesiveness, a defective basement membrane, defective regulation of protease synthesis, or an ag-

---

not formed. Bar, 50 μm. (From Fisher and Kollar, 1985; reproduced with permission of The Company of Biologists Limited.)

FIG. 6. The newborn *pf/pf* mutant epidermis is greatly thickened and undifferentiated. A network of cells including blood vessels (bv) extends throughout the mutant epidermis. Bar, 50 μm.

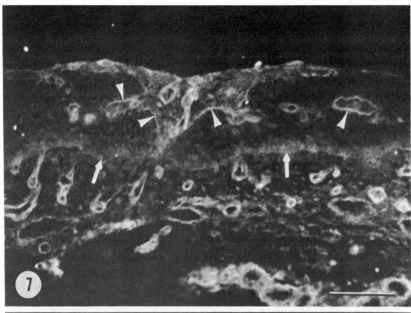

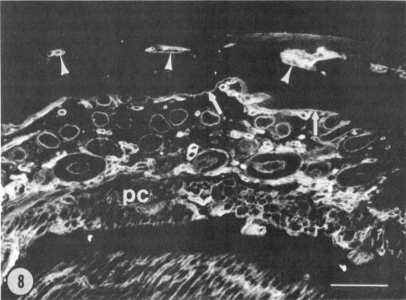

Fig. 7. Indirect immunofluorescence localization of anti-laminin binding in 16 day *pf/pf* epidermis highlights the DEJ (arrows) as well as the interface of the invading cell population and the mutant epidermis (arrowheads). Bar, 50 μm. (Anti-laminin was provided by Dr. Hinda Kleinman, National Institutes of Health.)

Fig. 8. Immunofluorescence localization of anti-type IV collagen binding in the newborn mutant epidermis reveals binding to the basal lamina at the DEJ (arrows) as well as to the basal lamina that is deposited wherever the network of dermal cells meets the

gressive, invasive cell type from the dermis are all possible candidates. The unusual dermal cell alignment at the DEJ at 14–15 days of development (Fig. 4) suggests they are attracted by the epidermis. Since the defect is first detectable at the onset of epidermal stratification, this process may be the one that is primarily affected by the *pf* gene. Finally, as early as 13–14 days of development degenerating epidermal cells may be found in the thinnest areas of the mutant epidermis (Fisher and Kollar, 1985). These may be areas through which dermal cells enter the mutant epidermis; however, direct evidence for this is lacking.

2. Local Response of the Mutant Epidermis to Dermal Components

The distribution of two major components of the basal lamina, laminin and type IV collagen, have been established in the developing *pf/pf* mutant skin (Fisher and Kollar, 1985). In all cases examined these antigens were recognized at the interface between the epidermal cells and the invading cell population. At 15–16 days of development laminin was found at the DEJ, and wherever the invading cell population contacted the mutant epidermis (Fig. 7). Even the most superficial cells of the mutant epidermis were found to deposit a basal lamina wherever they contacted the ectopic cell population. The newborn mutant skin had a similar distribution of basal lamina antigens. Laminin and type IV collagen were found deposited wherever the network of ectopic dermal cells contacted the epidermis (Fig. 8). The basal laminae of blood vessels and nerves are often highlighted in these areas. These findings have been confirmed by ultrastructural observations; an ultrastructurally normal basal lamina was consistently found at the interface of the invading cell population and the epidermis (Fisher *et al.*, 1984; Fisher and Kollar, 1985).

Thus it appears that a local epidermal cell reaction occurs as the ectopic, invading cells enter the mutant epidermis at 15–16 days of development. It is generally accepted that as cells depart the basal cell layer they become committed to terminal differentiation (Green, 1980; Watt, 1984). For this reason it is surprising to find cells synthesizing a basal lamina in the outermost aspects of the mutant epidermis (Figs. 7 and 8; Fisher and Kollar, 1985). It is likely that these cells have other properties of basal cells (e.g. expression of basal cell specific keratins) as well. An important question raised by this observation concerns

---

mutant epidermis. The basal lamina of blood vessels is also highlighted in these areas. The subcutaneous panniculus carnosus (pc) muscle and numerous hair follicles and vessels in the dermis are also delineated by anti-type IV binding. Bar, 100 μm. (Anti-type IV collagen was provided by Dr. George Martin, National Institutes of Health.)

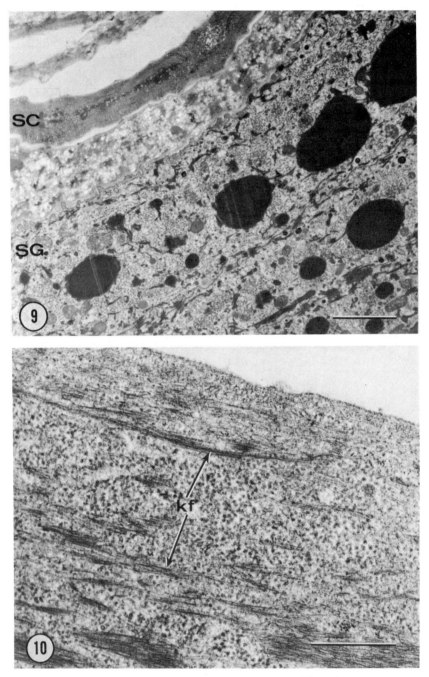

Fɪɢ. 9. Electron micrograph of the stratum granulosum (SG) and stratum corneum (SC) of a normal newborn mouse. The stratum granulosum has keratohyalin granules and dense bundles of keratin filaments, and the stratum corneum displays the typical

whether suprabasal cells revert to basal cells when the invading cell population is encountered, or whether basal cells are merely pushed into the mutant epidermis ahead of the invading front of cells. Knowing that the dermis and the dermal extracellular matrix strongly influence the epidermis, it is not unreasonable to suggest that an outwardly migrating epidermal cell, particularly an embryonic cell, would revert to a basal cell phenotype when the ectopic dermal cells are encountered.

The invasion of dermal cells undoubtedly contributes to the thickening of the mutant epidermis. The abnormal architecture of the mutant epidermis, with the apparent enrichment of basal cells, probably contributes to an increase in the number of cells in the proliferating cell population. In addition, hyperplasia, resulting from the insult of epidermal invasion, probably leads to an increased mitotic activity. Finally, the failure of terminal differentiation no doubt increases the total number of viable cells in the mutant epidermis since no cells are dying and sloughing.

B. ABNORMAL KERATINIZATION

1. Light and Electron Microscopy Studies

A comparison of newborn normal skin to newborn *pf/pf* mutant skin reveals striking differences in epidermal differentiation. Normal epidermis is ~50 μm thick with prominent granular and cornified layers (Fig. 3). Ultrastructurally, dense bundles of keratin filaments are present in the granular cells, and the keratin filaments of the stratum corneum are associated with a dense, interfilamentous matrix (Fig. 9). The newborn *pf/pf* epidermis, in contrast, is hyperplastic and, while it varies greatly in thickness, is often five- to sevenfold thicker than the normal newborn epidermis (Fig. 6). In addition, the newborn *pf/pf* epidermis completely lacks a stratum corneum. The most superficial cells of the newborn mutant epidermis contain abundant keratin filaments, but these do not occur in dense bundles and are not associated with electron-dense material (Fig. 10; Fisher *et al.*, 1984). Other hallmarks of differentiation, such as lamellar granules and cornified cell envelopes, are also missing from these cells.

"keratin pattern" of filaments embedded in an electron-dense matrix. Bar, 2 μm. (From Fisher *et al.*, 1984; reproduced with permission of Academic Press.)

    FIG. 10. Electron micrograph of the outermost region of the *pf/pf* newborn epidermis. While abundant keratin filaments are present they are not found in dense bundles or associated with a dense matrix. Bar, 0.5 μm.

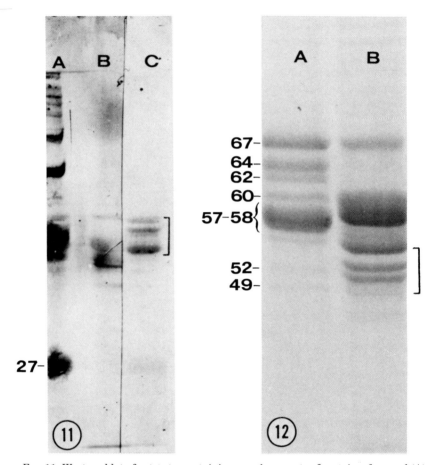

FIG. 11. Western blot of extracts, containing equal amounts of protein, of normal (A) and *pf/pf* mutant (B) epidermis using anti-rat filaggrin. In normal epidermal extracts filaggrin is found in the 27-kDa region, and the higher molecular weight precursors (profilaggrin) are also detected. No filaggrin is detected in the *pf/pf* mutant extracts. Some binding of the antibody occurs in the keratin region (bracket) of the *pf/pf* epidermal extracts (B). However this binding is thought to be nonspecific since similar binding is obtained for blots of extracts of normal epidermis (C) using preimmune serum. (Antibody provided by Dr. Beverly Dale, University of Washington.)

FIG. 12. Coomassie blue-stained SDS–polyacrilamide gel of keratins from normal (A) and *pf/pf* mutant (B) head epidermis. The normal epidermis has approximately eight keratins between 67 and 49 kDa. The mutant epidermal extracts are missing the 64- and 62-kDa keratins and have a prominent band at 60 kDa that is reduced or absent from the extracts of normal epidermis. In addition, the *pf/pf* epidermis has several prominent bands (bracket) between 47 and 54 kDa.

2. Biochemical and Immunofluorescent Observations of Filaggrin and Keratins

Filaggrin migrates to the 27-kDa position upon sodium dodecyl sulfate–polyacrylamide gel electrophoresis (SDS–PAGE) of 8 M urea extracts of normal newborn epidermis (Steinert et al., 1981; Holbrook et al., 1982). This band is missing from similar preparations of newborn pf/pf mutant epidermis (Fisher et al., 1984). Profilaggrin is also absent from newborn pf/pf epidermis as determined by the absence of a granular layer, by the failure of the epidermis to bind anti-rat filaggrin antibodies (Fisher et al., 1984), and by immunoblot analysis of 8 M urea extracts of mutant epidermis (Fig. 11). Thus, the failure of the pf/pf mutant epidermis to keratinize is reflected in its deficiency of filaggrin and profilaggrin.

The failure of pf/pf epidermis to keratinize is also reflected in its keratin composition. Keratins of newborn normal and mutant skin were analyzed following exhaustive extraction of the water-insoluble proteins with high-salt buffer, according to a modification of the technique of Schweizer and Winter (1982b). Epidermis was homogenized in a 10 mM Tris–HCl buffer (pH 8.0) containing 1.5 M KCl, 10 mM NaCl, 2 mM dithiothreitol, 0.5% Triton X-100, and 0.5 mM phenylmethylsulfonyl fluoride. The samples were centrifuged, the supernatants were discarded, and the pellets were rehomogenized. The process repeated four times. The keratins were then dissolved from the resulting water-insoluble pellet in a buffer containing 5% SDS, 5% 2-mercaptoethanol, and 10% glycerol, and run on 12% polyacrylamide gels according to Laemmli.

Normal newborn epidermis has the typical keratin electrophoretic profile of eight prominent bands ranging in size from 49 to 68 kDa (Fig. 12; Schweizer and Winter, 1982a,b; Breitkreutz et al., 1984). The keratins of the newborn pf/pf epidermis, on the other hand, vary from the normal epidermal keratins in several respects (Fig. 12): the 64- and 62-kDa keratins are absent, and several prominent keratin bands between 55 and 49 kDa, which are either missing or greatly reduced in the normal newborn epidermis, are present. There are also differences between normal and pf/pf keratins in the poorly resolved region around 60–57 kDa.

A protein that migrates at 60 kDa in extracts of mutant epidermis is missing or reduced in extracts of normal epidermis (Fig. 12). This protein may represent a murine equivalent of the "hyperplastic" keratins that appear in diseased human epidermis (Sun et al., 1983). The differences between the keratins of mutants and normal littermates may be summarized as follows: the 64- and 62-kDa keratins of normal epidermis are missing from mutant epidermis, a 60-kDa epidermal keratin found in mutants is missing from normal littermates, and mutant epidermis appears to accumulate several keratins in the lower molecular weight range.

It is clear that at least three of the four major stratum corneum keratins, the 64-, 62-, and the 57-kDa keratins, are not expressed in the newborn mutant epidermis. Since these keratins are not coded by their own mRNA (Roop *et al.*, 1983; Schweizer *et al.*, 1984), do not incorporate amino acids during short-term incubations (Bladon *et al.*, 1982; Breitkreutz *et al.*, 1984), and are structurally related to the 67- and 58-kDa keratins (Bowden *et al.*, 1984), their absence is most likely due to a failure of posttranslational processing and not to a failure of keratin gene expression. However, degradation has not been ruled out as the reason for the absence of these keratins.

It is unclear whether the accumulation of lower molecular weight keratins (47,000–54,000) in the *pf/pf* epidermis is due to an accumulation of degraded keratins or to an enhanced synthesis of keratins in this molecular weight range. The latter explanation, however, is the more attractive one in that epidermal basal cells and transplantable squamous cell carcinomas synthesize an abundance of keratins of similar molecular weight (Schweizer *et al.*, 1984). Since the mutant epidermis fails to terminally differentiate and is enriched in basal cells due to its unique structure, it may be expected that the keratins of the *pf/pf* mutant would reflect an enhanced basal cell phenotype.

The epidermal keratin profile of the *pf/pf* epidermis is remarkably similar to that of the normal, 16-day embryonic mouse (Schweizer and Winter, 1982b). The *pf/pf* mutant does not produce those keratins associated with the formation of the stratum corneum. The lack of filaggrin production and the absence of morphological markers of differentiation, such as cornified cell envelopes and lamellar granules, also suggest that the *pf/pf* epidermis does not mature past 15–16 days of development. The most attractive hypothesis explaining these abnormalities is that the network of ectopic cells throughout the mutant epidermis, with the abnormal epidermal architecture and polarity that results, suspends the progress of epidermal differentiation. Epidermal processes such as cell movement and proliferation are no doubt affected by the abnormal structure of the *pf/pf* epidermis. In addition, cues that an epidermal cell may normally receive concerning its position in the epidermis, relative to the dermis, would be completely altered in the *pf/pf* epidermis. For instance an epidermal cell may regulate its differentiative state from such diverse environmental cues as substrate properties (Lillie *et al.*, 1982), accommodation of substrate to cell shape change (Emerman *et al.*, 1979), distance from available dermal factors (Wessels, 1962), and oxygen gradients (Taylor *et al.*, 1978). In fact, epidermal differentiation is probably influenced by all of these factors, and others as well. Because of the unusual nature of the *pf/pf* epidermal structure, all of these elements may provide abnormal positional information to epidermal cells.

It is important that tissue architecture not be ignored as an important factor in the process of epithelial differentiation, particularly in light of the demonstrations that tissue (Emerman and Pitelka, 1977) and cell shape (Ben-Ze'ev, 1984) can profoundly influence cell metabolism and pathways of differentiation. Thus, the failure of *pf/pf* mutant epidermis to keratinize could be explained as occurring secondary to other epidermal alterations. Indeed, an important step toward understanding the action of the *pf* gene comes with the realization that, when transplanted to a normal animal, the *pf/pf* epidermis has the potential to differentiate normally (*vide infra*).

III. Localization of Expression of the *pf* Gene

A. Tissue Recombination and Grafting Studies

It is of interest to determine whether the *pf* gene primarily affects keratinization and/or its major products, or whether these defects appear secondary to the expression of the mutation. Furthermore, it is important to identify the tissue(s) in which the *pf* gene is expressed and to determine the developmental stage of expression of the abnormal gene (e.g., expression may be transient) before experiments are initiated to determine the function of the gene. For these reasons, reciprocal heterogenetic tissue recombinations were constructed from the epidermis and dermis of 15 day *pf/pf* mutants and normal littermates, and were grafted to the anterior chamber of the eye of normal adult mice from the *pf* colony (Fisher *et al.*, 1984). In all cases examined, whether mutant dermis was associated with normal epidermis (8 grafts) or normal dermis was associated with mutant epidermis (11 grafts), a keratinizing epidermis was formed. Surprisingly, the control combinations of mutant epidermis and mutant dermis (5 grafts) also formed a normal, keratinizing epidermis complete with stratum granulosum and stratum corneum. These results strongly suggest that the *pf* gene is not expressed in either the epidermis or the dermis. Not only were the heterogenetic tissue recombinations capable of forming an

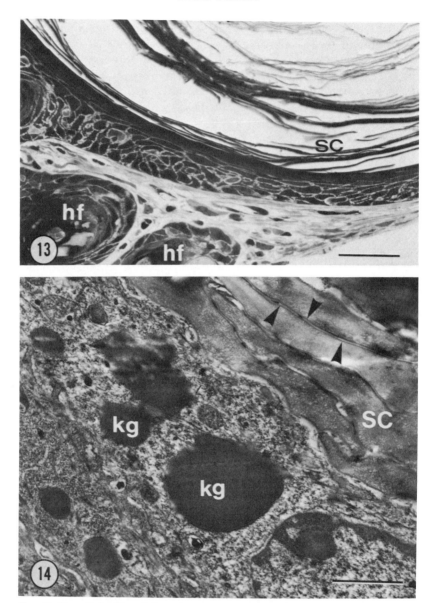

FIG. 13. The *pf/pf* epidermis keratinizes rapidly when grafted to a normal, adult host. A normal granular layer and stratum corneum (SC) form. Well-formed hair follicles (hf) also develop. Bar, 100 μm.

FIG. 14. Electron micrograph of grafted *pf/pf* epidermis. A well-formed granular layer containing well-developed keratohyalin granules (kg) and a well-developed stratum corneum (SC) with a typical "keratin pattern" and cornified cell envelopes (arrowheads) are found in the grafted mutant epidermis. Bar, 1 μm.

organized, histologically normal epidermis, complete with a stratum granulosum and a stratum corneum, but the reconstructed, entirely mutant skin also demonstrated the ability to regain a normal phenotype. Thus, simply removing the mutant skin from the mutant environment by grafting to a normal animal appeared to be enough to reverse the *pf/pf* epidermal phenotype.

B. RECOVERY OF A NORMAL PHENOTYPE

A more extensive grafting study was then initiated in which whole, unmanipulated 14–15 day embryonic *pf/pf* mutant skin was grafted directly to the anterior chamber of the eye or beneath the kidney capsule of normal animals. An identical result was obtained; grafts were found to keratinize normally within 7 days as observed by light (Fig. 13) and electron (Fig. 14) microscopy, and by their ability to bind antibodies directed against filaggrin (Fisher *et al.*, 1984). Grafts of newborn *pf/pf* mutant skin responded similarly (Fisher, unpublished observation). These results indicate that the ability of the *pf/pf* mutant epidermis to keratinize is not primarily affected by the *pf* gene. Therefore, the major proteins of keratinization, filaggrin and the keratins, are not encoded or directly affected by the *pf* gene. The recovery of the ability to bind anti-filaggrin supports this presumption for filaggrin; biochemical evidence for the keratins should be obtained shortly.

There are several interpretations of the grafting data in relation to the site of expression of the *pf* gene. The most attractive interpretation, perhaps because of its simplicity, is that the *pf* gene is expressed systemically. Removal of the *pf/pf* mutant skin from the mutant environment, by grafting to a normal animal, results in normal keratinization. Systemic factors, e.g., epidermal growth factor, can have profound influence on epidermal growth and proliferation (Cohen, 1965) as well as on keratinization (Cohen and Elliot, 1963). It is easy to imagine that a systemic factor could be affected by the *pf* gene resulting in subsequent epidermal defects.

The grafting studies also suggest alternative explanations. The *pf* gene may be expressed transiently at 13–15 days of development, allowing invasion of the epidermis to occur. Once the invasion was complete, the blood vessels that accompanied the invading cells would help to anchor and nourish the dermal cell population in the epidermis. In this scheme the failure of keratinization would then occur secondary to the various affects the foreign cells exert on epidermal physiology. The process of grafting, however, would effectively bypass the critical period of epidermal invasion. If the grafting was performed during the period of invasion (14–16 days), the period would have ended by the time the graft healed, and linkage with the host vasculature would be impossible. If grafting occurred after the critical invasion period (17 days to birth), the foreign cells would be cut off from their blood supply, and would die and slough. Further invasion would be impossible since the critical period would be over, and normal keratinization would then be observed. Thus, in this scheme, abnormal keratinization is directly dependent on the presence of the ectopic cell population.

The interactions that occur between tissues during development may be conveniently divided into two categories: instructive and permissive (Saxen, 1977). Instructive interactions actually determine the course of development and differentiation of a tissue, while permissive interactions provide the proper environment so that the normal course of differentiation may proceed. It is clear that the *pf/pf* epidermis has been exposed to the appropriate instructive influences during the course of its development. Not only does the *pf/pf* epidermis express epidermal-specific keratins (e.g., 67-kDa keratin) and form hair follicles, but it also has the capacity to rapidly keratinize when grafted to a normal animal. Thus the *pf/pf* epidermis is lacking an environment that is permissive for keratinization, and the nonpermissive conditions are overcome by merely grafting to a normal environment.

Development occurs as a cascade of events from the moment of fertilization through organogenesis. Developmental events are influenced by events that precede them and affect events that follow them. It is not surprising, then, that the abnormalities of keratinization in the *pf/pf* mutant occur secondary to the action of the *pf* gene. Our studies illustrate the dependence of a fundamental process, keratinization, on the developmental history of the tissue. In addition, study of the *pf/pf* mutant may lead to insights into the roles of tissue architecture and dermal–epidermal interactions in the regulation of epidermal differentiation. The contribution of molecular biology to our understanding of epidermal differentiation cannot be denied. However, we must be reasonable in our expectations of this technology. When all of the keratin genes are cloned and sequenced and all of the regulatory sequences identified, we will still need to explain how expression of these genes is developmentally regulated. We must identify when and where the developmentally significant cell and tissue interactions are occurring, and how the information from these interactions is coded and transduced so that the appropriate genes are eventually expressed. Our understanding of development, either normal or abnormal, will remain grossly inadequate until we come to understand such phenomena.

IV. The Relationship of the Pupoid Fetus (*pf*) Mutation to the Repeated Epilation (*Er*) Mutation of the Mouse

A. COMPARATIVE EFFECTS OF THE *pf* AND *Er* GENES ON KERATINIZATION

The *Er* mutation of the mouse behaves as an autosomal, semidominant gene (Hunsicker, 1960). Animals homozygous for the repeated epilation mutation (*Er/Er*), like the *pf/pf* mutants, die at birth. Heterozygotes, unlike the *pf* heterozygotes, undergo repeated periods of hair loss and regrowth. There are many phenotypic similarities between *Er/Er* mutant and *pf/pf* mutant mice. Both animals are cocooned in a smooth, stretched skin which appears to restrict limb outgrowth and cause adhesion of limbs to the body wall (Meredith, 1964; Guenet *et al.,* 1979; Holbrook *et al.,* 1982). In addition, abnormal craniofacial development, including abnormal vibrissae development and fusion of epithelia of the oral cavity and of the eye, occurs in both *pf/pf* and *Er/Er* mice (Guenet *et al.,* 1979; Holbrook *et al.,* 1982; Kollar, 1983; Tassin *et al.,* 1983). These abnormalities give the two different mutants a nearly identical gross appearance.

Of particular interest are the similar effects of the *pf* and *Er* genes on epidermal development. Not only are the initial phases of abnormal gene expression alike, but abnormal epidermal keratinization is very similar in both mutants. Like the *pf/pf* mutant, the onset of abnormal epidermal development in the *Er/Er* mouse occurs at 12–13 days of development (Holbrook *et al.,* 1982; Salzgeber and Guenet, 1984). This is the period of transition from a simple epithelium to a multilayered epidermis. During this period the *Er/Er* epidermis stratifies abnormally, varying between two and eight cell layers (Holbrook *et al.,* 1982). The *Er/Er* mutant subsequently develops a disorganized, hyperplastic epidermis that is variable in thickness and fails to keratinize by birth (Fig. 15; Holbrook *et al.,* 1982), again like the *pf/pf* mutant.

The 18 day *Er/Er* epidermis has an abnormal, discontinuous granular layer of variable thickness that lies just beneath the outermost epidermal cells (Fig. 15; Holbrook *et al.,* 1982). This finding is in contrast to the *pf/pf* mutant which forms only sparse, small keratohyalin granules that, when present, usually lie three to five cell layers above the dermal/epidermal junction (compare Figs. 15 and 6). Nevertheless, like the *pf/pf* mutant, *Er* homozygotes do not form a stratum corneum (Fig. 16; Holbrook *et al.,* 1982) even though a few, isolated cornified cells may be found in various positions among the granular and spinous cells of the *Er/Er* epidermis.

The similarity between *pf/pf* and *Er/Er* mutants is reflected in the

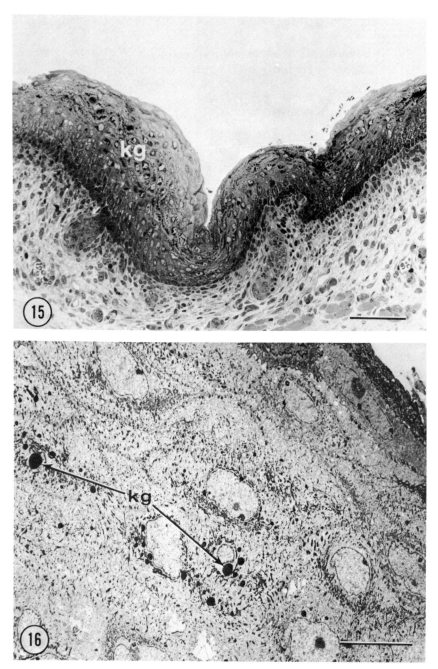

FIG. 15. Newborn *Er/Er* mutant epidermis is thickened and has a hyperplastic granular layer containing keratohyalin granules (kg) that may extend to the outermost aspects of the epidermis. A stratum corneum is not detected. Bar, 100 μm. (Micrograph courtesy of Dr. Karen A. Holbrook, University of Washington.)

biochemical composition of the epidermis as well. SDS–PAGE of whole epidermal extracts of *pf/pf* epidermis (Fisher *et al.*, 1984) and *Er/Er* epidermis (Holbrook *et al.*, 1982) are virtually identical. Not only do both mutants lack the filaggrin band, but they also have prominent bands in the low molecular weight (40,000–55,000) keratin region. These bands in 18 day *Er/Er* epidermis are probably keratins, as they are in the *pf/pf* mutant (Fig. 12). Finally, the 64- and 62-kDa stratum corneum keratins are missing from the 18 day *Er/Er* epidermis, just as they are from the *pf/pf* epidermis, reflecting the undifferentiated nature of the *Er/Er* epidermis.

An apparent difference between the two mutants occurs in filaggrin synthesis and metabolism (Holbrook *et al.*, 1982; Fisher *et al.*, 1984). The 18 day *Er/Er* epidermis binds anti-filaggrin much better than does *pf/pf* epidermis. Immunoblot analysis of extracts of *Er/Er* epidermis reveals the absence of filaggrin but an accumulation of profilaggrin, a result suggesting that the lack of filaggrin is due to a failure of posttranslational processing of profilaggrin. Immunoblot analysis of *pf/pf* epidermal extracts, in contrast, fails to detect significant amounts of filaggrin and profilaggrin (Fig. 11), indicating that net synthesis of filaggrin, and its precursors, is greatly diminished. Thus, in terms of filaggrin production, both the *Er/Er* and *pf/pf* epidermis respond to their mutant environments in similar, yet different, fashions; similar because net filaggrin production is diminished in both mutants, and different because this same end is achieved by unique means.

Er/Er skin is also similar to *pf/pf* skin in its response to grafting to a normal animal. Preliminary results indicate that newborn *Er/Er* epidermis will keratinize normally, as determined by light (Fig. 17) and electron (Fig. 18) microscopy, when grafted to the anterior chamber of the eye of a normal host. Thus, as in the case of the *pf/pf* mutant, these results suggest that the local epidermal environment of the *Er/Er* mutant is not permissive for keratinization.

B. ARE THE *pf* AND *Er* GENES ALLELES?

The *pf* (Green, 1982) and *Er* (Eicher and Fox, 1978) mutations have been mapped to the same region of chromosome 4, strongly suggesting a close relationship between these genes. Interestingly, preliminary data suggest that the *pf* and *Er* genes are not alleles. Three crosses

FIG. 16. Electron micrograph of the newborn *Er/Er* mutant epidermis showing keratohyalin granules (kg) and dense bundles of keratin filaments. However, a stratum corneum does not form. Dense, nucleated, uncornified cells may be found on the surface of the epidermis. Bar, 10 μm. (Micrograph courtesy of Karen A. Holbrook.)

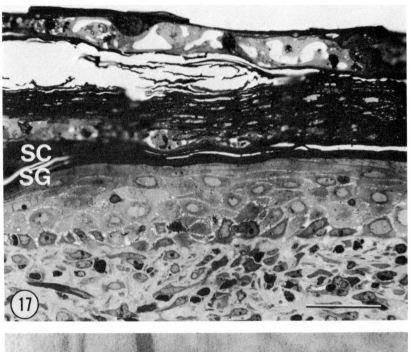

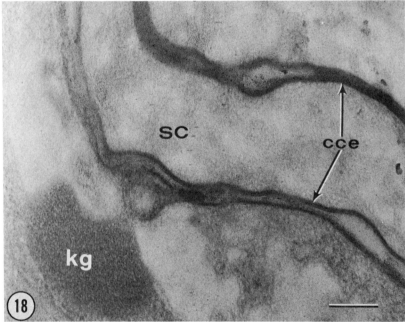

FIG. 17. Newborn *Er/Er* mutant skin grafted to the anterior chamber of the eye of an adult host for 13 days. The normal appearing epidermis has formed a well-developed stratum granulosum (SG) and stratum corneum (SC). Bar, 50 μm.

between $pf/+$ and $Er/+$ animals yielded no identifiable homozygotes. Litter sizes were normal and, in one case, the litter was examined at 15 days of gestation and no signs of resorption were noted. Although these data are preliminary they strongly suggest that the pf and Er genes are not alleles. Further allelism tests should confirm these findings.

The extent of the relationship between these genes is still unclear. It is certain, however, that these genes are related by their similar, powerful effects on tissues of ectodermal origin, and by their location on chromosome 4 of the mouse. By understanding more of the relationship between these genes, and by comparing their abnormal effects on epithelial differentiation, we hope to gain insight into how the corresponding normal genes participate in the regulation of epithelial differentiation.

V. Prospects for the Future

The pf/pf epidermal keratins should be examined immunohistochemically. In this way keratin expression can be studied relative to epidermal architecture. The basal cell-specific keratins should be examined to determine if they colocalize with the basal lamina secreting epidermal cells. By examining these and other markers in this way it can be determined if epidermal cells mature as cells move away from the ectopic dermal cells in the mutant epidermis.

The relationship of the pf and Er genes should be explored further. The similarities and differences of the effects of these genes on keratinization must be reconciled with their different influences upon epidermal structure. In addition, the nature of the allelic relationship of these genes must be confirmed. More complimentation tests should solidify the preliminary data indicating that these genes are non-allelic. In addition, with the appearance of a cDNA probe to a gene localized on mouse chromosome 4, it will be possible to directly assay the structure of these two genes in genomic DNA blots. The genetic structure of the t haplotypes of mouse chromosome 17 has already been analyzed in such a manner using cDNA probes to H-2 class I genes (Shin *et al.*, 1982).

The early events in the development of the abnormal phenotype of the pf mutant need to be examined. The abnormal stratification of the epidermis at 13–14 days of development and the subsequent invasion

---

FIG. 18. Electron micrograph of grafted Er/Er mutant skin. A normal stratum corneum (SC) that displays a typical "keratin pattern" and cornified cell envelopes (cce) has formed. Keratohyalin granules (kg) are found in the stratum granulosum. Bar, 0.2 μm.

of the mutant epidermis should be examined in greater detail. The mutant epidermis should be tested for chemotrophic activity for a variety of embryonic cell types, and also should be assayed for its ability to elicit angiogenesis. Conversely, the proteolytic activity of the dermal cells of the mutant should be tested during the period of active epidermal invasion. Plasminogen activator and collagenase activities, two enzyme activities associated with capillary endothelial cells and proposed to play an important role during endothelial cell invasion of tissues (Gross *et al.*, 1982), are proteases that may play an important role in the etiology of the *pf/pf* mutant phenotype. Finally, cell culture studies should be initiated in an effort to identify a *pf/pf* mutant cell population that retains an abnormal phenotype. Once such a mutant cell population is identified, studies can be initiated to identify the abnormal or missing products of the *pf* gene.

Addendum

Significant progress in the study of keratin expression in *pf/pf* and *Er/Er* mutants has been made since this chapter was submitted for publication (Fisher *et al.*, 1986). Briefly, both the *pf/pf* and *Er/Er* mutants show similar abnormalities in keratin processing and expression. Both mutants fail to process the 67-kDa keratin (K1) into the 64- and 62-kDa keratins. Furthermore, the onset of expression of the "differentiation-specific" keratins (67 kDa [K1] and 59 kDa [K 10]) is delayed in both mutants; few suprabasal epidermal cells of 17-days mutants (*pf/pf* or *Er/Er*) express these keratins, while all viable suprabasal epidermal cells of normal littermates accumulate high levels of these keratins. In addition, a pair of keratins (60 kDa [K6] and 50 kDa [K16]) not detected in normal epidermis is found in abundance in the both *pf/pf* and *Er/Er* epidermis. Finally, grafting of either *pf/pf* or *Er/Er* skin for short periods of time results in epidermal keratin electrophoretic profiles that are indistinguishable from those of grafted normal skin. These findings strongly support the observations reviewed in this chapter and suggest that grafting *pf/pf* or *Er/Er* epidermis to normal animals results in reorganization of the epidermis and expression of a normal phenotype.

ACKNOWLEDGMENTS

The author is thankful to Drs. Karen A. Holbrook and Beverly A. Dale for their critical review of the manuscript. Dr. Edward J. Kollar is gratefully acknowledged for his guidance throughout the course of this work. The author is supported by NIH Grant HD-17664 and is the recipient of a National Research Service Award (AR 07892).

REFERENCES

Ball, R. C., Walker, G. K., and Bernstein, I. A. (1978). *J. Biol. Chem.* **253**, 5861–5868.
Balmain, A., Loehren, C., Fischer, J., and Alonso, A. (1977). *Dev. Biol.* **60**, 442–452.
Ben-Ze'Ev, A. (1984). *J. Cell Biol.* **99**, 1424–1433.
Billingham, R. E., and Silvers, W. K. (1973). *J. Invest. Dermatol.* **60**, 509–575.
Bladon, P. T., Bowden, P. E., Cunliffe, W. J., and Wood, E. J. (1982). *Biochem. J.* **208**, 179–187.

Bowden, P. E., Quinlan, R. A., Breitkreutz, D., and Fusenig, N. E. (1984). *Eur. J. Biochem.* **142**, 29–36.

Breitkreutz, D. A., Bohnert, A., Herzmann, E., Bowden, P. E., Boukamp, P., and Fusenig, N. E. (1984). *Differentiation* **26**, 154–169.

Briggaman, R. A. (1981). *Birth Defects Orig. Art. Ser.* **17**, 39–60.

Briggaman, R. A., and Wheeler, C. E. (1968). *J. Invest. Dermatol.* **51**, 454–465.

Briggaman, R. A., Dalldorf, F. G., and Wheeler, C. E. (1971). *J. Cell Biol.* **51**, 384–395.

Brody, I. (1959). *J. Ultrastruct. Res.* **2**, 482–511.

Cohen, S. (1965). *Dev. Biol.* **12**, 394–407.

Cohen, S., and Elliott, G. A. (1963). *J. Invest. Dermatol.* **40**, 1–5.

Dale, B. A. (1977). *Biochim. Biophys. Acta* **491**, 193–204.

DuBrul, E. F. (1972). *J. Exp. Zool.* **181**, 141–158.

Eicher, E. M., and Fox, S. (1978). *Mouse News Lett.* **58**, 50.

Emerman, J. T., and Pitelka, D. R. (1977). *In Vitro* **13**, 316–328.

Emerman, J. T., Burwen, S. J., and Pitelka, D. R. (1979). *Tissue Cell* **11**, 109–119.

Fisher, C., and Kollar, E. J. (1985). *J. Embryol. Exp. Morphol.* (in press).

Fisher, C., Dale, B. A., and Kollar, E. J. (1984). *Dev. Biol.* **102**, 290–299.

Fisher, C., Jones, A., Roop, D., and Dale, B. A. (1986). *J. Cell Biol.* **103** (5, part 2), 560a.

Franke, W. W., Schiller, D. L., Moll, R., Winter, S., Schmid, E., Engelbrecht, I., Denk, H., Krepler, R., and Platzer, B. (1981). *J. Mol. Biol.* **153**, 933–959.

Fuchs, E., and Green, H. (1980). *Cell* **19**, 1033–1042.

Fukuyama, K., and Epstein, W. L. (1973). *J. Ultrastruct. Res.* **51**, 314–325.

Fukuyama, K., and Epstein, W. L. (1975). *J. Invest. Dermatol.* **65**, 113–117.

Green, H. (1980). *Harvey Lect.* **74**, 101–139.

Green, H., Fuchs, E., and Watt, F. (1981). *Cold Spring Harbor Symp. Quant. Biol.* **46**, 293–302.

Green, M. C. (1982). "Genetic Variants and Strains of the Laboratory Mouse." Fischer, Stuttgart.

Gross, J. L., Moscatelli, D., Jaffe, E. A., and Rifkin, D. B. (1982). *J. Cell Biol.* **95**, 974–981.

Guenet, J.-L., Salzgeber, B., and Tassin, M. T. (1979). *J. Hered.* **70**, 90–94.

Hirone, T., and Taniguchi (1980). *In* "Current Problems in Dermatology" (I. A. Bernstein and M. Seigi, eds.), Vol. 10, pp. 151–169. Karger, Basel.

Holbrook, K. A., Dale, B. A., and Brown, K. S. (1982). *J. Cell Biol.* **92**, 387–397.

Hunsicker, P. R. (1960). *Mouse Newslett.* **23**, 58.

Kollar, E. J. (1966). *J. Invest. Dermatol.* **46**, 254–262.

Kollar, E. J. (1970). *J. Invest. Dermatol.* **55**, 374–378.

Kollar, E. J. (1983). *In* "Epithelial–Mesenchymal Interactions in Development" (R. H. Sawyer and J. F. Fallon, eds.), pp. 27–49. Praeger, New York.

Lillie, J. H., MacCallum, D. K., and Jepson, A. (1980). *Exp. Cell Res.* **125**, 153–165.

Lillie, J. H., MacCallum, D. K., and Jepson, A. (1982). *Eur. J. Cell Biol.* **29**, 50–60.

Lonsdale-Eccles, J. D., Resing, K. A., Meek, R. L., and Dale, B. A. (1984a). *Biochemistry* **23**, 1239–1245.

Lonsdale-Eccles, J. D., Teller, D. C., and Dale, B. A. (1984b). *Biochemistry* **21**, 5940–5948.

McGloughlin, C. B. (1961a). *J. Embryol. Exp. Morphol.* **9**, 370–384.

McGloughlin, C. B. (1961b). *J. Embryol. Exp. Morphol.* **9**, 385–408.

Matoltsy, A. G., and Matoltsy, N. M. (1970). *J. Cell Biol.* **47**, 593–603.

Matoltsy, A. G., and Parakkal, P. F. (1967). *In* "Ultrastructure of Normal and Abnormal Skin" (A. S. Zelickson, ed.), pp. 76–104. Lea & Febiger, Philadelphia.

Meredith, R. (1964). *Mouse News Lett.* **31**, 25.

Rice, R. H., and Green, H. (1977). *Cell* **11**, 417–423.

Roop, D. R., Hawley-Nelson, P., Cheng, C. K., and Yuspa, S. H. (1983). *Proc. Natl. Acad. Sci. U.S.A.* **80**, 716–720.

Salzgeber, B., and Guenet, J.-L. (1984). *J. Craniofac. Genet. Dev. Biol.* **4**, 95–114.

Sawyer, R. H. (1975). *J. Exp. Zool.* **191**, 141–147.

Saxen, L. (1977). *In* "Cell and Tissue Interactions" (J. W. Lash and M. M. Burger, eds.), pp. 1–10. Raven, New York.

Schweizer, J., and Winter, H. (1982a). *Cancer Res.* **42**, 1517–1529.

Schweizer, J., and Winter, H. (1982b). *Differentiation* **22**, 19–24.

Schweizer, J., Kinjo, M., Furstenberger, G., and Winter, H. (1984). *Cell* **37**, 159–170.

Shin, H.-S., Stavnezer, J., Artzt, K., and Bennett, D. (1982). *Cell* **29**, 969–976.

Sengel, P. (1976). "Morphogenesis of Skin." Cambridge Univ. Press, London.

Steinert, P. M., Cantieri, J. S., Teller, D. C., Lonsdale-Eccles, J. D., and Dale, B. A. (1981). *Proc. Natl. Acad. Sci. U.S.A.* **78**, 4097–4101.

Sun, T.-T., Eichner, R., Nelson, W. G., Tseng, S. C. G., Weiss, R. A., Jarvinen, M., and Woodcock-Mitchell, J. (1983). *J. Invest. Dermatol.* **81**, 109s–115s.

Tassin, M. T., Salzgeber, B., and Guenet, J.-L. (1983). *J. Craniofac. Genet. Dev. Biol.* **3**, 289–307.

Taylor, W. G., Camalier, R. F., and Sanford, K. K. (1978). *In Vitro* **14**, 352.

Tseng, S. C. G., Jarvinen, M. J., Nelson, W. G., Huang, J.-W., Woodcock-Mitchell, J., and Sun, T.-T. (1982). *Cell* **30**, 361–372.

Watson, P. J., and Ede, D. A. (1977). *J. Anat. (London)* **124**, 229.

Watt, F. (1984). *J. Cell Biol.* **98**, 16–21.

Wessels, N. K. (1962). *Dev. Biol.* **4**, 87–107.

CHAPTER 11

EXPRESSION OF β-KERATIN GENES DURING DEVELOPMENT OF AVIAN SKIN APPENDAGES

Rose B. Shames and Roger H. Sawyer

DEPARTMENT OF BIOLOGY
UNIVERSITY OF SOUTH CAROLINA
COLUMBIA, SOUTH CAROLINA 29208

I. Introduction

The now classic experiments of Sengel (1958) and Rawles (1963) clearly demonstrated the significance of epidermal–dermal interactions in the morphogenesis of avian feathers and scales. Although the dermal component of these integumental structures undergoes its own differentiative changes, it is the epidermis of feathers and scales which undergoes the most obvious changes to ultimately make up the bulk of these skin appendages. The major product of the epidermal cells which make up feathers and most avian scales is β-keratin.

With the advent of recombinant DNA technology, a great deal of knowledge has now been gained on the molecular biology of the β-keratin genes of feathers and scales. Information has recently become available on the number, organization, and structure of the feather and scale β-keratin genes (Gregg and Rogers, 1986). Several lines of evidence indicate that the synthesis of β-keratins is controlled at the level of transcription, and DNA sequences have been identified which may be of significance for control at this level (Gregg and Rogers, 1986). Since the β-keratin genes of feathers differ from those of scales, some mechanism must operate to select the appropriate set of genes for expression. When and how does this mechanism work and what is its relation to the epidermal–dermal interactions governing morphogenesis?

In this chapter we first present brief background information on the basic developmental programs of feathers and scales, on tissue recombination experiments using the scaleless (*sc/sc*) mutant line of chickens which is defective in the development of its scales and feathers, and on the molecular biology of the avian β-keratins. With this

CURRENT TOPICS IN
DEVELOPMENTAL BIOLOGY, VOL. 22

background information, we then present what we have learned about the relationship between various developmental events and the tissue-specific expression of β-keratin genes. We have monitored gene expression during scale development by determining the appearance, abundance, and location of mRNA for β-keratin using a DNA probe (pCSK-12, a generous gift from Dr. George Rogers, University of Adelaide) and RNA probes which we generated from pCSK-12.

II. Development of the Avian Skin Appendages

A. DEVELOPMENT OF FEATHERS AND SCALES

The development of feathers and scales on the avian foot is dependent on epidermal–dermal tissue interactions. Without the continual association of these two layers, morphogenesis, histogenesis, and biochemical differentiation of feathers or the various types of scales do not occur (for reviews, see Dhouailly, 1984; Sengel, 1976, 1986; Sawyer and Fallon, 1983; Sawyer *et al.*, 1986). Feathers first appear as hexagonally arranged epidermal placodes which are 250 μm in diameter when viewed from the surface, and are accompanied by dermal condensations (Sengel and Rusaouen, 1968). Wessells (1965) demonstrated that these dermal condensations and accompanying epidermal placodes undergo a "nonproliferation" phase during which their cells do not incorporate tritiated thymidine ([³H]TdR) for some 20 hours. The role of the nonproliferation phase is unknown. Feather development continues with outgrowth of the placodes and their dermal cores to give rise to the feather filaments. With continued elongation of the feather filament (stages 34 to 36; Hamburger and Hamilton, 1951), differentiation of barb ridges begins at the tip of the feather filament. X-Ray diffraction analyses (Bell and Thathachari, 1963), fine structural studies (Matulionis, 1970), and immunohistochemical studies (Haake *et al.*, 1984) all demonstrated that the morphogenetic events of feather development precede the appearance of β-keratins. Bell and Thathachari (1963) raised the question whether the initial inductive events of feather development also "triggered" the expression of the β-keratin genes.

Studies of scale development have become more complex since it has been shown that there are at least five different patterns of scale development on the legs and feet of the chicken (Sawyer *et al.*, 1986). In this chapter we will present studies on two types of scale, the reticulate scale and scutate scale. Reticulate scales develop without the formation of epidermal placodes or dermal condensations and when mature they produce only α-keratins. By contrast, the scutate scales form epidermal placodes without dermal condensations and when mature produce β-keratins only on the outer, platelike epidermal surfaces. The epidermal placodes of scutate scales are populations of elongated nonproliferating basal cells (Sawyer, 1972a,b) which accumulate by movement of proliferating cells from proximal interplacode regions into placode regions (Tanaka and Kato, 1983a,b). Formation of these placodes sets in motion the morphogenesis of the scale. The placodes become asymmetrical, marking the elevation of a scale primordium (stage 37). A definitive scale ridge then forms (stage 38), which over several days elongates distally to give the shape of the overlapping scutate scale. By stage 39 the scale has well-developed outer, hinge, and inner epidermal surfaces. The morphological events which occur from stage 36 to 39 not only are producing obvious changes in the shape of the epidermal appendages, but are having profound effects on the underlying dermis. The dermis must be associated with developing scutate scale epidermis until stage 39 in order to acquire the competency to promote further histogenesis and biochemical differentiation of scutate scales.

B. STUDIES WITH THE SCALELESS (sc/sc) MUTANT

The embryos of the scaleless (sc/sc) line of chickens (Abbott and Asmundson, 1957) provide an extremely useful genetic system for studying the relationships between morphogenesis and terminal differentiation of scutate scales (Sawyer, 1979, 1983). The sc/sc trait blocks epidermal placode formation and all subsequent morphogenetic events, with the consequence that scale β-keratins are not produced in the mature skin (Sawyer et al., 1974b, 1986). β-Keratins are found in the embryonic subperiderm of sc/sc epidermis. Reciprocal epidermal–dermal recombination experiments between normal and sc/sc embryos have demonstrated (1) that the sc/sc defect is initially expressed by the epidermis (Sengel and Abbott, 1963; Goetinck and Abbott, 1963); (2) that this epidermal defect manifests itself only as an inability to form placodes, since scaleless epidermis will synthesize scale β-keratins when instructed to do so by a normal scutate scale dermis (McAleese and Sawyer, 1981, 1982); and (3) that the sc/sc dermis eventually becomes defective in its ability to induce the formation of scutate scales if it remains associated with sc/sc epidermis after $9\frac{1}{2}$ days of incubation, the period during which placodes normally form (Dhouailly and Sawyer, 1984).

III. Keratins of Avian Skin Appendages

A. General Picture

Studying the role of tissue interactions in skin development requires a method to critically evaluate the final differentiated state of a particular tissue. In the case of avian skin, there are a variety of specialized tissues (Sawyer *et al.*, 1986) where the differentiated state may be defined not only by characteristic shape, but also by histogenic expression and distribution of keratins. Keratins are a group of fibrous, water-insoluble intracellular proteins. The α-keratins are a family in this group that range from 40,000 to 70,000 in molecular weight and display an α-type X-ray diffraction pattern. The filaments of α-keratin have a diameter of 8–11 nm. These proteins are found in nearly all vertebrate epithelia (Moll *et al.*, 1982; Franke *et al.*, 1981; Parakkal and Alexander, 1972). The β-keratins are another family that have been found in certain epidermises of birds and reptiles. These proteins form filaments of 3–4 nm and fall in the molecular weight range of 10,000–25,000. They display a β-type X-ray diffraction pattern, and are rich in cysteine which leads to formation of disulfide bonds within and between polypeptides (Rudall, 1947; Fraser *et al.*, 1972).

B. Molecular Studies on Feather β-Keratin

Recent investigations (Gregg and Rogers, 1986) into the molecular structure of the β-keratins have demonstrated that these proteins are members of multigene families. They are found closely linked on the chromosome, display a high degree of sequence homology, and have related functions. In general, the β-keratins can be subdivided into two groups based on size of the individual polypeptides. The smaller group, molecular weight of approximately 10,000, is found predominantly in feathers, while the larger group, molecular weight between 14,000 and 25,000, is found predominantly in scales. Thus far, 11 genes for feather β-keratin have been identified in a tandem array on the chromosome (Molloy *et al.*, 1982) and all the genes have the same organization. The 5' untranslated regions are approximately 60 base pairs in length. Between residues 37 and 38 the genes are interrupted by an intervening sequence of 340–360 base pairs with the first 37 base pairs of the genes displaying rigid sequence conservation. The protein coding regions contain 297 base pairs and display greater than 95% homology. The amino termini and carboxy termini are cysteine rich and show greater sequence variation than the central region which has no cysteine. It is the central region that is responsible for the β-pleated sheet secondary structure of the proteins. The greatest sequence differences between feather genes are found in the 3′ untranslated regions, which are 440–460 base pairs long.

C. MOLECULAR STUDIES ON SCALE β-KERATIN

The scale β-keratin genes are also members of a multigene family (Wilton *et al.*, 1985; Walker and Bridgen, 1976). Wilton has isolated a genomic clone with at least four scale β-keratin genes (Wilton, 1984). The organization of these genes is identical to the feather β-keratin genes and there is strong sequence homology between the coding regions of the two types (Gregg *et al.*, 1984). The most striking difference between the coding regions of feather and scale genes is a domain between residues 77 and 128 in the scale genes that is absent from feather genes. This additional sequence consists of units of 39 base pairs, rich in glycine and tyrosine, which are repeated approximately four times. The domain of repeated units accounts for the larger size of scale β-keratins and for differences in secondary structure between the scale and feather β-keratins. In feather β-keratin, residues 28–63 form a unit of structure called a β-pleated sheet. A single polypeptide chain is twisted into four parallel chains, each of eight amino acids. These units or sheets line up following a right-handed helical path. Two sets, running in opposite directions, associate to form a filament core of 3 nm diameter (Fraser and McRae, 1980). The scale β-keratin forms the same core structure, but in addition, the domain of glycine–tyrosine repeats takes up a β-conformation as it wraps itself on the outside of the core filament. The hydrophobic nature of the repeated domain probably establishes strong interfilament binding.

The data on sequence homology between scale and feather β-keratins suggest that feather β-keratin genes may have evolved from scale β-keratin genes by deletion of the repeated domain in the coding region followed by gene duplications (Gregg *et al.*, 1983). In spite of the differences in size of the coding regions, the mRNAs for scale and feather β-keratins are the same. The length of β-keratin mRNA seems to have been maintained by adjusting the size of the 3′ untranslated regions.

IV. Expression of β-Keratin mRNA during Scale Development

Molecular studies have provided insight into the complexity of the β-keratin gene families and have pointed out that control mechanisms must exist to coordinate expression of these related genes. An analysis of tissue from adult birds (Walker and Bridgen, 1976) identified at least nine scale β-keratin genes, and a study of tissue from 17-day (stage 43) embryonic birds identified at least 12 scale β-keratin genes (Wilton *et al.*, 1985). Since β-keratin is the major product of terminal differentiation in certain scale types, it is essential to know which β-keratin polypeptides are expressed in a specific tissue, when they are expressed, and how they are distributed over the appendage in order to be able to critically evaluate the outcome of experiments such as heterotypic tissue recombinations which are designed to study the role of tissue interactions in the development of skin appendages.

A. Studies with the β-Keratin Probe pCSK-12

We have begun to study the timing of appearance of mRNA for β-keratins in the developing skin of normal anterior metatarsus (NAM), *sc/sc* anterior metatarsus (ScAM), and normal footpad (NFP) regions. Our approach has been to hybridize a β-keratin-specific, ^{32}P-labeled cDNA probe to RNA which had been isolated at certain stages and from specific regions of developing skin. The probe for β-keratin was pCSK-12 which was isolated by Wilton (1984). This hybrid plasmid was isolated after inserting cDNA, constructed from a 15 S RNA fraction of total RNA from shank and tarsal skin of stage 43 chick embryos, into the *Pst*I site of pBR322. The 15 S RNA fraction directed cell-free synthesis of translation products which comigrated with scale β-keratin markers on SDS–polyacrylamide gels and urea–polyacrylamide gels. The total insert was 613 base pairs, which included coding sequences for 66 amino acids at the carboxy terminal end (about one-half of the scale keratin molecule) and some noncoding sequences at the 3′ end of the gene. A glycine–tyrosine-rich domain of 39 base pairs, repeated exactly three times in this probe, provided identification of pCSK-12 as a molecular probe for scale β-keratin.

In a recent study (Shames and Sawyer, 1986), we used dot blot hybridization to follow the appearances of β-keratin mRNA in NAM skin (Fig. 1). The hybridization signal remained at background levels from stage 36 to 39. At stage 40, an accumulation of β-keratin mRNA began and then increased until stage 43. From stage 43 to 46 the amount of β-keratin mRNA remained high. Northern blot hybridization was used to compare the expression of β-keratin mRNA in anterior metatarsal skin from scaleless and normal embryos (Shames and Sawyer, 1986). As before, mRNA for β-keratin in NAM skin was not detected at stages 38 or 39, but began to appear at stage 40 and was present through stages 43 and 45 and in newly hatched chicks. The pattern of expression in ScAM skin was quite different; a signal for β-keratin mRNA was not detected at stages 38 or 40. However, at stage 42 there was an intense signal which was diminished by stage 44 and

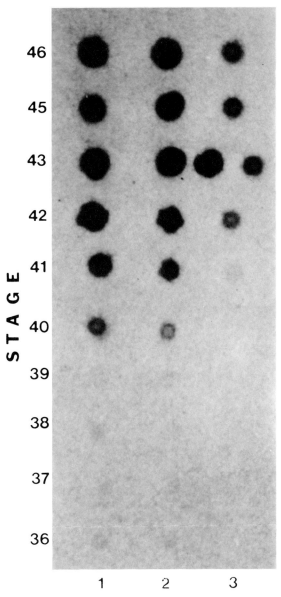

FIG. 1. RNA was extracted from normal anterior metatarsal (NAM) skin at the indicated developmental stages, then immobilized onto nitrocellulose paper, and finally hybridized to ^{32}P-labeled pCSK-12. The dots in lanes 1, 2, and 3 represent 2, 1, and 0.125 μg RNA, respectively. (After Shames and Sawyer, 1986.)

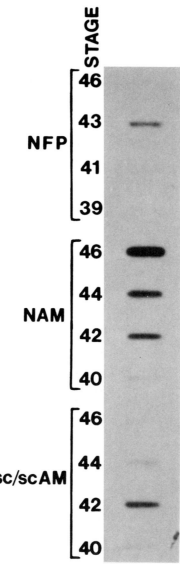

Fig. 2. RNA was extracted from NAM, normal footpad (NFP), and scaleless anterior metatarsal (ScAM) skin at the indicated developmental stages. After immobilizing the RNA (2 μg) to nitrocellulose paper, it was hybridized to ^{32}P-labeled pCSK-12.

was absent by hatching. Compared to normal, mRNA for ScAM skin β-keratin appeared at a later developmental time and unlike normal disappeared before the end of embryonic development. The pattern of expression of β-keratin mRNA in developing NFP skin was the same as observed in developing ScAM skin (Fig. 2). β-Keratin mRNA accumulated for a 1- or 2-day interval and then disappeared before the end of embryonic development.

B. RELATION OF β-KERATIN GENE EXPRESSION TO MORPHOGENESIS, HISTOGENESIS, AND CYTODIFFERENTIATION

Figure 3 summarizes the developmental pattern of mRNA expression in scutate scales and relates this pattern to the current picture of the morphogenesis, histogenesis, and cytodifferentiation of the scale. Development of NAM skin into scutate scales is initially characterized by the appearance of epidermal placodes. This process is well under way by stage 36, and yet there is no evidence of expression of mRNA for β-keratins. By stage 37, the placodes become asymmetrical and the contour of the epidermis takes on an undulating appearance. Again, there is no evidence of β-keratin gene expression. Formation of a definitive scale ridge occurs at stage 38. The epidermis is now divided into distinct layers: a layer of basal cells (stratum basale), the first layer of suprabasal cells (subperiderm), secondary periderm, and primary periderm. By stage 39, the scale has well-developed outer, hinge, and inner epidermal surfaces. There is still no evidence for the accumulation of β-keratin mRNA. However, it is at this stage that the dermis is totally competent to induce foreign epithelia to stratify and differentiate a beta stratum (Sawyer et al., 1986). The morphological, histological, and biochemical events which have occurred to produce the stage 39 scutate scale have, in some way, affected the dermis so that it is now competent to promote further histogenesis and terminal cytodifferentiation (keratinization) which characterize the beta stratum of scutate scales.

O'Guin (1984) had demonstrated with immunohistochemistry using an antiserum to β-keratins that β-keratin polypeptides first appear in the subepidermal cells of the scutate scale at stage 41. This observation provided direct evidence in support of early X-ray diffraction (Bell and Thathachari, 1963) and biochemical (Kemp and Rogers, 1972; Dhouailly et al., 1978) studies which concluded that much of the morphogenesis of the scutate scale is completed before β-keratin genes are expressed. The possibility still remained, however, that the inductive event responsible for the formation of the epidermal placodes also resulted in the transcription of the β-keratin genes whose products

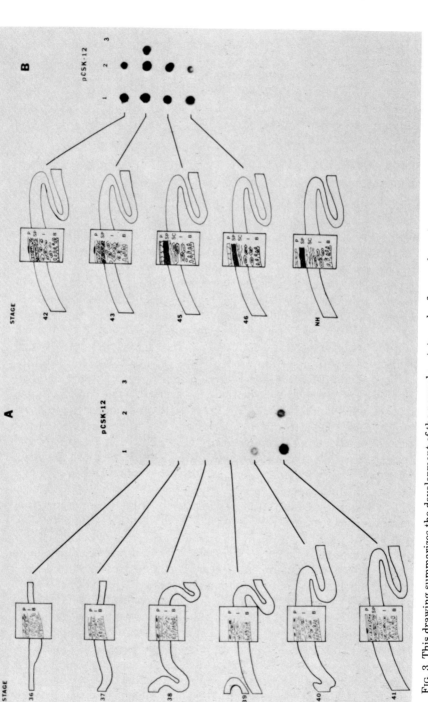

Fig. 3. This drawing summarizes the development of the normal scutate scales from embryonic stage 36 to 41 (A) and stage 42 to newly hatched chick (B) and relates the various stages of morphogenesis and histogenesis to appearance of mRNA for β-keratin. (After Shames and Sawyer, 1986.)

would be found at a later time due to translation of stored mRNA. The studies of Shames and Sawyer (1986) rule out this possibility, further strengthening the view that the search for the mechanism that signals β-keratin gene expression in scutate scales must be directed to the developmental events that occur after formation of the definitive scale ridge at stage 38. The lack of mRNA for β-keratin in epidermal cells during the formative steps clearly demonstrates that morphological events, though necessary, are not directly linked to expression of the β-keratin genes.

At stage 40, elongation of the scale ridge has progressed so that inner and outer surfaces are more distinct. mRNA for β-keratin appears for the first time at this stage of development. By stage 41, the scales have taken on a definite overlapping appearance and terminal cytodifferentiation of the two peridermal layers and the subperiderm has clearly begun. The amount of mRNA for β-keratin has increased greatly. Both fine structural (Sawyer and Abbott, 1972; Sawyer et al., 1974a,b) and immunohistochemical (O'Guin, 1984) data have demonstrated that β-keratinization first begins in the subperidermal cells at stage 41. The peridermal layers, the subperiderm, and the thin alpha stratum of the outer scale surface are sloughed around the time of hatching, stage 47, or soon thereafter (Sawyer et al., 1974a, 1986). Most likely, the mRNA for β-keratin seen at stages 40–41 is present in the subperidermal cells, since they are the first cells to fill with β-keratin filaments. We believe that the high level of β-keratin mRNA that continues beyond stages 40 and 41 represents β-keratin mRNA made in cells which will give rise to the beta stratum. The close correlation between the time of appearance of β-keratin mRNA and actual β-keratinization of the cells suggests again (Gregg and Rogers, 1986) that β-keratin synthesis is controlled at the level of keratin mRNA transcription. The expression of β-keratin genes seems to be linked to events of stratification and cytodifferentiation more directly than events of morphogenesis. Only as the cells take their positions in discrete layers within the epidermis do they express the β-keratin genes associated with terminal differentiation.

Appearance of mRNA for β-keratin in developing ScAM and NFP skin also correlates with observed β-keratinization of the cells (Fig. 4). At stage 36, ScAM skin shows no evidence of epidermal placode formation. By stage 39, when scale ridges have formed and are elongating in the NAM skin, the sc/sc epidermis still shows no sign of placode or scale ridge formation. There is no detectable level of β-keratin mRNA in these tissues until stage 41, a day later than in the corresponding normal tissue. The lag in sc/sc subperidermal development follows the

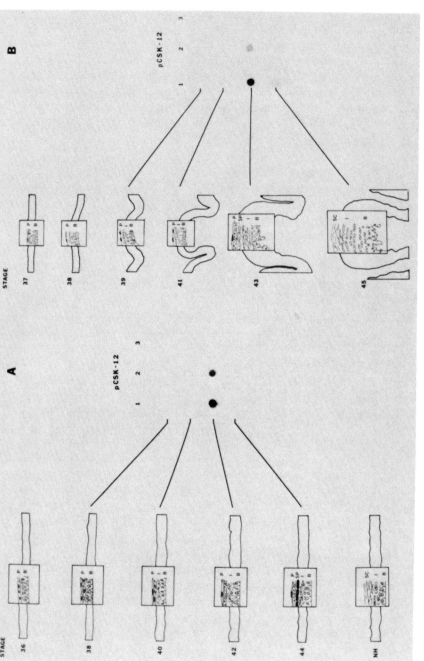

FIG. 4. This drawing summarizes the development of scaleless anterior metatarsal skin from embryonic stage 36 to newly hatched chicks (A) and normal reticulate scales from stage embryonic 37 to 45 (B) and relates the various stages of morphogenesis and histogenesis to appearance of mRNA for β-keratin. (After Shames and Sawyer, 1986.)

overall 24-hour lag in *sc/sc* development (Sawyer and Abbott, 1972). By stage 44, the subperidermal cells have enlarged and are filled with 3-nm β-keratin filaments (Sawyer *et al.*, 1974b; O'Guin, 1984), but the level of β-keratin mRNA has diminished and by hatching there is no detectable level of β-keratin mRNA in ScAM skin. The burst of β-keratin mRNA at stages 41 and 42 corresponds to β-keratinization of the subperiderm.

Development of NFP epidermis (Fig. 4B) begins with a layer of cuboidal basal cells and a surface layer of flattened peridermal cells. There is no evidence of placode formation. At stages 38, the epidermis begins to become undulated in appearance and by stage 39 radially symmetrical anlagen of reticulate scales are prominent. The epidermis becomes multilayered and a subperidermal layer forms under the peridermal layers. mRNA for β-keratin appears between stages 42 and 43 and β-keratinization of the subperiderm is observed at stages 42–43 (O'Guin, 1984; Sawyer *et al.*, 1984). By stage 45, mRNA levels for β-keratin have diminished. As in ScAM skin, appearance of β-keratin mRNA in the reticulate scale epidermis is linked in time with β-keratinization of the subperiderm.

V. Localization of β-Keratin mRNA in Developing Scutate Scales

During scutate scale development, the onset of β-keratin gene expression is linked to events of histogenesis that occur after the scale has taken its shape. At stage 40, when β-keratin mRNA accumulation is first detected, the scutate scale already has an overlapping structure with clearly defined outer and inner surfaces. As development proceeds, the scale ridge continues to elongate and the epidermal cells continue to stratify and differentiate. The cells of the outer scale surface proliferate to a greater extent than the cells of the inner scale surface.

During stratification of the epidermal layers, β-keratins are synthesized. Previous work has shown that on the outer scale surface, β-keratins accumulate in the stratum intermedium and stratum corneum, which are several cell layers from the basement membrane (O'Guin *et al.*, 1982). Since epidermal–dermal interactions are required for β-keratinization of the outer surface of the scale (Sawyer *et al.*, 1984), the regulatory influences of the dermis must be transmitted through several cell layers. This "long distance" influence of dermis on differentiation of the beta stratum may act on cells still in contact with basement membrane but translation of the β-keratin mRNA is delayed until the cells move to the stratum intermedium. *In situ* hybridization of scutate scale mRNA with a probe complementary to

PstI
↓
TGC A GC CCT TAC TCC TAC CGG TAC AAC AGG TAC CGC CGT GGC AGC TGC GGG CCC TGC TAA

Cys Ser Pro Tyr Ser Tyr Arg Tyr Asn Arg Tyr Arg Arg Gly Ser Cys Gly Pro Cys

GCCAAGCAGAAATATTCCCCTCATGGAAGAGAATCACCAATGGGTTCCCAACAGAAGATCTCCATGTTGCTCTGATTCAAG

ACTACTGAGCTGTTTCTCTTCAGCCCCATCAAATTTATCCTCTCAATTCTACTTTCAGTTTCTACTATAATGCTTCTCCCTT

CATGTTTCCATCATACCTTGTGTAAATGTAACAAAACTGCA GAAATAA
↑
PstI

Fig. 5. The sequence of a β-keratin-specific, 260-base pair fragment isolated from pCSK-12 and inserted into pT7-1 is shown.

β-keratin mRNA would provide data to support or reject this hypothesis.

To this end, an ^{3}H-labeled RNA probe was generated that was complementary to β-keratin mRNA. This was done by isolating a β-keratin-specific, 260-bp fragment from pCSK-12 (Fig. 5) and inserting it into the vector pT7-1, at a site adjacent to the T7 polymerase promoter. Using T7 RNA polymerase and the recombinant plasmid, a ^{3}H-labeled RNA probe was transcribed *in vitro*. This probe hybridized to mRNA isolated from NAM skin of the developing chick embryo, whereas an ^{3}H-labeled RNA probe transcribed *in vitro* from the parent template, pT7-1, did not hybridize to mRNA extracted from embryonic NAM skin. The β-keratin-specific RNA probe was hybridized *in situ* to cellular RNAs of stage 46 scutate scale (Angerer *et al.*, 1984) (Fig. 6). As shown by the location of grains, β-keratin mRNA was present only in the epidermal cells that had moved several layers above the stratum basale of the outer scale surface. This result reinforces the hypothesis that β-keratin gene expression occurs during histogenesis of the scale, and only in cell layers that have moved away from the germinative population.

VI. Identification of a β-Keratin Polypeptide by Hybrid Selection with pCSK-12

Detergent-insoluble proteins extracted from NAM skin have been analyzed by two-dimensional gel electrophoresis according to the method of O'Farrell *et al.* (1977). The large array of polypeptides visualized in this way fall into two molecular weight groups, the 50,000–70,000 group which consists predominantly of α-keratins (not shown)

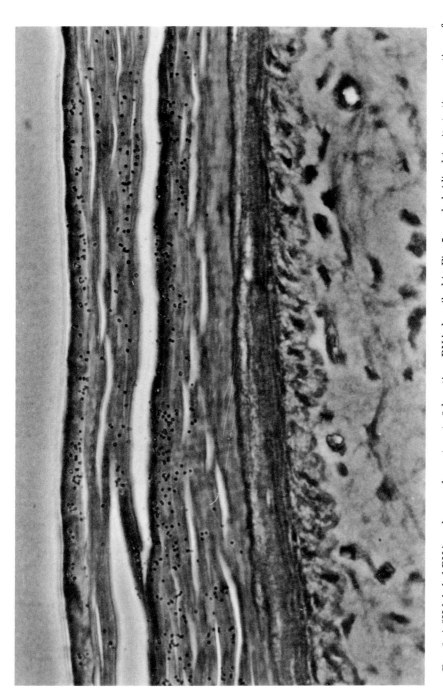

Fig. 6. A ³H-labeled RNA probe complementary to β-keratin mRNA described in Fig. 5 was hybridized *in situ* to tissue sections of stage 46 embryonic scutate scale. Grains appear only over the stratum intermedium and stratum corneum.

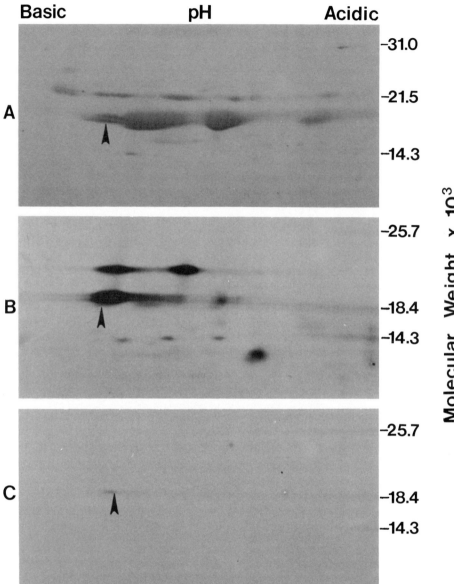

FIG. 7. (A) Two-dimensional gel electrophoresis of detergent insoluble polypeptides from NAM skin of posthatched chicks. First dimension, nonequilibrium pH gradient electrophoresis; second dimension, SDS–polyacrylamide gel (only the bottom half of a two-dimensional 15–20% gel is shown). After electrophoresis in the second dimension the gel was fixed, stained with Coomassie brilliant blue G-250, and dried under vacuum.

which have been described by O'Guin *et al.* (this volume), and a 10,000–25,000 group which is predominantly β-keratins, as described by Haake (1985) and Haake *et al.* (1986). Figure 7A shows the low molecular weight group of detergent-insoluble polypeptides that were extracted from the scutate scale epidermis of hatched chickens. RNA extracted from NAM skin was translated *in vitro* using the wheat germ lysate system and [³H]leucine as a marker. Proteins synthesized in this way are shown in Fig. 7B. When total RNA from NAM skin was first hybrid selected with pCSK-12, and then translated *in vitro,* the spot shown in Fig. 7C was detected. Therefore, this polypeptide is a β-keratin and is the product of the β-keratin gene, sβK III, whose partial sequence is contained in pcSK-12 (Wilton, 1984). This polypeptide reacts strongly with our anti-β-keratin antiserum (O'Guin *et al.,* 1982; O'Guin, 1984), as do several of the other polypeptides in the molecular weight range of 10,000–25,000 (Haake, 1985).

VII. Concluding Remarks

The mechanisms by which tissue interactions direct the formation of the epidermis and its appendages remain obscure. However, application of molecular biology to this problem is adding significantly to our understanding of the developmental events that are most directly associated with onset of terminal differentiation as signaled by transcription of β-keratin genes. For example, we now have direct evidence that the early stages of scutate scale development are not accompanied by expression of any β-keratin genes. Even subperidermal cells which may be formed as early as day 11 (stage 37) do not elaborate β-keratin mRNA until stage 40 and do not produce β-keratins until stage 41.

We have also determined that the scale β-keratin genes are expressed only in epidermal cells which are located above the proliferating population of basal cells. Are the basal cells committed to produce β-keratins once they migrate to the appropriate layer, and if so when does this germinative basal population become "determined"? We are presently using tissue recombination techniques in conjunction with

---

The molecular weight markers in the second dimension were lysozyme (14.3K), soybean trypsin (21.5K), and carbonic anhydrase (31.0K). (B) RNA was extracted from NAM skin of stage 45 embryos and translated *in vitro* using [³H] leucine as the radiolabeled marker. Following electrophoresis, the gel was fixed, treated with En³Hance (NEN), dried, and exposed to X-ray film for 12 days. The ¹⁴C-labeled molecular weight markers in the second dimension were lysozyme (14.3K), β-lactoglobulin (18.4K), and α-chymotrypsinogen (25.7K). (C) RNA was extracted from stage 46 NAM skin, hybrid selected with pCSK-12, and translated *in vitro* with [³H]leucine. The translation products were analyzed as stated in B.

our immunological and molecular probes to answer these questions.

Since β-keratins are encoded by a large family of genes, another important question relates to the mechanisms by which developmental events affect the expression of specific β-keratin genes. Work is under way to define the particular β-keratins expressed in different skin appendages, and to identify and sequence the corresponding genes in order to find relationships that might provide insight into how selective terminal differentiation is controlled by associated developmental events.

ACKNOWLEDGMENTS

This work was supported by Grant PCM 83-09068 from NSF and Grant 1RO1HD18129 from NICHD. The authors wish to thank Ms. Anita Jennings for her technical assistance, Mr. Clint Cook for his photographic work, and Ms. Betty Branham for typing the manuscript.

REFERENCES

Abbott, U. K., and Asmundson, V. S. (1957). J. Hered. 18, 63–70.
Angerer, R. C., Cox, K. H., and Angerer, L. M. (1984). Genet. Eng. 7.
Bell, E., and Thathachari, Y. T. (1963). J. Cell Biol. 16, 215–223.
Dhouailly, D. (1984). In "Pattern Formation, A Primer in Developmental Biology" (G. M. Malacinski and S. V. Bryant, eds.). Macmillan, New York.
Dhouailly, D., and Sawyer, R. H. (1984). Dev. Biol. 105, 343–350.
Dhouailly, D., Rogers, G. E., and Sengel, P. (1978). Dev. Biol. 65, 58–68.
Franke, W. W., Schiller, D. L., Moll, R., Winter, S., Schmid, E., Engelbrecht, I., Denk, H., Krepler, R., and Platzer, B. (1981). J. Mol. Biol. 153, 933–959.
Fraser, R. D. B., and MacRae, T. P. (1980). "The Skin of Vertebrates" (R. I. C. Spearman and P. A. Riley, eds.), pp. 67–86. Academic Press, New York.
Fraser, R. D. B., McRae, T. P., and Rogers, G. E. (1972). "Keratins, Their Composition, Structure and Biosynthesis." Thomas, Springfield, Illinois.
Goetinck, P. F., and Abbott, U. K. (1963). J. Exp. Zool. 154, 7–19.
Gregg, K., and Rogers, G. E. (1986). In "Biology of the Integument, Vol. II. Vertebrates" (J. Bereiter-Hahn, A. G. Matoltsy, and K. S. Richards, eds.), pp. 666–694. Springer-Verlag, Berlin.
Gregg, K., Wilton, S. D., Rogers, G. E., and Molloy, P. L. (1983). In "Manipulation and Expression of Genes in Eukaryotes" (P. Nagley, A. W. Linnema, W. J. Peacock, and J. A. Pateman, eds.), pp. 65–72. Academic Press, New York.
Gregg, K., Wilton, S. D., Parry, D. A. D., and Rogers, G. E. (1984). EMBO J. 3, 175–178.
Haake, A. R. (1985). Ph.D. dissertation, University of South Carolina, Columbia.
Haake, A. R., König, G., and Sawyer, R. H. (1984). Dev. Biol. 106, 406–413.
Haake, A. R., Knapp, L. W., and Sawyer, R. H. (1987). Submitted.
Hamburger, V., and Hamilton, H. L. (1951). J. Morphol. 88, 49–92.
Kemp, D. J., and Rogers, G. E. (1972). Biochemistry 11, 969–975.
McAleese, S. R., and Sawyer, R. H. (1981). Science 214, 1033–1034.
McAleese, S. R., and Sawyer, R. H. (1982). Dev. Biol. 89, 493–502.
Matulionis, D. H. (1970). Z. Anat. Entwicklungsgesch. 132, 107–157.
Moll, R., Franke, W. W., Schiller, D. L., Geiger, B., and Krepler, R. (1982). Cell 31, 11–24.

Molloy, P. L., Powell, B. C., Gregg, K., Barone, D., and Rogers, G. E. (1982). *Nucleic Acids Res.* **10**, 6007–6021.

O'Farrell, P. Z., Goodman, H. M., and O'Farrell, P. H. (1977). *Cell* **12**, 1133–1142.

O'Guin, W. M. (1984). Ph.D. dissertation, University of South Carolina, Columbia, South Carolina.

O'Guin, W. M., Knapp, L. W., and Sawyer, R. H. (1982). *J. Exp. Zool.* **220**, 371–376.

Parakkal, P. F., and Alexander, N. J. (1972). "Keratinization, A Survey of Vertebrate Epithelia." Academic Press, New York.

Rawles, M. E. (1963). *J. Embryol. Exp. Morphol.* **2**, 765–789.

Rudall, K. M. (1947). *Biochim. Biophys. Acta* **1**, 549–562.

Sawyer, R. H. (1972a). *J. Exp. Zool.* **181**, 365–384.

Sawyer, R. H. (1972b). *J. Exp. Zool.* **181**, 385–408.

Sawyer, R. H. (1979). *Dev. Biol.* **68**, 1–15.

Sawyer, R. H. (1983). *In* "Epithelial–Mesenchymal Interactions in Development" (R. H. Sawyer and J. F. Fallon, eds.), pp. 115–146. Praeger, New York.

Sawyer, R. H., and Abbott, U. K. (1972). *J. Exp. Zool.* **181**, 99–110.

Sawyer, R. H., and Fallon, J. F. (1983). "Epithelial–Mesenchymal Interactions in Development." Praeger, New York.

Sawyer, R. H., Abbott, U. K., and Fry, G. N. (1974a). *J. Exp. Zool.* **190**, 57–70.

Sawyer, R. H., Abbott, U. K., and Fry, G. N. (1974b). *J. Exp. Zool.* **190**, 71–78.

Sawyer, R. H., O'Guin, W. M., and Knapp, L. W. (1984). *Dev. Biol.* **101**, 8–18.

Sawyer, R. H., Knapp, L. W., and O'Guin, W. M. (1986). *In* "Biology of the Integument, Vol. II. Vertebrates" (J. Bereiter-Hahn, A. G. Maltotsy, and K. S. Richards, eds.), pp. 194–238. Springer-Verlag, Berlin.

Sengel, P. (1958). *Ann. Sci. Nat. Zool.* **20**, 421–514.

Sengel, P. (1976). "Morphogenesis of Skin" (M. Abercrombie, D. R. Newth, and J. G. Torrey, eds.). Cambridge Univ. Press, London.

Sengel, P. (1986). *In* "Biology of the Integument, Vol. II. Vertebrates" (J. Bereiter-Hahn, M. S. Matoltsy, and K. S. Richards, eds.). Springer-Verlag, Berlin.

Sengel, P., and Abbott, U. K. (1963). *J. Hered.* **54**, 254–262.

Sengel, P., and Rusaouen, M. (1968). *C. R. Acad. Sci. Ser. D* **266**, 795–797.

Shames, R. B., and Sawyer, R. H. (1986). *Dev. Biol.* **116**, 15–22.

Tanaka, S., and Kato, Y. (1983a). *J. Exp. Zool.* **225**, 257–269.

Tanaka, S., and Kato, Y. (1983b). *J. Exp. Zool.* **225**, 271–283.

Walker, I. D., and Bridgen, J. (1976). *Eur. J. Biochem.* **67**, 283–293.

Wessells, N. K. (1965). *Dev. Biol.* **12**, 131–153.

Wilton, S. D. (1984). Ph.D. dissertation. Department of Biochemistry, University of Adelaide, South Australia.

Wilton, S. D., Crocker, L. A., and Rogers, G. E. (1985). *Biochim. Biophys. Acta* **824**, 201–208.

CHAPTER 12

CONCLUDING REMARKS AND FUTURE DIRECTIONS

A. Gedeon Matoltsy

DEPARTMENT OF DERMATOLOGY
BOSTON UNIVERSITY SCHOOL OF MEDICINE
BOSTON, MASSACHUSETTS 02118

I. Introduction

During the past decades several new components of keratinizing tissues have been characterized by ultrastructural studies, and their constituents have been analyzed *in vitro* by new biochemical, immunofluorescent, and genetic engineering methods. The mammalian epidermis, hair, and wool and avian epidermis, scales, and feathers have been the most studied tissues. But valuable information has also been obtained on the epidermis of other vertebrates, the scale, shell, and claw of reptiles, beak and claw of aves, and hoof, quill, and horn of mammals. As a result, our knowledge has broadened considerably about the structure and function of keratinizing tissues, and new concepts have been developed about keratin and the keratinization process.

In this chapter comparative aspects of keratinization in the epidermis of representatives of various vertebrate classes are discussed. Attention is focused on the superficial cell layer that is in direct contact with the environment and provides protection for the organism. In most vertebrates the superficial cells are cornified and filled with a filament network embedded into a matrix and encased by a thickened cell envelope. Between the cornified cells an intercellular substance is found. These structural components are closely associated and may be regarded as a multicomponent protective system (PS). Its constituents are schematically illustrated in Fig. 1 as seen in the mammalian epidermis. In the following sections, evolutionary aspects are listed and the complexity of PS is emphasized. Properties of the components are also described, and unresolved problems are presented to initiate further studies.

CURRENT TOPICS IN
DEVELOPMENTAL BIOLOGY, VOL. 22

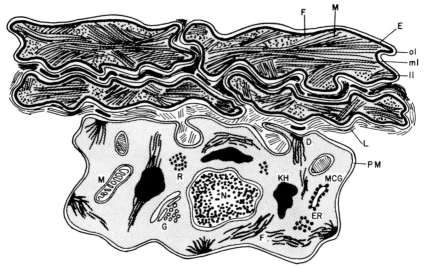

Fig. 1. Schematic illustration of the mammalian stratum corneum and a differentiated granular cell in the initial stage of transformation. Horny cells are filled with
filaments (F) and an amorphous matrix (M). The envelope (E) consists of thin outer (ol)
and mid leaflets (ml), and a thickened inner leaflet (il). The intercellular space is filled
with 2-nm parallel leaflets (L) derived from membrane-coating granules (MCG). The
granular cell contains filament bundles (F), keratohyalin granules (KH), mitochondria
(M), Golgi vesicles (G), rough-surfaced endoplasmic reticulum (ER), and free ribosomes
(R) encased by a triple-layered plasma membrane (PM) attached to horny cells by desmosomes (D). (Reproduced from Matoltsy, 1980.)

II. Components of the Protective System
of the Vertebrate Epidermis

A complete PS evolved about 350 million years ago in the amphibian epidermis, consisting of a filamentous network embedded into
mucus and encased by a thickened cell envelope surrounded by mucus
(Fig. 2). The network is formed during transformation of differentiated cells into horny cells by aggregation of filaments, and the matrix
is formed mainly by dispersion of large mucous granules. The plasma
membrane thickens and the content of small mucous granules is discharged into the intercellular spaces at the initial stage of the transformation process. Components of PS, however, had evolved much earlier, in the epidermal cells of some fish, because in the epidermal
thickenings of these fish is a loose filamentous network encased by a
thickened envelope in superficial cells. Thus constituents of PS such as
the filament and envelope protein were first expressed by fish epidermal cells approximately 450 million years ago. The rest of the fish

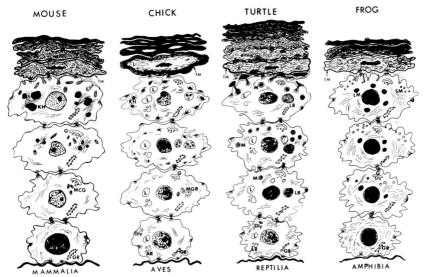

FIG. 2. Schematic illustration of characteristic structural changes of epidermal cells of representatives of the different vertebrate classes. (Redrawn from Matoltsy and Huszar, 1972.) *Amphibia*: In basal cells filaments are abundant and the granular endoplasmic reticulum (GR) is poorly developed. During differentiation, the Golgi vesicles (G) increase in amount and many mucous granules are formed. Large mucous granules (LM) appear in the perinuclear cytoplasm, whereas small mucous granules (SM) appear at the cell periphery. The latter are discharged into the intercellular space. Horny cells, encased by a thickened plasma membrane (TM), contain remnants of cell organelles, filaments, and mucus dispersed in the interfilamentous space. *Reptilia*: Basal cells contain relatively few filaments, lipid droplets (L), and glycogen (Gly). Both granular (GR) and agranular (AR) endoplasmic reticulum are present. During differentiation mucous granules (M), lamellar bodies (LB), and lipid droplets (L) are formed. The content of lipid droplets is retained along with some of the content of mucous granules and lamellar bodies. Mucous granules and lamellar bodies migrate toward the cell periphery and release their content into the intercellular spaces. Horny cells with a thickened membrane (TM) are filled with filaments, lipid, mucus, and lamellae of LB. The intercellular material consists of mucus and polar lipids of LB. *Aves*: Both granular (GR) and agranular (AR) endoplasmic reticulum are present in basal cells. Filaments, lipid droplets (L), and glycogen particles (Gly) are relatively few. The cytoplasm shows compartmentalization during differentiation. An increase is seen in Golgi vesicles (G) and other synthetic organelles. Multigranular bodies (MGB) containing lamellated granules and relatively large lipid droplets (L) appear early in the central part of the cytoplasm. Filament bundles preferentially occur at the cell periphery. Keratohyalin (KH) is deposited in the vicinity of filament bundles at the periphery. The content of MGB is emptied into the intercellular spaces. Horny cells with a thickened plasma membrane (TM) are filled with lipid, filaments, and an amorphous matrix. The latter is derived from keratohyalin. *Mammalia*: In basal cells filaments are abundant; granular endoplasmic reticulum (GR) is scanty. During differentiation, Golgi vesicles (G) increase in number, and membrane-coating granules (MCG) appear early. Later, keratohyalin accumulates in the form of granules (KH). MCG migrate toward the cell periphery and their contents are discharged into the intercellular space. When the cells enter the horny stage, the plasma membrane thickens (TM). The horny cells are filled with filaments and an amorphous matrix mainly derived from keratohyalin.

epidermis is a nonkeratinizing epithelium consisting of filament-form-ing cells and different secretory cells. The superficial cells are covered by mucus of secretory cells, and their plasma membrane is not thick-ened.

The PS of the reptilian epidermis, as it is found in turtles, reveals a remarkable transitional stage between PS of the amphibian and avian epidermis (Fig. 2). Filamentous networks and thickened envelopes are similar. The matrix contains mucus, as in amphibia, and lipids as in aves and in addition a specific constituent consisting of thin leaflets. Mucus and lipids are derived from dispersed mucous granules and lipid droplets, respectively, while the leaflets are formed from retained content of lamellar bodies of transforming epidermal cells. The inter-cellular spaces are filled with secreted mucus as in amphibia and thin leaflets as in aves. The latter are derived from the discharged content of lamellar bodies (which are comparable to multivesicular bodies of avian epidermal cells). It is noteworthy that leaflets in the inter-cellular space appeared for the first time in chelonia, about 300 million years ago. In reptiles other than chelonia, a PS comparable to that seen in amphibia, aves, and mammals is not formed because in basal epi-dermal cells α- and β-keratins appear in cycles and β-keratin-contain-ing cornified cells form the protective layer.

The most characteristic feature of the avian PS is the presence of large quantities of lipids in the matrix, derived from numerous lipid droplets of differentiating cells. Furthermore, keratohyalin appears in the matrix, having evolved in aves approximately 225 million years ago. The intercellular material consists of thin leaflets as mentioned above. The PS of the mammalian epidermis consists of a well-devel-oped filamentous network, an amorphous matrix derived from ker-atohyalin granules, and thickened cell envelopes. The intercellular spaces are filled with thin leaflets formed from the discharged content of membrane-coating granules of differentiated epidermal cells (Figs. 1 and 2).

A. THE FILAMENTOUS NETWORK

The molecular biology of epidermal keratin was established in 1947 by the pioneering work of Rudall, who showed that the filamen-tous network of PS of vertebrates consists of α-keratin. Rudall pre-pared thin films of epidermal cells by drying them on glass plates. Cells were collected by scraping the skin surface of lamprey, perch, *Triturus,* frog, toad, snake, guinea fowl, cow, and humans. Each sam-ple was studied by high-angle X-ray diffraction methods, which re-vealed an α-keratin diffraction pattern. He concluded that the presence of α-type fiborus protein in the epidermis distinguishes all vertebrates and that variations of the structure of this protein may be regarded as changes that have occurred during evolution of a molecular species. Recently Rudall's work was confirmed and extended by the finding that α-keratin polypeptides are extractable from the epidermis of all vertebrate classes and that each contains conserved regions which cross-react with antibodies specific for human α-keratin polypeptides. It was also shown that such polypeptides are encoded by a multigene family in which genes increase in number from 2 to 10 during evolution (Fuchs et al., 1981; Fuchs and Marchuk, 1983).

Mammalian epidermal keratin polypeptides were first isolated in 1952 by Rudall by the use of 6 M urea solution. Their average M_r was estimated at 60,000. It was thought for a long time that epidermal cells express only one type of α-keratin chain, and according to the classical concept (Giroud and Leblond, 1951) such chains become cross-linked by disulfide bonds to form an insoluble framework in cornified cells. During the last decade it was shown that several different types of chains are synthesized in the mammalian epidermis, ranging in M_r from 50,000 to 70,000. With regard to the filamentous framework of PS, the most significant discovery has been the observation that the number and weight of chains increase during differentiation of epidermal cells; low M_r chains become "eliminated" and high M_r chains become reduced in weight by postsynthetic modification prior to transformation of differentiated cells into cornified cells (Fuchs and Green, 1980; Bowden and Cunliffe, 1981; Skerrow and Skerrow, 1983). Thus the filamentous framework of PS is formed by a group of specific α-keratin polypeptides.

It is also significant that newly synthesized chains assemble instantly into filaments so that filaments of different chain composition accumulate in epidermal cells during the course of their differentiation. As a consequence, the network of PS consists of filaments of heterogeneous composition. The subunits of such filaments were thought to consist of three-chain building blocks (Skerrow et al., 1973; Steinert, 1978). Numerous studies provided direct evidence for a three-chain building block, including analysis of proteolytic fragments of prekeratin, and studies of stoichiometry of chains, their cross-linking, reassembly, handedness of outer helix, and linear density of filaments. However Ahmadi and Speakman (1978) studied a wool fiber fragment and proposed that α-keratin building blocks consist of four chains arranged in two two-chain units. Gruen and Woods (1983) reached a similar conclusion on the basis of their cross-linking studies of epidermal keratin of bovine hoof. This new concept is receiving support by indirect evidence, such as the expression of keratin polypeptides in pairs in the mammalian epidermis and other epithelial tissues (Sun *et al.*, 1984), and by the makeup of subfamilies of epidermal keratin, such as type I and type II keratins (Fuchs and Marchuk, 1983).

In the formation of the filamentous network of PS, at present we do not know precisely the mechanisms involved in "elimination" and reduction of M_r of α-keratin polypeptide chains, how many chains interact to form a building block of filaments, and how many protofibrils are present in a filament. Clarification of these questions would greatly enhance our knowledge about the function of PS in mammals.

It is also questionable whether the chains are cross-linked by disulfide bonds in the network of PS, as held in the classic concept. A mechanism has not been presented that would explain conversion of -SH groups to disulfide bonds, and evidence is also lacking for the site of such cross-links. Disulfide bonds would be unlikely to form at cysteine-rich terminal regions of chains as proposed for wool keratin, because such regions of epidermal keratin chains contain glycine and serine residues. The requirement for the use of reducing agent for dissociation and extraction of keratin chains from horny cells is indirect evidence for stabilization of keratin by disulfide bonds. It would be a direct evidence against disulfide bonds if filaments were *not* embedded into sulfur rich-proteins in mammals and horny cells were not encased by an envelope containing abundant disulfide bonds. In horny cells of the frog, epidermis filaments are embedded in mucus and the resistant envelope contains a negligible amount of cystine (Matoltsy, 1977). The α-keratin polypeptides are extractable from these cells with denaturing agents that do not contain any reducing agent. Apparently the network of PS in the frog is not stabilized by disulfide bonds. Whether a similar condition exists in the filamentous framework of other vertebrates, including mammals, remains to be determined.

B. The Matrix

The most variable and least known constituent of PS of vertebrates is the matrix. Mucus and lipids from the matrix have not been isolated and analyzed *in vitro*. The presence of mucus in amphibia and chelonia is based primarily on positive PAS reaction and the presence of lipids on stains binding to neutral lipids. Since the ultrastructure of leaflets in the turtle closely resembles that seen in the intercellular spaces of mammalian stratum corneum (Matoltsy and Bednarz, 1975), it can be assumed that the leaflets consist of polar lipids.

Keratohyalin of aves and mammals does not react specifically with histological stains. In the avian epidermis, keratohyalin granules are not visible in the light microscope because they are of submicroscopic dimensions. Also, the chemical composition of avian keratohyalin has not been studied. Thus, most of our knowledge about keratohyalin is derived from studies of mammalian keratohyalin granules. It is generally agreed that keratohyalin is an amorphous protein containing polypeptides of approximately M_r 20,000. Significant differences prevail, however, in the interpretation of its amino acid composition and functional role. Originally, Brody (1960) proposed that kerohyalin in the matrix of cornified cells consists of sulfur-rich protein. This concept received support primarily by identification of sulfur *in situ* in keratohyalin granules through X-ray microanalysis, incorporation of labeled cysteine, and amino acid analysis of isolated keratohyalin granules, which revealed large amounts of cystine residues (Matoltsy and Matoltsy, 1970, 1972). It has been also assumed that disulfide bonds of keratohyalin may stabilize the structure of the filament–matrix complex and maintain permanency of orientation of the network. Another concept was developed after the finding that keratohyalin granules are labeled extensively *in situ* by [^{3}H]histidine (Fukuyama *et al.*, 1965), and after a histidine-rich protein was isolated from the epidermis (Hoober and Bernstein, 1966) and the stratum corneum (Dale *et al.*, 1978). Since this protein (also called filaggrin) produces aggregation when it is mixed with isolated filaments *in vitro* it was considered involved in stabilization of the network of PS. The mechanism involved in filament aggregation has not been explained, but it does not seem to be specific, as poly(L-lysine) produces comparable aggregation of filaments (Aebi *et al.*, 1983). Although some investigators favor the view that keratohyalin is a mixture of both sulfur-rich and histidine-rich proteins, more work is required to identify its molecular structure and function.

C. THE ENVELOPE OF HORNY CELLS

Attention was focused on the functional role of the membrane of horny cells when researchers in a fractionation study of human calluses noted that about 5% of the callus did not dissolve for a week in 0.1 N NaOH and could not be completely hydrolyzed at 110°C in 6 N HCl for 24 hours. Examination of this highly resistant residual material by phase-contrast microscope revealed ghosts of horny cells and membrane fragments (Matoltsy and Balsamo, 1955; Matoltsy and Matolsy, 1966). Since the material contained cystine residues in large amounts it was thought to be firmly stabilized by disulfide bonds and that such bonds were responsible for its high resistance. Later research demonstrated that its resistant nature did not change after reduction of the disulfide bonds, and it was concluded that some "unknown" highly resistant bond is present. Resistant envelopes have been isolated from the epidermis of all vertebrate classes except fish. Differences were found in amino acid composition (Matoltsy, 1977), suggesting that the envelope may contain several different proteins.

The resistant chemical bond that stabilizes the envelope was identified by Rice and Green in 1977 as an ϵ-(γ-glutamyl)lysine cross-link. They found that the bond is formed by activation of transglutaminase by calcium in a soluble precursor protein called involucrin. Subsequently several other membrane-associated proteins were isolated which were rendered insoluble by comparable cross-links. Antisera raised to these proteins showed that they are synthesized by differentiating cells and that they occur in large amounts at the periphery of granular cells (Watt and Green, 1982). Further studies of envelope proteins would greatly enhance our knowledge about PS of vertebrates, because these are in direct contact with the environment and protect the integrity of horny cells.

D. THE INTERCELLULAR SUBSTANCE

Attention was focused on the presence of lamellar intercellular material after it was noted that reptilian, avian, and mammalian epidermal cells produce submicroscopic granules filled with parallel lamellae and that these are discharged into the intercellular spaces prior to their transformation into horny cells. Preservation of lamellae has been difficult during tissue processing; therefore their structure and function remained unexplained for a long time. Since they readily dissolved in organic solvents it was suspected that they contain lipids. The presence of polar lipids became apparent after Lavker (1976) succeeded to preserve the discharged content and found that it formed multiple bileaflets, similar in structure to the plasma membrane. The content of the granules was well preserved the first time by Landmann (1984). He found that the major broad lamellae do not terminate at the encasing membrane, but split into halves, bend back, and fuse with halves of adjacent major lamellae and encase the intersepting minor thin lamella. Thus these granules are not filled with parallel disks, but rather with unilamellar liposomes. It has been proposed by several investigators that the bileaflets form a permeability barrier in the stratum corneum. The best evidence for this was provided by Squier (1973) by demonstrating that water-soluble substances enter only the spaces between the superficial cells and do not penetrate into the basal portion of the horny layer.

Yardley and Summerly (1981) proposed that the permeability barrier consists of ceramides. Glycolipids and sphingolipids have been assumed to be involved in unstacking of liposomes and formation of bileaflets (Wertz and Downing, 1982; Wertz *et al.*, 1984). Since mammals were used for these studies, information is not available about polar lipids of the permeability barrier in reptiles and aves.

III. Conclusion

The complexity of the stratum corneum, as described above, clearly shows that protection cannot be attributed solely to keratin, and that there are several other substances which play a significant role and assure survival of vertebrates in their particular environment. Variations of constituents of the protective system of the epidermis during evolution are related primarily to the changing environment of the evolving groups. Development of a flexible and extensible filamentous network anchored to a highly resistant envelope was essential for stabilization of the entire protective system in tightly interdigitated horny cells connected by desmosomes. Mucus was required to prevent desiccation of land vertebrates such as amphibia and chelonia. Lipids, particularly polar lipids, were needed to form a permeability barrier for maintaining homeostasis of reptiles, aves, and mammals. We do not know how the environmental factors activated or repressed groups of genes in response to extrinsic and intrinsic signals and how constituents of the protective system were formed, retained, and replaced. However, we do know that during differentiation epidermal cell gene expression proceeds in an orderly and coordinated manner in each vertebrate. The most interesting and valuable direction in future research would be characterization of genes of epidermal cells and explanation of regulation of gene expression.

ACKNOWLEDGMENTS

The author wishes to thank Mrs. Margit N. Matoltsy for her help in preparation and critical reading of the manuscript. The author's work referred to in this paper was supported by grants from the National Institute of Arthritis, Metabolism, and Digestive Diseases, U. S. Public Health Service.

REFERENCES

Aebi, U., Fowler, W. E., Rew, P., and Sun, T.-T. (1983). *J. Cell Biol.* **97**, 1131–1143.
Ahmadi, B., and Speakman, P. T. (1978). *FEBS Lett.* **94**, 365–367.
Brody, I. (1960). *J. Ultrastruct. Res.* **4**, 264–297.
Bowden, P. E., and Cunliffe, W. J. (1981). *Biochem. J.* **199**, 145–154.
Dale, B. A., Holbrook, K. A., and Steinert, P. M. (1978). *Nature (London)* **276**, 729–731.
Fuchs, E. V., and Green, H. (1980). *Cell* **19**, 617–625.
Fuchs, E., and Marchuk, D. (1983). *Proc. Natl. Acad. Sci. U.S.A.* **80**, 5857–5861.
Fuchs, E. V., Coppock, S. M., Green, H., and Cleveland, D. W. (1981). *Cell* **27**, 75–84.

Fukuyama, K., Nakamura, T., and Bernstein, I. A. (1965). *Anat. Rec.* **152**, 525–536.
Giroud, A., and Leblond, C. P. (1951). *Ann. N.Y. Acad. Sci.* **53**, 613–626.
Gruen, L. C., and Woods, E. F. (1983). *Biochem. J.* **209**, 587–595.
Hoober, J. K., and Bernstein, I. A. (1966). *Proc. Natl. Acad. Sci. U.S.A.* **56**, 594–601.
Landmann, L. (1984). *Eur. J. Cell Biol.* **33**, 258–264.
Lavker, R. M. (1976). *J. Ultrastruct. Res.* **5**, 79–86.
Matoltsy, A. G. (1977). *In* "Biochemistry of Cutaneous Epidermal Differention" (M. Seiji and I. A. Bernstein, eds.), pp. 93–109. Univ. of Tokyo Press, Tokyo.
Matoltsy, A. G. (1980). *Linn. Soc. Symp. Ser.* (9), 57–66.
Matoltsy, A. G., and Balsamo, C. A. (1955). *J. Biophys. Biochem. Cytol.* **1**, 339–360.
Matoltsy, A. G., and Bednarz, J. A. (1975). *J. Ultrastruct. Res.* **53**, 128–132.
Matoltsy, A. G., and Huszar, T. (1972). *J. Ultrastruct. Res.* **38**, 87–101.
Matoltsy, A. G., and Matoltsy, M. N. (1966). *J. Invest. Dermatol.* **46**, 127–129.
Matoltsy, A. G., and Matoltsy, M. N. (1970). *J. Cell Biol.* **47**, 593–603.
Matoltsy, A. G., and Matoltsy, M. N. (1972). *J. Ultrastruct. Res.* **41**, 550–560.
Rice, R. H., and Green, H. (1977). *Cell* **11**, 417–422.
Rudall, K. M. (1947). *Biochim. Biophys. Acta* **1**, 549–562.
Rudall, K. M. (1952). *Adv. Protein Chem.* **7**, 253–290.
Skerrow, D., and Skerrow, C. J. (1983). *Exp. Cell Res.* **43**, 27–35.
Skerrow, D., Matoltsy, A. G., and Matoltsy, M. N. (1973). *J. Biol. Chem.* **248**, 4820–4826.
Squier, C. A. (1973). *J. Ultrastruct. Res.* **43**, 160–177.
Steinert, P. M. (1978). *J. Mol. Biol.* **123**, 49–70.
Sun, T.-T., Eichner, R., Schermer, A., Cooper, D., Nelson, W. G., and Weiss, R. A. (1984). *In* "The Cancer Cell" (A. Levine, W. Topp, G. Vande Woude, and J. D. Watson, eds.), pp. 169–176. Cold Spring Harbor Lab., Cold Spring Harbor, New York.
Watt, F. M., and Green, H. (1982). *Nature (London)* **295**, 434–436.
Wertz, P. W., and Downing, D. T. (1982). *Science* **217**, 1261–1262.
Wertz, P. W., Downing, D. T., Freinkel, R. K., and Traczyk, T. N. (1984). *J. Invest. Dermatol.* **83**, 193–195.
Yardley, H. J., and Summerly, R. (1981). *Pharmacol. Ther.* **13**, 357–383.

INDEX